Epidemics in Colonial America

Noah Webster. From the Toner Collection in the Library of Congress.

Epidemics in Colonial America

By JOHN DUFFY

LOUISIANA STATE UNIVERSITY PRESS
Baton Rouge

ISBN 0-8071-0205-9
Library of Congress Catalog Card Number 53-9904

Manufactured in the United States of America
1971 printing

To Corinna

Preface

While examining colonial records, I was struck by the frequent references to epidemic sicknesses. A check of secondary materials revealed that no comprehensive study of colonial epidemics has been made since the publication in 1799 of Noah Webster's work, *A Brief History of Epidemic and Pestilential Diseases; with the Principal Phenomena of the Physical World, Which Precede and Accompany Them, and Observations Deduced from the Facts Stated.*

On delving into the colonial source materials, it became apparent that evidence of colonial epidemics was to be found in all types of contemporary records—correspondence, diaries, journals, histories, descriptions, newspapers, official records, *et al.* Obviously not all of these sources have been mined, but a wide range of materials was examined during the years of research and should afford a reasonably accurate picture.

Epidemic sicknesses played a disastrous part in colonial life, and it has been my endeavor to determine which diseases were involved, to clarify them in order of importance, and to show both collectively and singly their effect upon colonial development. From a social and economic standpoint infectious disorders were evidently costly. Not so apparent was the influence upon the religious thinking of the omnipresent threat of death through recurring epidemics. However, before the ramifications of colonial epidemics can be explored, the factual groundwork must be laid.

In the course of several years' work, a number of obligations have been incurred. Part of the research was financed with the aid of a university fellowship from the University of California at Los Angeles. Later a travel grant from the American Philosophical Society brought the research to completion. Northwestern State College of Louisiana gave some assistance in typing. Special thanks are due to Professors Frank J. Klingberg and the late Louis Knott Koontz of the University of California at Los Angeles, who guided this study in its early stages, and to Dr. Ernest Caulfield of West Hartford, Connecticut, and Professor Richard H. Shryock of Johns Hopkins University for their valuable suggestions. The staff members of all libraries visited were both kind and helpful, as was Miss Joan Doyle of the Louisiana State University Press, whose deft touches miraculously transformed academese into English. Above all was the help of my wife Corinne, an excellent research assistant and an able critic.

JOHN DUFFY

Contents

Epidemics in Colonial America

CHAPTER I

Introduction

The tragic role played by sickness and disease in the history of the American colonies has long been recognized. No attempt has been made to minimize its importance, yet surprisingly little is known of the extent and virulence of the prevailing sicknesses. Medical historians ordinarily survey the field of medicine from a professional viewpoint, emphasizing the state of medical knowledge, eminent physicians, medical education societies, and publications. Epidemic diseases have been dealt with very cursorily, usually one short chapter sufficing for the entire colonial period. Evidence of epidemics in the main lies outside the general medical records and consequently has been overlooked by many medical writers. State medical histories have proved more complete, but much additional work is necessary.

Recently a start has been made on the study of specific diseases. Among the monographic studies of this type are St. Julien Ravenel Childs's book on malaria and colonization in the Carolina low country; P. M. Ashburn's study of diseases in the Americas, which concentrates largely upon South America; the work on smallpox and the American Indians by E. Wagner and Allen E. Stearn; and Ernest Caulfield's thorough study of the diphtheria and scarlet fever epidemics in New England, 1735 to 1740. However, there is still no standard work dealing with epidemics in America comparable to John J. Heagerty's study of diseases in Canada, or Charles Creighton's classic work on English epidemics. The latter work, although now over fifty years old, is still invaluable.[1]

Epidemic disorders visited death and destruction upon the American colonies with relentless regularity. The nature of diseases was understood, but the treatment justified the aphorism of Dr. William Douglass that "more die of the practitioner than of the natural course of the disease." Colonial America made little contribution to medical knowledge, although by the time of the Revolution the colonies were developing some first-rate physicians and surgeons. The best medical men were trained in Great Britain, the majority at Edinburgh. But, although European pioneers were enlarging the boundaries of medical knowledge, contemporary medical practices were unable to alleviate the high mortality from epidemic infections.[2]

[1] St. Julien Ravenel Childs, *Malaria and Colonization in the Carolina Low Country, 1526–1696* (Baltimore, 1940), in Johns Hopkins University *Studies in Historical and Political Science*, Ser. 58, No. 1; P. M. Ashburn, *The Ranks of Death, A Medical History of the Conquest of America* (New York, 1947); E. Wagner Stearn and Allen E. Stearn, *The Effect of Smallpox on the Destiny of the Amerindian* (Boston, 1945); Ernest Caulfield, *A True History of the Terrible Epidemic vulgarly called The Throat Distemper . . .* (New Haven, 1939); John J. Heagerty, *Four Centuries of Medical History in Canada . . .* (Toronto, 1928), 2 vols.; Charles Creighton, *A History of Epidemics in Britain* (Cambridge, 1894), 2 vols.

[2] William Douglass, *A Summary, historical and political, of the first planting, progressive improvements, and present state of the British Settlements in North America* (London, 1760), 2 vols. (hereinafter cited as *British Settlements)*; see also Joseph Meredith Toner Collection, Division of Manuscripts, Library of Congress. In his manuscript "Notes on the History of Medicine" Toner lists sixty Americans who graduated from the University of Edinburgh between the years 1744 and 1775.

During the seventeenth century William Harvey and Marcello Malpighi demonstrated the circulation of blood,[3] and Leeuwenhoek introduced the use of the microscope. Pioneer work was done in chemistry and histology. The introduction into Europe of cinchona, or Jesuits' bark, gave medicine an important weapon. Surgery, which had fallen into considerable disrepute, attained professional standing in France by the end of the century.

The famous seventeenth-century English physician, Thomas Sydenham (1624–89), left his imprint on both British and colonial medical practice far into the eighteenth century. For the medical theorizing of the period he substituted observation, and his accumulated experience became his chief reliance in carrying on his work and developing his ideas. The cause of all disease he laid to morbific or peccant matter. This substance either entered the body in particles of air, thus tainting the blood, or else was caused by fermentation and putrefaction of retained humors. Sweating, purging, and bleeding were Sydenham's remedies for this condition. Although using phlebotomy, or bleeding, he did not practice it as severely as so many of his contemporaries and successors. To Sydenham goes much of the credit for introducing Jesuits' bark into England and overcoming the prejudice that the contemporary name for cinchona bark automatically aroused in Protestant England. He was also one of the first to advocate fresh air in the sickroom, and he avoided the loathsome admixtures so often prescribed by his colleagues. In common with other physicians of his day he attributed epidemics to geographic and meteorological conditions. Although his contributions to the field were lim-

[3] Although Harvey first announced his ideas on the circulation of blood in 1616, the question was still debated as late as 1699. See Edward Eggleston, *The Transit of Civilization from England to America in the Seventeenth Century* (New York, 1901), 48–49.

ited, Sydenham can be placed among the founders of epidemiology.

In the eighteenth century the most influential physician was Hermann Boerhaave (1668–1738). Since one of his pupils founded the Edinburgh Medical School, he has been acclaimed by an English medical historian as the father of British medicine.[4] He accepted the best from all the medical theories of the time. In general, Boerhaave maintained that disease was an imbalance of "natural activities." Phlebotomy and purging to reduce acidity and purify the system were his basic cures for all disorders. Boerhaave was followed by William Cullen and John Brown, whose ideas gained wide acceptance both in Europe and America, but neither they nor their contemporaries contributed much of permanent value.

Surgeons had little social standing either in Europe or in America during most of the colonial period. Because medieval church laws forbade the shedding of blood by ecclesiastics, and because all the students of medieval universities took clerical orders, there occurred a separation of surgery from medicine which was to continue into the nineteenth century. A physician was a university man, but a surgeon was merely a skilled craftsman. Surgery, which was associated with barbering and bonesetting, was included among the manual trades. In fact, it was not until 1745 that English barbers and surgeons officially separated into two distinct companies. The surgeon's work was limited to setting bones, performing amputations, cutting ulcers and boils, and treating open wounds. He was compelled to work without anesthetics and had no inkling of the value of cleanliness. A leading medical historian estimated that the unhygenic conditions under which surgeons worked caused

[4] Charles Singer, *A Short History of Medicine* (New York, 1928), 140.

death in 70 per cent of cases of compound fractures and 50 per cent of all amputations. It is not surprising to find a South Carolina missionary reporting in 1751 to the Society for the Propagation of the Gospel that he was "under the severe hand of the Surgeon." [5]

Medicine, as already stated, was a university subject taught from a purely theoretical standpoint without the benefit of actual bedside observation. In America, however, the lack of medical schools necessitated the apprentice system, whereby the young medical student learned his art through daily practical contact with patients. Indeed, relatively few of the colonial doctors were medical school graduates. For example, of the ten practitioners in Boston in 1721 only one held a doctor's degree. By the time of the Revolution it is estimated that only four hundred of the approximately thirty-five hundred practicing medical men possessed the M.D. degree.[6] Obviously, then, the distinction between physicians as university men and surgeons as craftsmen could not be maintained in the colonies. The freer atmosphere in the colonies too, was not conducive to rigid social distinctions between the two branches of medicine.

The leadership of France in surgery in the late seventeenth century continued for many years, and it was not until well into the eighteenth that the genius of William Hunter (1718–83) and his brother, John (1728–93), enabled Great Britain to forge ahead in this field. During the Revolution, American medical men had a chance to acquire

[5] M. G. Seelig, *Medicine, An Historical Outline* (Baltimore, 1931), 163; William Cotes to Secretary, St. George's, South Carolina, April 17, 1751, in Society for the Propagation of the Gospel in Foreign Parts MSS., Library of Congress Phototranscripts, London Letters, B19, fp. 305 (hereinafter cited as S.P.G. MSS. with appropriate designation of letters).

[6] Francis R. Packard, *History of Medicine in the United States*, 2 vols. (New York, 1931), I, 273.

the skills of European surgeons who served on both sides of the conflict. Soon American surgeons were making notable additions to surgical knowledge, which, like medicine, had been in a static condition before American independence.

In brief, medical practice advanced little during most of the colonial era. Dr. William Douglass wrote that when he asked a local doctor for the routine practice in New England, "he told me their practice was very uniform, bleeding, vomiting, blistering, purging, anodyne, etc. if the illness continued there was repetendi, and finally murderandi." In the same ironic vein Douglass reported that the New England physicians "follow Sydenham too much in giving paregoricks, after catharticks, which is playing fast and loose." [7]

The most-used drugs—calomel, mercury, opium, ipecac, rattlesnake root, and Jesuits' bark—were administered, as were all other medicines, in unbelievable quantities. Prescriptions were compounded in a haphazard fashion, and no one thought of measuring the amount of drugs with any degree of accuracy. As one writer has expressed it, "the asbestos stomachs and colossal minds of our forefathers were much above such petty minuteness." Hence one encounters such phrases as "enough to lie on a penknife's point," "the bigth of a walnut," or "a pretty draught." [8]

Prescriptions containing nauseating ingredients were given for many illnesses. Cotton Mather, the well-known New England leader, wrote a medical treatise in which he advocated dung and urine as two of the best medicines for human ailments. Human excreta, he declared, was "a Remedy for Humane Bodies that is hardly to be paralleled,"

[7] Douglass, *British Settlements*, II, 352.

[8] Henry F. Long, "The Physicians of Topsfield, with some account of Early Medical Practice," in *Historical Collections* of the Essex Institute, Salem, Mass., XLVII (1911), 209.

and urine had virtues far beyond all the waters of medicinal springs. Purging was an essential of medical treatment. A physician's bill sent to a patient by a Dr. Pasteur of Williamsburg, Virginia, in 1747 itemized thirty-two drugs administered in the course of the patient's illness: no less than eighteen of these drugs were purgatives.[9]

Phlebotomy was another indispensable method of treatment, used both extensively and intensively. On occasion doctors prescribed that the patient be bled to unconsciousness. The taking of twenty to forty ounces of blood was a normal treatment, and not infrequently the amount was much greater. In view of the heroic measures usually taken with the patient (or victim), one shudders at the implications in prescriptions which order "copious bleeding" or "brisk purging." The effect of violent vomiting, purging, and bleeding upon a patient already weakened by illness can only be imagined.

The current medical practices and the large number of quack doctors contributed to the disrepute in which the colonial medical profession was held. In 1706 William Byrd wrote: "There be some men indeed that are call'd Doctors: but they are generally discarded Surgeons of Ships, that know nothing above very common Remedys." A few years later John Oldmixon stated: "The *Virginians* have but few Doctors among them, and they reckon it among their Blessings, fancying the Number of their Diseases would increase with that of their Physicians." Toward the close of the colonial period an observer in New York declared that few physicians in the province were noted for their skill and that "quacks abound like locusts in Egypt." In 1709 one of the

[9] Ralph Boas and Louise Boas, *Cotton Mather, Keeper of the Puritan Conscience* (New York and London, 1928), 46–47; "Jones Papers," in *Virginia Magazine of History and Biography*, XXVI (1918), 70–80.

missionaries for the Society for the Propagation of the Gospel in Foreign Parts "had the misfortune to take Physick of a pretended Phisitian wch. work't so violently that it gave him 100 vomits and as many stools, brought the Convulsions on him, wch. soon carryed him off, and caused him to purge till he was Interr'd." [10] Cases similar to this one were only too frequent.

As indicated above, despite the apprentice system and the immigration of physicians from Great Britain, the colonies constantly suffered from a dearth of trained men. This shortage of medical practitioners is shown in the letters of the S.P.G. missionaries, who were often called upon to minister to the physical, as well as spiritual, needs of their flocks. The Reverend Henry Lucas wrote from New England in 1716, "My little Knowledge in Physick has given me a great Opportunity of conversing wth. Men by wch. I have done that, wch. by preaching I could not have done." Christopher Bridge, ministering to the people in Rye, New York, complained to the Society that he received very little cash from his parishioners and expended nearly all of it on medicine for them. As late as 1764 a missionary in western New York wrote: "As there is no Doctor here when any English or Indians are sick and infirm if they apply to me I visit them in their distress and ye poor Indians in a special manner & freely to all—Dear Sir this requires some Druggs." [11]

[10] William Byrd to the Royal Society, Virginia, April 20, 1706, in Sloane MSS., B. Miscel., MS. copy, Library of Congress; John Oldmixon, *The British Empire in America*, 2 vols. (London, 1741), I, 429; William Smith, *The History of the Province of New York* (London, 1776), 272–73; Bradford to Secretary, New York, September 12, 1709, in S.P.G. MSS., A5, fpp. 141–50.

[11] Henry Lucas to Secretary, Newbury, New England, July 24, 1716, in S.P.G. MSS., A11–12, fp. 311; Christopher Bridge to Secretary, Rye, N. Y., October 31, 1716, *ibid.*, A12, fp. 146; Cornelius Bennett to Secretary, Mohawk Castle, January 7, 1764, *ibid.*, B22, fp. 129.

This combination of minister-physician was not always appreciated by the parishioners. The wardens of the church at Perth Amboy, New Jersey, wrote to the Society in 1769 objecting to the appointment of their new pastor on the grounds that he practiced "physick." Their previous minister had been "bred to Physick" and the congregation had found that it interfered with his clerical duties.[12]

Possibly an even larger factor in the excessive mortality rate than the inadequate medical knowledge was malnutrition, which paved the way for epidemic disorders. Actual famine was a constant threat to the early settlers; and scurvy, beriberi, and other dietary sicknesses scourged the colonists. Thomas Prince in his history of early New England emphasized the problem of food. Of 1628 he recorded, "This Year the Massachusetts Planters at London send several Servants to Naumkeak; but for want of wholesome Diet and convenient Lodgings, many die of Scurvys and other Distempers." Again in 1631 he stated, "The Poorer Sort of People . . . by long lying in Tents and small huts are much afflicted with Scurvy, and many Die, especially at Boston and Charleston." [13]

Although the eighteenth century brought some improvement, scurvy was a constant threat throughout the entire colonial period. Thomas Hassell, a South Carolina missionary, wrote to the Society in 1717 that, although his health was improved, he was still suffering from the scurvy, a distemper, he said, "very difficult to cure in this sickly clymate and the more in those whose business requires a sedentary life, as the clergy's does." From Brookhaven,

[12] Church Wardens to Secretary, Perth Amboy, N. J., June 16, 1769, *ibid.*, B24, pt. 2, fp. 882.

[13] Thomas Prince, *A Chronological History of New-England . . .*, 2 vols. (Boston, 1736 and 1755), I, 171; II, 19 (Volume II was published under the subtitle *Annals of New England).*

Connecticut, another missionary reported in 1726: "My Leggs swell & and my Body somewhat, wch. I doe in some Measure impute to the Dyet of this Country, whose meat is salt Beef & Pork, its drink is Cyder one part of the year & Molasses Beer all the rest." William Douglass was cognizant of the inadequate diet in New England for he recorded a few years later: "In New England (some parts of Connecticut excepted) the general subsistence of the poorer people (which contributes much towards their endemial psorick disorders) is salt pork and Indian beans, with bread of Indian corn meal, and pottage of this meal with milk for breakfast and supper." Cadwallader Colden, another keen medical observer, stated in a letter to Dr. John Mitchell in 1745 that "the scurvy is exceedin[gly] common in North America & hardly anybody [is] free of it & often mistaken for other Diseases." [14]

The notorious inefficiency in the provisioning of colonial armies rendered their dietary problems acute. The commanding officer at Oswego wrote to the governor of New York in 1753 that the French army in Ohio was incapacitated from sickness, and many were dying from scurvy caused by bad provisions.[15] With dietary diseases undermining the health of the colonial population, it is not surprising that outbreaks of contagious sicknesses claimed many lives.

The disastrous effect of disease and sickness among the

[14] Thomas Hassell to Secretary, St. Thomas, S. C., December 20, 1717, in S.P.G. MSS., A13, fpp. 105–106; Thomas Standard to Secretary, Brookhaven, Conn., October, 1726, *ibid.*, A19, fpp. 324–25; Douglass, *British Settlements*, II, 206; *The Letters and Papers of Cadwallader Colden*, 9 vols. (New York, 1918–37), VIII (1937), 335–36, in *Collections* of the New-York Historical Society (1917–35), hereinafter cited as *Colden Papers*.

[15] E. B. O'Callaghan (ed.), *Documents Relative to the Colonial History of the State of New-York* . . . , 11 vols. (Albany, 1856–61), VI, 825 (hereinafter cited as *Documents Relative to Colonial History*).

early settlers is clearly illustrated in the case of the first colony, Virginia. "Tidewater Virginia for the English settlers was a pest-ridden place," according to a recent historian. "The low and marshy ground, the swarming mosquitoes, the hot sun, the unwholesome drinking water combined to produce an unending epidemic of dysentery and malaria." The same writer described the famine and wars, which decimated the population, and added: "But by far the most terrible scourge was the 'sicknesse' that swept over Virginia year after year, leaving in its wake horrible suffering and devastation."[16] The statistics gathered by Alexander Brown demonstrate more effectively than words the sickness and death among the early colonists. From December, 1606, to May, 1618, a total of 1,800 persons sailed for Virginia. Approximately 100 returned to England, and 1,100 died on the passage or in the colony. When a census was taken on December 28, 1618, the population of the colony was only 600. From 1619 to 1625 another 4,749 immigrants arrived, and yet the population in the latter year was only 1,025. By the end of the century 100,000 settlers had arrived in Virginia; but, despite the normal increase occasioned by an extremely high birthrate, the total population had reached only 75,000.[17]

Health conditions improved after the mid-century, for Governor Berkeley testified in 1671 that "there is not oft seasoned hands (as we term them) that die now, whereas heretofore not one of five escaped the first year." [18] The governor's estimate of an 80 per cent mortality among new-

[16] Thomas J. Wertenbaker, *The Planters of Colonial Virginia* (Princeton, 1922), 39; *id.*, *Virginia under the Stuarts* (Princeton, 1914),2.

[17] Alexander Brown, *The First Republic in America* (Boston and New York, 1898), 285, 612.

[18] William Waller Hening (ed.), *The Statutes at Large . . .*, 13 vols. (Richmond, 1819), II, 513.

comers in the early days of the settlements is borne out by the figures already cited for the first twenty years.

The excessive fatalities among newly arrived settlers is easily explained. The colonists had to endure a long passage on crowded and filthy ships on which the limited supply of food carried often did not suffice for the extended journey and, in any case, was deficient from a dietetic standpoint. Typhus and other diseases frequently developed among the passengers and, after taking many lives on board ship, were usually landed with the survivors to infect those settlers already in the colonies. In 1636 the governor of Virginia wrote that much of the blame for sickness in the colonies could be laid to the merchants who overcrowded their vessels leaving England. These ships landed crowds of filthy and sick passengers with the result, as the governor expressed it, "that where the most pestered shipps vent their passengers they carry with them almost a general mortality." [19] The vessels coming to North America had the alternative of sailing direct to the New World and subjecting the crews and passengers to the inevitable scurvy or of traveling by way of the Antilles and thereby acquiring fresh water and fruits. Unfortunately, the benefits derived from this southern route were counteracted by the possibility of exposure to yellow fever and other tropical diseases during the stopover.

Upon landing in the new country, the settler found little improvement in the food supply, inadequate clothing and shelter, a climate subject to both extreme heat and extreme cold, and a continuation of the crowded, unsanitary living conditions which he had encountered on board ship. Malaria, dysentery, and other diseases usually proved fatal

[19] Wyndham B. Blanton, *Medicine in Virginia in the Seventeenth Century* (Richmond, 1930), 35.

in more instances than in the old country, possibly a result of the trying conditions which the newly arrived immigrant faced. In the later colonial period, yellow fever, a completely new disease and consequently one to which they had no immunity, plagued many of the colonists.

Once introduced into the colonies, contagious diseases flourished and were certain to reach epidemic proportions. Some of the disorders were omnipresent, constantly threatening the comfort and safety of the people. Others appeared at intervals and were rendered more severe and terrifying because of this characteristic. Year after year, "winter" and "summer" sicknesses visited the colonies. The conditions described in Virginia were typical of all, varied only slightly by climatic and other geographical factors.

As the colonies became established and living standards rose, health conditions improved. Nevertheless, colonial Americans remained subject to such familiar European diseases as smallpox, measles, and influenza while at the same time they endured new and more fatal infections in the form of yellow fever and pernicious malaria.

CHAPTER II

Smallpox

The European Scourge

Of the many diseases plaguing Europe and North America from 1600 to 1775, few of them were as universal or as fatal as smallpox. It is hard to realize that a disease so rare today in western countries could have been one of the chief scourges of the seventeenth and eighteenth centuries. Yet an examination of the records shows that smallpox was a perpetual threat to public health. Because of its high mortality rate and the possibility of disfigurement for life, this malady was regarded with terror. In England, as on the Continent, large cities were the centers of the infection, and in them it was endemic; the countryside, too, was periodically ravaged. Although endemic in many places, the disease recurrently flared up into epidemic proportions, as is shown by the London and Edinburgh Bills of Mortality.[1] In the American colonies, smallpox spread in waves, and an epidemic in one or more sections of the country was to be expected.

Variola, to give it its technical name, is an acute infectious disease characterized by fever and eruptions. The

[1] Bills of Mortality are the records of deaths periodically published by the municipalities. The London Bills, which were first printed in 1628, are the earliest and best known. The bills were issued weekly, monthly, and annually. Usually the reason for death was stated, and often the victims were classified within age limits.

eruptions leave the distinct scars from which the common name is derived. In the early seventeenth century smallpox was occasionally confused with syphilis. Gradually, as the two diseases were differentiated, syphilis became known in England as the "large pox" or "French pox" and variola as "small pox." A temperature of 103 degrees or higher, a quick pulse, an intense headache, vomiting, and pains in the loins and back are the symptoms for about three days. On the third or fourth day the typical eruptions appear, usually coming first on the forehead and at the roots of the hair and gradually spreading over the body. The eruptions are dark red spots which eventually develop into papules, or pimples. The distinctive nature of the symptoms made the disorder easily identifiable, and for this reason ample material exists for a study of its ravages.

The actual cause of smallpox is still unknown, and it is usually classed as a filter-passing virus. At times, the disease almost seems to be generated spontaneously. "When a sufficient number of unvaccinated people accumulate in any community," one medical historian has reported, "an epidemic of smallpox almost invariably follows, which only differs from the epidemics that formerly devastated whole countries because everywhere the majority of the population have been vaccinated. The virus of smallpox appears to be ubiquitous, and is one of the most certain of infections. Practically 100 per cent of individuals not protected by vaccination will acquire the infection when once exposed to the disease." [2] Smallpox recognizes no age barriers and is apparently a contact disease; unsanitary conditions and overcrowding favor its spread. The best protection is either a previous attack—since one attack usually confers immu-

[2] Edward B. Vedder, *Medicine, Its Contribution to Civilization* (Baltimore, 1929), 56.

nity—or vaccination, although the immunity thus conferred weakens with the passage of time. This loss of immunity explains periodic outbreaks in population centers. The worst cases appear at the beginning of an epidemic, among persons having the least resistance or immunity. Periodic vaccination, then, is a necessity for complete protection from the infection, as was demonstrated by the outbreaks of smallpox among American troops in Europe and the Far East during World War II.

The place of origin of smallpox is not known, but either Central Africa or India is the probable hearth area. The first definite reference to smallpox occurs at the beginning of the tenth century, though it may have scourged mankind since the beginning of history. Eruptions on the skin of an Egyptian mummy of the twentieth dynasty (1200–1100 B.C.) indicate smallpox, and an epidemic brought back by the Roman army sent against the Parthians in 164 A.D. is attributed by some medical authorities to this same disorder. The first accurate description of the disease was made by a famous Persian scholar, Rhazes (850–923), who by present-day standards convincingly identified both smallpox and measles.[3]

Although the early history of smallpox in Europe is obscure, by the fifteenth and sixteenth centuries it emerged as a major threat to both the Old World and the New. About fifteen years after Columbus made his initial voyage, it reached the West Indies and soon became endemic. In 1520 the Spaniards carried the infection into Mexico, where it began a career which was ultimately to result in the deaths of an estimated three million natives in Central and South

[3] Wade W. Oliver, *Stalkers of Pestilence, the Story of Man's Ideas of Infection* (New York, 1930), 9–10; Ralph N. Major, *Disease and Destiny* (New York and London, 1936), 107–11; David Riesman, *The Story of Medicine in the Middle Ages* (New York, 1936), 50–51; Seelig, *Medicine*, 51.

America.[4] Its appearance in North America coincided with white settlement, and English, French, Dutch, and Swedish colonists alike succumbed to it.

The disease steadily became more virulent on the Continent and in the British Isles, becoming a serious problem in England after the Stuart restoration. No one has expressed more vividly than Macaulay the terror it aroused:

> That disease, over which science has since achieved a succession of glorious and beneficent victories, was then the most terrible of all the ministers of death. The havoc of the plague had been far more rapid: but plague had visited our shores only once or twice within living memory; and the smallpox was always present, filling the churchyards with corpses, tormenting with constant fears all whom it had not yet stricken, leaving on those whose lives it spared the hideous traces of its power, turning the babe into a changeling at which the mother shuddered, and making the eyes and cheeks of the betrothed maiden objects of horror to the lover.[5]

Although Macaulay was doubtless carried away by his own descriptive powers, smallpox was a leading cause of suffering and death until well into the nineteenth century.

By the beginning of the eighteenth century smallpox was endemic in nearly all major cities in the British Isles and, because of the extensive commercial and social intercourse with the mother country, recurrent in the American colonies. The frequent quarantining of ships in American ports because of smallpox and other infections attests to the relationship between trade and the spread of this plague. A brief survey of smallpox conditions in England throws light on its migration to America and lays the foundation

[4] Major, *Disease and Destiny*, 113; Blanton, *Medicine in Virginia in the Seventeenth Century*, 60; Stearn and Stearn, *Effect of Smallpox*, 14.

[5] Thomas Babington Macaulay, *The History of England from the Accession of James II*, 5 vols. (Philadelphia, 1887 ed.), IV, 575.

for a comparative study of the disease at home and in the colonies.

Although interest in population and mortality figures was a late eighteenth-century development, as an examination of the annual volumes of the Royal Society of London shows, contemporary observers made many estimates of the effects of smallpox on the population. The Comte de la Condamine, a famous eighteenth-century French mathematician and scientist, declared in an essay that "every tenth person and one tenth of all mankind was killed, crippled or disfigured by smallpox." Dr. James Jurin, secretary of the Royal Society and probably a more accurate observer, in 1723 published the results of a study of the London Bills of Mortality for the previous forty-two years showing that one fourteenth of the total population in and around London died of smallpox. The death rate among those infected, according to Jurin's statistics, was two out of every eleven. In the same year another member of the society, after investigating smallpox in Leeds, Halifax, and several other English towns, claimed an even higher mortality ratio of one death for every five smallpox cases.[6] A report published in the *Gentlemen's Magazine* in 1747 estimated that the deaths ran from 15 to 20 per cent of the cases. Dr. Richard Brocklesby, Physician to the Army, in his book published in 1763 stated that in the army one out of every four smallpox victims died, a figure which he attributed to the hard life and intemperance of the soldiers. The highest estimate was that given by the Reverend J. Aikin, who wrote in 1774 that his studies in Hastings indicated a 40 per cent fatality rate for smallpox.[7] Despite the continued

[6] Wyndham B. Blanton, *Medicine in Virginia in the Eighteenth Century* (Richmond, 1931), 60; James Jurin, Secretary, to Dr. Caleb Cotesworth, in *Philosophical Transactions of the Royal Society of London*, XXXII (1720–23), 213–24 (hereinafter cited as *Philosophical Transactions*); *ibid.*, 49–52.

presence of smallpox in London, the inhabitants developed no special resistance to the disorder. The percentage of fatalities among the victims in London was not appreciably below that of localities where the disease struck only occasionally.

William Douglass in his *Summary History*, written in the middle of the eighteenth century, threw some interesting light on smallpox in Europe. He stated that physicians were seldom called in except for particularly bad cases, since the infection was considered a children's disease comparable to teething and worms. Few adults were infected because childhood exposure was almost inevitable, and the high mortality rate among smallpox victims made it a chief cause for the excessive infant fatalities.[8]

The London Bills of Mortality, critically used, provide excellent information on the extent of smallpox in and around the city. Although the cause of death is often not clear ("convulsions," for example, is frequently given), smallpox and measles were differentiated, and the smallpox figures are reasonably accurate.[9]

From 1731 to 1765 there were only two years in which the number of smallpox deaths listed in the London Bills was less than 1,000. For several years the toll was over 3,000, and in 1751 the high mark of 3,538 was recorded. The total annual London deaths in this period ranged from 17,576 in 1757 to 32,169 in 1741, with an average of about

[7] *Gentlemen's Magazine*, XVII (1747), 623; "Review of Dr. Brocklesby's *Aeconomical and Medical Observations*," *ibid.*, XXXIII (1763), 633–38; Reverend J. Aiken, "Bill of Mortality for the town of Warrington, 1773," communicated to the secretary of the Royal Society by Dr. Percival, May 19, 1774, in *Philosophical Transactions*, LXIV, Pt. 2 (1774), 438–44.

[8] Douglass, *British Settlements*, II, 402 n. In referring to children's diseases it should be noted that the London Bills of Mortality show that almost 50 per cent of the total deaths occurred among children below the age of five.

[9] "Account of the Weather . . . in December, 1751," in *Gentlemen's Magazine*, XXI (1751, supplement), 577–78.

23,300 per year. The average number of deaths from smallpox in this period was approximately 2,080. In short, about 9 per cent, or one out of each eleven deaths occurring in London from 1731 to 1765, was attributed to smallpox.[10] Although this ratio is slightly higher than Dr. Jurin's calculations covering the forty-two years prior to 1723, it bears out his conclusions.

The long intervals between smallpox outbreaks in the colonies resulted in the growth of a large body of non-immunes, few of whom escaped the infection during an epidemic. This high case incidence brought many deaths and led to the popular colonial misconception that smallpox was peculiarly fatal to Americans. In actuality the death rate in the colonies was, if anything, slightly lower than that in England. Because of its irregular appearance in the colonies, the disorder was far more dreaded than in England: even the rumor of a smallpox epidemic caused consternation among the colonists. In London, where the annual number of deaths from smallpox rarely was under a thousand, the disease was a familiar evil.

Despite the contemporary opinion, even among medical men, that the American colonists were far more susceptible to smallpox than were the English, the estimates of the death rate among American colonials were lower than some of those given for England. In 1765 Dr. Benjamin Gale wrote to Dr. John Huxham, the English physician, that one in every seven or eight infected with smallpox in America died. The study made by William Douglass showed a death ratio of one out of every seven cases in the Boston epidemic of 1721. This latter outbreak was one of the worst in colonial history. Naturally the colonists were terrified

[10] London Bills of Mortality from 1731 to 1765 published in *Gentlemen's Magazine* for the same years, Vols. I to XXXV.

at the prospect of a smallpox epidemic, and wholesale flights from town on the appearance of the disease were not unusual. During the Boston epidemic of 1721 about nine hundred people left town, and in the outbreak of 1751 it was estimated that over eighteen hundred fled to the country.[11]

If smallpox was severe among the whites, it was devastating to the Indians. It was not unusual for half a tribe to be wiped out, and occasionally the entire group was practically eliminated. A letter from South Carolina written in March, 1699, stated that smallpox was "said to have swept away a whole neighboring [Indian] nation, all to 5 or 6 which ran away and left their dead unburied, lying upon the ground for the vultures to devour." A smallpox epidemic in 1738 reportedly killed one half of the Cherokee Indians in the vicinity of Charleston, South Carolina.[12] The decimation of the Indians by smallpox will be considered in detail in connection with the middle and southern colonies rather than with New England, which was relatively isolated from the western frontier.

Variolation: the Precursor to Vaccination

It was no accident that the eighteenth century, the age of rationalism and experimentation, should see the introduction of vaccination, the means by which man achieved

[11] Dr. Benjamin Gale to Dr. John Huxham, New York, May 23, 1765, in *Philosophical Transactions*, LV (1765), 193–204; Douglass, *British Settlements*, II, 397–99; I, 530–31.

[12] Mrs. Afra Coming to sister, South Carolina, March 6, 1699, quoted in Edward McCrady, *The History of South Carolina under the Proprietary Government, 1670–1719* (New York, 1897), 308; "A Treaty Between Virginia and the Catawbas and Cherokees, 1756," in *Virginia Magazine of History and Biography*, XIII (1906), 227n. See also John Duffy, "Smallpox and the Indians in the American Colonies," in *Bulletin of the History of Medicine*, XXV (1951), 324–41.

his first victory over contagious diseases. The way for Edward Jenner's first use of this smallpox preventive was prepared by a long series of experiments with another and more drastic method of curbing smallpox, a treatment known as variolation or smallpox inoculation. The technique consisted of transplanting pus from the pustules of a smallpox victim into an incision or puncture in the skin of a healthy person. The resultant infection was usually mild and chances for survival far greater than in cases of infection through ordinary contact. Since the normal case fatality rate ranged anywhere from ten to fifty per cent and the ubiquitous nature of the smallpox virus made infection almost certain during epidemics, thousands of persons resorted to variolation as the lesser of two evils. First used about 1720, the practice steadily increased and continued well into the nineteenth century, long after the introduction of vaccination.

Among the early medical historians the practice of variolation has been treated primarily as an unsuccessful medical innovation, which, after a number of sporadic trials, eventually was displaced by vaccination. This picture, however, is not accurate. In England, where variolation was restricted to a relatively small percentage of the upper classes during the eighteenth century, the practice was of doubtful value; but in the British American colonies, where it was given a more extensive trial, it was an important factor in reducing smallpox fatalities.

In recent years the early origins of variolation have been thoroughly explored, and it is obvious that the introduction of inoculation was no chance happening. Granting the remarkable increase in the number of smallpox victims, it was inevitable that the protective devices discovered by the Negroes and other long-suffering victims of the disease would be adopted by Europeans. A recent study shows conclusively that a number of leading Englishmen, including some reputable physicians, were acquainted with the practice of variolation as early as 1700. In the years 1714 and 1716 letters to the Royal Society from Turkey and Greece confirmed previous rumors of the use of inoculation in that area and described the technique in some detail. One of these, written by Emanuel Timonius from Constantinople in 1714, stressed the necessity for inoculating only those in good health for the best results.[1] Interestingly enough, this latter fact was rediscovered time after time, each physician reporting it as an important contribution to the technique of variolation.

These accounts, however, aroused only academic interest in England until Lady Mary Montagu, wife of the English ambassador to Turkey, successfully experimented on her own son. As a close friend of Princess Caroline, Lady Mary was able to gain the support of the royal family. After experimenting with seven convicts and eleven pauper children, Princess Caroline had her two children inoculated, thereby insuring acceptance of the practice by a good share of England's fashion-conscious upper class.[2]

A further impetus to the cause of inoculation was given by Dr. James Jurin, whose interest led the Royal Society to publish considerable material relating to variolation after 1727 and thus enabled the movement to survive a series of setbacks in the late 1720's. Among the most interesting letters printed in the Society's *Proceedings* were those from two Welsh medical men. Dr. Perrot Williams of Haverford West, Pembrokeshire, Wales, wrote to the Society in 1722

[1] R. P. Stearns, "Remarks upon the Introduction of Inoculation for Smallpox in England," in *Bulletin of the History of Medicine*, XXIV (1950), 103–22; Letter from Emanuel Timonius, Constantinople, December, 1713, in *Philosophical Transactions*, XXIX (1714–16), 72–76.

[2] Creighton, *History of Epidemics*, I, 460–61 n.

that he had long been familiar with the practice. He declared that inoculation had been "commonly practiced by the Inhabitants of this Part of Wales time out of mind, though by another Name, viz. that of buying the Disease," and he cited the testimonials of many older residents to prove his statement. Richard Wright, a surgeon at Haverford West, also wrote to the Society in a similar vein and added that two large villages in the neighborhood were particularly noted for this custom.[3]

Despite its endorsement in influential circles, a violent controversy broke out on the issue of inoculation, and a bitter pamphlet war ensued on both sides of the Atlantic. The protagonists judiciously selected and amassed evidence supporting their particular viewpoints; the successes and failures of the practice in the American colonies supplied ammunition to both sides in England, and, correspondingly, American writers on both sides of the issue were able to reinforce their arguments by citing English examples.

The best history of variolation in England is still found in the classic work on English epidemics by Charles Creighton, published over half a century ago. Creighton traced the growth of the inoculation movement in England and showed that after initial successes, several deaths among socially prominent families caused the practice to fall into disrepute in the years from 1728 to 1740.[4]

However, reports of the success of variolation during the smallpox epidemic in Charleston, South Carolina, in 1738 brought a revival. James Kilpatrick, a physician who had inoculated extensively during this outbreak, came to

[3] Dr. Perrot Williams to Secretary of the Royal Society, Haverford West, Pembrokeshire, Wales, September 28, 1722, and February 2, 1723, in *Philosophical Transactions*, XXXII (1722–23), 262–63, 265–66; Richard Wright to *id.*, Haverford West, Pembrokeshire, Wales, *ibid.*, 267.

[4] Creighton, *History of Epidemics*, II, 489, 504.

London in 1743 and soon achieved a reputation as a scientific inoculator. Kilpatrick, a man with a keen sense for publicity, wrote a series of pamphlets which served both to increase his own prestige and to publicize inoculation.[5] Partly because of his influence, variolation again became a fad among the British upper classes, and as the eighteenth century wore on, its use became well established.

Creighton considered variolation of very doubtful value, and insofar as England was concerned, he was essentially correct. He pointed out that the practice was restricted to a limited class because the high medical fees automatically ruled out the vast majority of Englishmen, who, for the most part, had little if any medical care. Only a few doctors recognized the necessity for general inoculation; and although sporadic attempts were made to provide free variolation service for the poor, the teeming thousands who lived in squalor and misery in the slums of the English cities and towns continued to propagate the infection. The English inoculation hospitals refused to accept children below the age of seven. Since the disease was both endemic and highly contagious, few children could reach seven without contracting it, and more than likely many of those who were inoculated at that age or beyond already possessed a high degree of natural immunity.

As the clinching point to his thesis that variolation was of little practical value, Creighton cited many instances of individuals falling prey to smallpox despite previous inoculation.[6] The temporary nature of smallpox immunity was,

[5] *Ibid.*, 491–92; Kilpatrick's first pamphlet published in 1743 is entitled *An Essay on Inoculation; Occasioned by the Smallpox being brought into S. Carolina in the year 1738* (London, 1743). After settling in London, he obtained an M.D. and later changed his name to Kirkpatrick. At different times he spelled his name Killpatrick or Kilpatrick.

[6] Creighton, *History of Epidemics*, II, 511–16.

however, not generally recognized in Creighton's day, and hence he was led astray in his conclusions. Had he made as thorough a study of the course of variolation in the American colonies as he did for England, it is more than likely that Creighton would have modified his views.

Although the two reports on variolation published in the *Philosophical Transactions* in 1714 and 1716 aroused only academic interest in England, they were directly responsible for the introduction of the practice into America. Dr. William Douglass, the only physician in Boston with a medical degree, lent his copy of the *Transactions* to Cotton Mather. Mather, after reading the reports on variolation, promptly wrote to Dr. John Woodward of the Royal Society in December, 1716:

> I am willing to confirm you, in a favorable opinion, of Dr. Timonius's Comunication; And therefore, I do assure you, that many months before I mett with any Intimations of treating ye Small-Pox, with ye Methods of Inoculation, any where in *Europe*, I had from a Servant of my own, an Account of its being practiced in *Africa*. Enquiring of my Negro-man *Anesimus*, who is a pretty intelligent Fellow, Whether he ever had ye Small-Pox; he answered, both, *Yes*, and *No;* and then told me, that he had undergone an operation, which had given him something of ye *Small-Pox*, and would forever preserve him from it; adding, That it was often used among ye Guramantese, & whoever had ye courage to use it, was forever free from ye fear of the Contagion. He described ye operation to me, and shew'd me in his Arm ye Scar, which it left upon him; and his Description of it, made it the same that afterwards I found related unto you by your Timonius.[7]

[7] Cotton Mather to John Woodward, Boston, December 16, 1716, quoted by George L. Kittredge in his introduction to Increase Mather's *Several Rea-*

Having heard of the practice from two entirely different sources, Mather became convinced of its soundness and urged it upon Douglass. But the physician, a conservative medical practitioner, refused to have anything to do with it—a view shared by nearly all of the other Boston medical men. The only physician who was willing to support Mather was Dr. Zabdiel Boylston. He, too, had discovered that some of the Negro slaves in Boston were familiar with the practice, and he made up his mind that he would give it a trial.

A serious smallpox outbreak in Boston in 1721 afforded the first opportunity for testing this new preventive, and Boylston inoculated both his and Mather's children. As soon as the news was made public, a "horrid clamour" arose from many people in Boston, who held that inoculation was a heathen practice and should not be adopted by Christians. Mather complained in his diary of "the monstrous and crying wickedness of this town, (a Town at this time strangely possessed with the Devil,) and the vile Abuse which I do myself particularly suffer from it, for nothing but my instructing our base Physicians, how to save many precious Lives." This "vile abuse" culminated in an attempt to bomb his house the following November. A "granado" with an attached note was hurled through one of his windows but fortunately did not explode. The bomb-thrower, however, did. "COTTON MATHER, You Dog, Dam you," he wrote, "I'll inoculate you with this, with a Pox to you." Far from deterring Mather, the threat served to fill his mind "with unutterable Joy at the prospect of . . . approaching martyr-

---

sons Proving that inoculating or transplanting the Small Pox, is a lawful practice, and that it has been blessed by God for the saving of many a life and Cotton Mather's *Sentiments on the Small Pox Inoculated* (Cleveland, 1921).

dom."[8] But the martyr's crown was withdrawn when the epidemic subsided and Mather was spared—or denied—this fate.

The two most articulate groups in the colonies were immediately at odds over the question of inoculation. The majority of the physicians were most skeptical, and their attitude is best expressed in the following excerpt from a letter written by Dr. William Douglass to Dr. Cadwallader Colden on May 1, 1722:

> I oppose this novel and dubious practice not being sufficiently assured of its safety and consequences; in short I reckon it a sin to propagate infection by this means and bring on my neighbor a distemper which might prove fatal and which perhaps he might escape (as many have done) in the ordinary way, and which he might certainly secure himself by removal in this Country where it prevails seldom. However, many of our clergy had got into it and they scorn to retract; I had them to appease, which occasioned great Heats (you may perhaps admire how they reconcile this with their doctrine of predestination).[9]

The ministers, as Douglass' letter indicates, welcomed the new prophylaxis and urged its use upon their reluctant congregations. The credit for the increasing use of vario-

[8] Worthington Chauncey Ford (ed.), *Diary of Cotton Mather*, 2 vols. (Boston, 1911–12), in Massachusetts Historical Society *Collections*, Ser. 7, VIII (1709–1724), 634, 657–59 (hereinafter cited as *Diary of Cotton Mather*, with appropriate years).

[9] William Douglass to Cadwallader Colden, Boston, May 1, 1722, in Jared Sparks (ed.), "Letters from Dr. William Douglas[s] to Dr. Cadwallader Colden of New York," in Massachusetts Historical Society *Collections*, Ser. 4, II (1854), 170. Douglass also wrote a pamphlet entitled *The Abuses and Scandals of some late Pamphlets in Favor of Inoculation of the Small Pox, Modestly obviated and Inoculation further considered in a Letter to A*[lexander] *S*[tuart], *M.D., F.R.S.* (Boston, 1722), in which he bitterly denounced Cotton Mather.

lation belongs in large measure to this support from the ministerial profession. They not only recommended it to their people but were among the first to follow their own precepts. Even as late as 1759 an S. P. G. missionary in New Jersey demonstrated its value to his congregation by inoculating his own children. He wrote subsequently to the Society that by his action he had removed the prejudices and scruples of many of his people, who were now following his example.[10]

Not all the churchmen supported the practice. One of them referred to inoculation in a sermon delivered in 1722 as "an unjustifiable act, an affliction of an evil, and a distrust of God's overruling care, to procure us a possible future good." Another declared in the same year that inoculation tended to promote "Vice and Immorality," since individuals set free from the fear of disease tended to lead "intemperate lives." A London pamphleteer, writing in support of inoculation, listed the following religious objections to the practice: "Is it not unlawful to make oneself sick? Ought we not to wait God's time? Can we not trust God? Are we taking God's work out of his hand? And finally, is not smallpox a judgment of God 'sent to punish us and humble us for our sins?' "[11] On the whole, however, insofar as the American colonies were concerned, the contention that

[10] Colin Campbell to the Secretary, Burlington, N. J., December 20, 1759, in S.P.G. MSS., B24, Pt. 1, fpp. 151–53.

[11] Packard, *History of Medicine*, I, 81; Edmund Massey, *A Sermon against the Dangerous and Sinful practice of Inoculation. Preach'd at St. Andrew's Holborn, on Sunday, July the 8th, 1722* (London, 1722), 24; William Cooper, *A reply to the objections made against taking the small pox in the way of inoculation from principles of conscience, etc.* (Boston, 1730). For an account of the introduction of inoculation into America and the subsequent controversy over it see John T. Barrett, "The Inoculation Controversy in Puritan New England," in *Bulletin of the History of Medicine*, XII (1942), 169–90.

smallpox inoculation was a denial of God's will appears to have come primarily from the laity rather than the clergy.

Despite considerable popular disapproval and the opposition of Douglass and other physicians, almost three hundred individuals were inoculated during the Boston epidemic of 1721.[12] Of this total only six died, giving a case fatality rate of about two per cent, which compared favorably with the fourteen per cent death rate among those infected by natural means. Not only Boston but a number of the adjacent towns also gave variolation a trial. Captain John Osborne of Roxbury told how the deaths of thirteen heads of families turned the people to inoculation; as a result forty-three men successfully used the method. A Mr. Walter, the local minister, was given credit for the experiment. Osborne wrote: "The Minister of the Town was the first that put it in Practice there, much against the Mind of his People at first, though afterwards they were very well pleas'd with it." Variolation was also tried in Salem, Massachusetts, in the summer of 1723. Thomas Robie, the local physician, reported in June that so far the method was proceeding satisfactorily and that those inoculated were doing very well, "some better than ever." [13]

Little is heard of variolation in the colonies from 1723 to 1730 when once again major epidemics of smallpox struck Boston, New York, and Philadelphia. The immediate effect was to revive interest in inoculation and hundreds of people turned to this drastic preventive. As early as February the *New England Weekly Journal* carried advertisements for

[12] Zabdiel Boylston, *An Historical Account of the Small-Pox Inoculated in New England, upon all sorts of persons, whites, blacks, and of all ages and constitutions. Etc.* (London, 1726), 40.

[13] "An account by Captain John Osborne of Roxbury, Massachusetts," in *Philosophical Transactions*, XXXII (1722–23), 225–27; Thomas Robie, physician in New England, to the Royal Society, Salem, Massachusetts, June 4, 1723, *ibid.*, XXXIII (1724–25), 67.

the sale of inoculation pamphlets and reprinted articles from English publications favoring inoculation. Shortly thereafter variolation must have been put into practice, since at a Boston town meeting in the middle of March the townsmen resolved that extreme care was to be taken with the use of variolation, and that the physicians were to report the names of all undergoing the operation.[14]

Not only Bostonians, but the residents of surrounding towns endeavored to forestall smallpox by inoculation, and on March 25 the selectmen found it necessary to caution outsiders:

> We being inform'd, That many Persons belonging to the Adjacent Towns intend to come into this Town to have the Small Pox Inoculated upon them, which we apprehend would be much to the damage of this Place, This is therefore to give Publick Notice, That if any Person or Persons, not belonging to this Town shall presume to come into it upon the aforesaid occasion, he or they shall be prosecuted according to Law.

By the time the outbreak in Boston had run its course, approximately four hundred persons had resorted to variolation. Of this group, twelve, or roughly 3 per cent, succumbed to the disease. This 3 per cent case fatality rate, while high from the standpoint of modern medicine, was definitely better than the 12.5 per cent rate suffered by the four thousand odd persons who caught the disease naturally.[15]

[14] *New England Weekly Journal*, No. 153, February 23, 1730, No. 156, March 16, 1730.

[15] Boston *Gazette*, No. 538, March 23–30, 1730; "Description of Boston," in Massachusetts Historical Society *Collections*, Ser. 1, III (1794), 292. In "A Collection of References to Scattered Medical Items and Contributions by early Medical Men found in American Newspapers and Periodicals Printed before 1800," Toner Collection, Library of Congress, the *Pennsylvania Gazette*, No. 82, June 4, 1730, is quoted as stating that 511 persons were inoculated in Boston with only 11 deaths.

In Philadelphia, Benjamin Franklin, whose inquiring mind made him receptive to innovations, was among the first to support the practice. "The practice of inoculation for the smallpox," declared his newspaper, the *Pennsylvania Gazette* in March, 1730, "begins to grow among us. J. Growden, Esq., the first patient of note, is now upon recovery, having had none but the most favorable symptoms during the whole course of the distemper, which is mentioned to show how groundless all those reports are that have been spread through the Province to the contrary." In 1736 one of Franklin's sons, a boy of four, died of smallpox, and it was rumored that the child's death had resulted from inoculation. Franklin, on hearing the rumor, immediately published a short article in his paper specifically denying it and reasserting his confidence in the practice of variolation. Late in 1736 the Boston *Gazette* reported: "We hear from Philadelphia that the Small Pox prevails very much there, and that for preventing its spreading in the Natural Way, they Inoculate with great success." Subsequently the *Gazette* declared that of the total of 129 persons in Philadelphia who had undergone inoculation in the winter of 1736–37 only one had died.[16]

The next large-scale application of inoculation came during the Charleston, South Carolina, smallpox epidemic of 1738. The figures vary as to the exact number submitting to the operation, but the most reliable account states that a total of 441 persons, 188 whites and 253 Negroes were inoculated during the course of the outbreak. Of those so treated, 9 whites and 7 Negroes—or not quite 4 per cent—succumbed. Among those who were infected by natural

[16] *Pennsylvania Gazette,* March 4, 1730, quoted in Packard, *History of Medicine,* I, 80; William Pepper, *The Medical Side of Benjamin Franklin* (Philadelphia, 1911), 15; Boston *Gazette,* No. 880, November 15–21, 1736, No. 923, September 12–19, 1737.

means during the attack the death toll was very heavy and the supporters of variolation found new encouragement.[17]

As already noted, it was in the course of this epidemic that Dr. James Kilpatrick first achieved the recognition which was to make him a leader in the revival of inoculation in England. In his account of the Charleston epidemic he asserted: "I shall, however, rather to come short than exceed, admit but 800 inoculated, which as I have said, is considerably short of the lowest estimate I have heard of: but it is certain, that of these, only six whites, and two negroes died." Kilpatrick, an ardent variolation practitioner, maintained that even these eight deaths resulted from causes other than inoculation. Creighton, who made only a superficial study of smallpox and smallpox inoculation in America, declared that some observers placed the number inoculated at 1,000.[18] Whatever the exact figure, variolation had evidently been tried on a fairly extensive scale and had again demonstrated its value.

By 1750 variolation was practiced in varying degrees in all the colonies. Benjamin Franklin wrote in September, 1750, that smallpox was in Philadelphia, but as "the Doctors inoculate apace" he thought they would soon drive the disease from the town. Within the decade from 1750 to 1760 variolation was given two major tests and emerged successful in both cases. The fourth smallpox epidemic to ravage Boston in the eighteenth century began early in 1752 and lasted until the end of the summer. In midsum-

[17] David Ramsay, *The History of South Carolina from its first Settlement in 1670 to the Year 1808*, 2 vols. (Charleston, 1809), II, 77 n.; the Boston *Weekly News-Letter*, No. 1809, November 16–23, 1738, lists 1,675 cases infected by natural means with 295 deaths. A total of 436 persons were inoculated and of these only 16 died.

[18] Kilpatrick, *Essay on Inoculation*, 33; Joseph Ioor Waring, "James Killpatrick and Smallpox Inoculation in Charleston," *Annals of Medical History*, N.S., X (1938), 303; Creighton, *History of Epidemics*, II, 490.

mer, when the worst was over, the selectmen made a careful check of the town and found that there had been a total of 7,653 cases during the outbreak. Of these, 5,544 had taken it naturally and another 2,109 were inoculated. The death tolls numbered 504 among the natural cases and 31 through inoculation, representing case fatality rates of 9.1 per cent and 1.5 per cent respectively.[19] Thus the Boston outbreak added further proof to the efficacy of variolation.

In 1760 a particularly virulent smallpox attack plagued Charleston, and, as in the case of Boston, the population turned in droves to inoculation. A local newspaper reported in March that "since last Monday, upwards of 2,000 persons have been inoculated for the Small Pox in this Town. One gentleman alone we are informed has upwards of 600 Patients." David Ramsay, in his history of South Carolina, declared that 1,500 were inoculated in one day. Indicating the widespread use of variolation, he added that "only ninety-two died under inoculation." [20]

The steadily increasing success of inoculation in Boston is clearly illustrated by a chart published at the end of the eighteenth century by the Massachusetts Historical Society:[21]

Date	*No. Inoculated*	*Deaths*	*Proportions*
1721	247	6	1 *in* 42
1730	400	12	1 *in* 33
1752	2,109	31	1 *in* 70
1764	4,977	46	1 *in* 108
1776	4,988	28	1 *in* 178
1778	2,121	19	1 *in* 112
1792	9,152	165	1 *in* 55

[19] Benjamin Franklin to the Reverend Samuel Johnson, Philadelphia, September, 1750, quoted in Pepper, *Medical Side of Franklin*, 26; Boston, *Weekly News-Letter*, No. 2614, July 30, 1752.

[20] Boston *News-Letter*, No. 2063, March 13, 1760; Ramsay, *History of South Carolina*, II, 79.

With the exception of the years 1776 and 1778, the number inoculated during smallpox epidemics rose steadily. The decrease in 1778 is obviously due to the relatively low number of nonimmunes left in the town after the two previous epidemics of 1764 and 1776. The figure of 2,121 for 1778 probably represents the additional births since 1776, plus the refugees and military personnel housed in Boston as a result of the vicissitudes of war. Up to 1776 the ratio of fatalities tended to decrease, but the rate of death rose sharply in the next two epidemics. The explanation probably lies in the fact that the early tendency had been to inoculate only the well. As the success of variolation became more evident, it was used with far less discretion, as the figure of 9,152 in 1792 indicates, and an increase in the mortality rate resulted.

The obvious success of variolation did not soothe the outcries against it, and criticism continued well past the middle of the century. The detractors of the practice were given ample ammunition through the careless techniques of many of the inoculators. It was not unusual after inoculation for a patient to continue "to do all Things, as at other times," taking only the precaution not to expose himself "unto the injuries of the Weather, if that be at all Tempestuous." As smallpox developed, the patient went to bed only when necessary. Even the event of retiring to bed did not inconvenience him greatly, for as one author explained, "Ordinarily the Patient sits up every Day, and entertains his Friends, yea ventures upon a Glass of Wine with them." [22]

[21] "Description of Boston," *loc. cit.*

[22] Henry Newman, "The Way of Proceeding in the Small Pox Inoculation in New England," *Philosophical Transactions*, XXXII (1722–23), 33–34. See also Solomon Drown, "A Long Journal of a Short Voyage from Providence to N. York. With an Account of my having the Small-Pox by Inoculation in that City . . . from September 10th to October 12th, 1772," in New-York Historical Society MSS.

One can well imagine the effect of two or three hundred active smallpox cases wandering around a community continuing to "do all Things, as at other times," or entertaining their friends in the sickroom. The healthy individual inoculated with smallpox usually suffered only a mild case, but the germs he passed on were virile and potent.

The abuses in the practice of variolation led to many attempts to prohibit or control it by means of proclamations and laws. At one time or another nearly all the colonies prohibited the practice, but many of the laws either lapsed or were subsequently amended or repealed. An example of these laws was one enacted during the smallpox epidemic of 1738 in Charleston, which prohibited smallpox inoculation in and around the city. The act was explicitly titled, "An Act for the better preventing of the spreading of the infection of the Small Pox in Charlestown." Governor George Clinton of New York issued a proclamation in 1747 "strictly prohibiting and forbidding all and every of the Doctors, Physicians, Surgeons, and Practitioners of Physick, and all and every other persons within this Province, to inoculate for small pox any persons or person within the City and County of New York, on pain of being prosecuted to the utmost rigour of the law." Because smallpox outbreaks were too frequently the result of careless inoculation, dozens of petitions were presented to the colonial legislatures, such as the one "setting forth the destructive Tendencies of Inoculation with the Small-Pox; and therefore praying that no such Practices may be allowed in Virginia," which was submitted to the Virginia House of Burgesses in 1769. The same Journal of the House later noted petitions from "divers inhabitants" opposing the practice.[23]

[23] Waring, "James Killpatrick and Smallpox Inoculation in Charleston," *loc cit.*, 303, 308n.; Proclamation of Governor George Clinton of New

The correspondence of William Nelson, the Virginia representative of English merchant John Norton, reveals the occasion for the Virginia petitions against inoculation during the late 1760's. On August 14, 1767, Nelson wrote:

> Our Country man Mr. Smith arrived in high Spirits: hath set up his hospital for Inoculation at Flat's Bay; and proposes to begin his business as soon as the weather grows cooler: But some People object to his bringing the infection to a Country or Neighbourhood that is free from it; If it comes by chance, then let him begin & prosper as fast as he pleases: However he goes to Baltimore soon with some of his own family; wch. he will begin upon there and bring with him matter enough to infect the world, A second Pandora's Box.

Unfortunately Nelson's fears were only too well founded, for the following February he reported: "Mr. John Smith hath rendered himself very blamable and unpopular suffering some of his Patients to go abroad too soon: so that the Distemper hath spread in two or three Parts of the Country: some of the College youths carried it to Wmsburgh where two or three have died, but by the care of the Magistrates it is stopped." [24] In light of the Virginia incident it is not surprising to find William Douglass writing that smallpox arrived in Boston in January, 1751, and that on March 23 "inoculation was let loose." However, despite his early bitter opposition to the practice, Douglass finally admitted its merits. "We may confidently pronounce," he wrote, "that

York, June 6, 1747, quoted in Packard, *History of Medicine,* I, 82; John P. Kennedy (ed.), *Journals of the House of Burgesses of Virginia,* 1766–69 (Richmond, 1909), 203, 269.

[24] William Nelson to John Norton, Virginia, August 14, 1767, in Francis Norton Mason (ed.), *John Norton & Sons, Merchants of London and Virginia* (Richmond, 1937), 31–32; *id.* to *id.*, February 27, 1768, *ibid.*, 38.

those who have had a genuine smallpox by inoculation never can have the smallpox again in a natural way, both by reason and experience."[25]

By 1760 the tendency was to regulate inoculation rather than to prohibit it. The laws usually prescribed the conditions under which variolation could be performed and set the duration of the quarantine period, and sometimes established minimum standards for the inoculation hospitals. Most of the early laws were rewritten or amended in the succeeding years, and by 1775 the practice was well established with reasonable legal safeguards for the public welfare in nearly all the Middle and Southern colonies.

New England, which had led the way in the use of variolation, later turned against it, and by 1790 its use was strictly forbidden in all the New England states. This prohibition may have resulted from the many infractions of the regulations, but the strictly enforced quarantine laws also served to keep smallpox under control ordinarily. In the Middle and Southern colonies, where the disease became far more prevalent in the latter part of the century, variolation was permitted at all times. Even in New England the laws were usually suspended during smallpox epidemics; at the time of the Boston outbreak in 1776 diarist William Cheever noted on November 24, that "Permission was given for Inoculation of the Small-Pox." During the Boston epidemics of 1778 and 1792 the laws were again relaxed, with over 9,000 resorting to inoculation during the latter outbreak.[26]

[25] Douglass, *British Settlements*, II, 397–98; Creighton, *History of Epidemics*, II, 486.

[26] William Currie, *An Historical Account of the Climates and Diseases of the United States of America, etc.* (Philadelphia, 1792), 3, 39–40; "William Cheever's Diary, 1775–1776," in Massachusetts Historical Society *Proceedings*, LX (1927), 95; "Description of Boston," *loc. cit.*

In addition to the legal restrictions placed upon inoculation, the physicians and surgeons at times voluntarily agreed to stop inoculating for a given period. Thus the physicians of Philadelphia met in September, 1774, and agreed to cease the practice during the sitting of the First Continental Congress, "as several of the Northern and Southern delegates are understood not to have had that disorder." However, once the Revolutionary War broke out, smallpox was soon carried to every colony, and as a result inoculation was practiced widely. In fact, on the recommendation of Dr. John Morgan, physician in chief of the American armies, Washington ordered a general inoculation of the American forces, and inoculation hospitals were established at various locations for this purpose.[27] This mass experiment is another indication of the colonial empirical approach to medical matters.

There is no question that smallpox inoculation was a great boon to eighteenth-century Americans. Although some improvement was made in medical treatment, variolation was the major factor in reducing fatalities from smallpox as the century advanced. Admittedly, uncontrolled inoculation was responsible for spreading the infection in the first thirty or forty years of its use, but smallpox epidemics steadily lessened in intensity, and with this decline came a corresponding diminishment of the terror which this plague had formerly aroused. By the end of the colonial period the procedure of inoculation was well standardized, and some of its practitioners even advertised their skill:

> Sutton and Lathom, Have open'd Apartments for Inoculation, where Patients will be carefully attended and every

[27] Packard, *History of Medicine*, I, 89; Morris C. Leikind, "Variolation in Europe and America," *Ciba Symposia*, III (1942), 1124.

Thing necessary provided. Their Price for Inoculation is Three Pounds four Shillings, New-York Currency.

As there may be some persons willing to be inoculated but who Cannot conveniently pay even so small a Sum as Half a Johannes, they are inform'd the Price shall be adapted to their Circumstances.

Mr. Lathom inoculates from Six Weeks old and every Month in the Year. For further Particulars, Application to be made to Mr. Lathom at his House on Broad-Street.[28]

Not only did variolation serve as a relatively effective check upon smallpox in the colonies, but it also paved the way for the immediate acceptance of vaccination both in England and in America. Although the earlier method was never tried on a large scale in Great Britain, physicians there were well acquainted with the techniques; when Edward Jenner made his revolutionary discovery of vaccination at the close of the century, his method was immediately accepted. The way for vaccination had been well prepared, and during his lifetime Jenner was awarded the honors and distinctions that had come to most of his predecessors only posthumously. In America vaccination first gained support in New England and the Middle colonies, and as it spread, it "broke up the inoculation of smallpox." By 1805, vaccination was reported to be in general use.[29] Thus variolation made its contribution to the preparation of both the Old World and the New for the process which was to subdue smallpox for all time.

[28] New York *Gazette and Weekly Mercury*, January 7, 1776, quoted in New-York Historical Society *Collections*, LXIX (1936), 305.

[29] Dr. [?] Fancher, "Progress of Vaccination in America," Massachusetts Historical Society *Collections*, Ser. 2, IV (1816), 97; Benjamin Rush, *Medical Inquiries and Observations*, 4 vols. (2d ed., Philadelphia, 1805), IV, 390.

Smallpox in New England

As with many other diseases, the date of the first smallpox outbreak in New England is still uncertain. Smallpox has been blamed for the devastation among the Indians prior to the landing of the *Mayflower*. However, the best existing evidence indicates that some other infection was the culprit and that smallpox did not begin its terrible course until it arrived with the mass migration to New England led by John Winthrop in 1630. Puritan Francis Higginson related in his account of the voyage that both his children were infected and that one of them subsequently died. The contagion seized a number of others on the ship, but Higginson was able to conclude, "Yet thanks be to God none dyed of it but my own childe." Another voyager wrote of his passage in March, 1631, that "we ware wondurfule seick as we cam at sea withe the small Poxe." He and his child barely survived the attack which took the lives of fourteen persons en route.[1] The presence of the disease on the ships coming from England was the factor which enabled the colonists later to pass through the first epidemic in the colony with relative ease.

It was not until four years afterward that this first major epidemic developed. At that time, according to William Bradford, three or four Dutch traders carried smallpox to the Indians on the Connecticut River, and soon the natives "fell sick of the small poxe, and dyed most miserably; for a sorer disease cannot befall them; they fear it worse than the plague; for usually they that have this dis-

[1] Herbert U. Williams, "Epidemics among Indians 1616–1620," in *Johns Hopkins Hospital Bulletin*, XX (1909), 340–49, after evaluating all available evidence concluded that the 1616 epidemic was bubonic plague; *The Hutchinson Papers* (Albany, 1865), 39–42.

ease have them in abundance . . . they dye like rotten sheep. . . . But by the marvelous goodness and providens of God not one of the English was so much as sicke, or in the least measure tainted with this disease. . . ." The English settlers had already gained immunity from previous exposure, but to contemporary observers it seemed a miraculous preservation. Though Bradford claimed that none of the English were affected, John Winthrop wrote his son that a young boy had "died of the small pox which are very rife at Newtowne." [2] The Dutch traders may have been responsible for taking the disease to the Indians, but it is not at all unlikely that the English shared at least part of the blame.

In the fall of 1638 the colony was plagued by "spotted feaver" and smallpox to such an extent that a fast was observed in December. In this same month Thomas Dudley wrote from Roxbury that there were a large number of cases of "spotted fever" and three of smallpox. John Brock of Dedham wrote that on his recovery from "spotted fever" in 1639 he was seized with smallpox, which "was a sore affliction" and which had brought death to many "that came with us." [3]

A general epidemic of smallpox struck the Massachusetts Bay colony in 1648–49. The severity of the attack varied from town to town, and in Boston the disease was relatively mild. "We blese god we are in some measure of

[2] J. Franklin Jameson (ed.), *Bradford's History of Plymouth Plantation, 1606–1646*, in *Original Narratives of Early American History Series* published by American Historical Association (New York, 1908), 312–13; John Winthrop to John Winthrop, Jr., December 12, 1634, in *Winthrop Papers*, 5 vols. (Boston, 1929–47), III, 177.

[3] Noah Webster, *A Brief History of Epidemic and Pestilential Diseases . . .*, 2 vols. (Hartford, 1799), I, 185; Thomas Dudley to John Winthrop, Roxbury, December 11, 1638, in *Winthrop Papers*, IV, 86; Clifford K. Shipton (ed.), "The Autobiographical Memoranda of John Brock, 1636–1659," in American Antiquarian Society *Proceedings*, LIII (1944), 98.

health," wrote Amos Richardson in October, 1649, "tho many among us in the towne are and have bin viseted with the small pox." In some of the outlying communities the infection was more virulent. A minister in Roxbury recorded in September "a general visitation by the small pox, whereof many died," and the Scituate and Barnstable church records show that a "Day of Humiliation" was declared on November 15 for, among other things, the "many Children in the Bey dyeing bye the Chin cough & the pockes."[4] The combination of smallpox and whooping cough undoubtedly took a heavy toll among the children born since the previous smallpox outbreak.

For almost twenty years the colonies remained relatively free of the infection. In 1666 the first cases of what was to become a major smallpox epidemic appeared in Boston, indicating that the infection was probably imported from England. However, the disease had prevailed among the French and Indians in Canada for the five previous years, and it may have arrived via the Indians. In any case it first spread in the summer and increased in virulence with the coming of winter. One diarist, John Hull, estimated the number of cases at "several hundreds" and the deaths "betwixt forty and fifty." Simon Bradstreet recorded in his journal that "the small poxe was exceeding rife . . . tho: it pleased god but few dyed of it. (There dyed about 40)." The number of fast days which were observed at this time indicates the seriousness of the attack.[5]

[4] Douglass, *British Settlements*, II, 382 n.; Webster, *A History of Epidemic Diseases*, I, 188; "Rev. Samuel Danforth's Records of the First Church in Roxbury, Mass.," in *New England Historical and Genealogical Register*, XXXIV (1880), 85; "Scituate and Barnstable Church Records," *ibid.*, X (1856), 38.

[5] Heagerty, *Four Centuries of Medical History*, I, 27; "Diary of John Hull," in American Antiquarian Society *Proceedings*, III (1857), 223; "[Simon] Bradstreet's Journal," *New England Historical and Genealogical Register*, IX (1855), 43.

Nine years later a few cases again appeared in New England. Increase Mather wrote, "The Ld. hath lifted up his hand agt. Boston in yt ye smallpox hath bin in ye harbor." The town of Gloucester, he added, was also infected.[6] Since none of his contemporaries mention the attack, it is very likely that the crude quarantine methods of the day proved effective in checking its spread.

Although Boston had successfully weathered the danger in 1675, it was not so fortunate two years later when the disease struck with full force. A number of English ships brought the infection into Charlestown in the summer of 1677; from there it soon spread across the Charles River to Boston. The main attack hit Charlestown during the winter of 1677–78, but in Boston the peak of the epidemic was not reached until the following September. On June 6, a public fast was decreed, for by this time more than 80 deaths had occurred in the two towns. It proved of little avail: Increase Mather stated in his diary that, by the end of July, 7 or 8 people were dying each week in Boston alone. By September the deaths had surged upwards; 30 persons died in one day, and 150 within a four-week period. John Hull noted in his journal on September 22 that "to this time, there were about eighty persons at Charltown that died of the small-pox, and about seven hundred that have had the disease." On October 3 he estimated that 180 deaths from the disease had occurred in Boston "in a little above a year's space since the disease began." Another journalist about the same time placed the death toll between 200 and 300, and declared that the sickness "rages still as much as ever." Samuel Sewall, who nearly lost his life to the disease

[6] Samuel A. Green (ed.), *Diary by Increase Mather, March, 1675–December, 1676. Together with extracts from another diary by him, 1674–1687* (Cambridge, 1900), 20–21.

in the fall of 1678, did not attempt an estimate of the loss in his diary, but he subsequently wrote to his son that "multitudes died." John Saffin grieved over the loss of his wife and two sons in 1678 from "that Deadly Disease of ye Small pox." [7]

Significantly none of the observers of the outbreak mention the presence of the infection outside Boston or Charlestown. The town records of Marblehead contain a quarantine notice issued in 1677 prohibiting the landing of passengers or seamen from a ship infected with smallpox, and in all likelihood similar restrictions were placed by the various New England communities against all persons coming from the epidemic areas.[8] Throughout the colonial period New England was by far the most successful in isolating epidemic infections, and it can safely be assumed that their methods proved effective in this case. One incidental result of the epidemic was the printing of the first medical work published in America, Thomas Thacher's pamphlet, *A Brief Rule to Guide the Common People of New England how to order themselves and theirs in the Small Pocks, or Measles.*

In the ensuing years a few isolated cases of smallpox are mentioned in the records but no outbreak of any significance occurred. For example, the selectmen of the town of Salem took action to prevent the landing of persons from infected ships in 1680, 1683, and 1685, and Increase Mather mentioned the disease in 1685–86. At Dover, New

[7] Green (ed.), *Diary by Increase Mather*, 49 ff.; "Diary of John Hull," *loc. cit.*, 243–45; "Bradstreet's Journal," *loc. cit.*, 48–49; Samuel Sewall to son, Boston, April 4, 1720, in *New England Historical and Genealogical Register*, I (1847), 113; The Note-Book of John Saffin, 1665–1708, in New-York Historical Society MSS., 9.

[8] "Documents Relating to Marblehead, Mass.," in *Historical Collections* of the Essex Institute, LIV (1918), 276.

Hampshire, two cases were reported by John Pike in this same winter, but each time the infection was checked.[9]

A major epidemic broke out in 1689–90 and soon became widespread in Canada and New England, and as far south as New York. It appeared in Massachusetts in October, 1689, following the arrival from the West Indies of a group of infected Negroes and slowly spread through Boston and the surrounding towns. The first public fast because of smallpox was decreed on March 6, and, as the epidemic increased in intensity during the summer months, the General Court proclaimed another one on July 10. *Public Occurrences,* America's first newspaper, declared that the epidemic was more widespread, but not so fatal, as the previous one of twelve years earlier. The editor estimated the death toll to be about 320 and added that the infection, which raged most in June, July, and August, attacked "all sorts of people," even "children in the bellies of Mothers." [10]

Salem was among the towns affected by the disease, and the town records of 1690 indicate that the selectmen were active in providing for the provisioning and care of the sick. Deaths from smallpox were reported in Hampton, New Hampshire, and other New England towns. In 1692 smallpox appeared in Portsmouth and Greenland, N. H.[11]

[9] "Salem Town Records, Town Meetings," *ibid.*, LXII (1926), 86–87; Green (ed.), *Diary by Increase Mather*, 49 ff.; "Journal of John Pike," in New Hampshire Historical Society *Collections,* III (1832), 42.

[10] Isaac Newton Stokes, *The Iconography of Manhattan Island, 1498–1909* (New York, 1922), IV, 357. Heagerty, *Four Centuries of Medical History,* I, 67, claims that New England troops developed smallpox while attacking Quebec in 1690 and later carried the disease to New England. See also Packard, *History of Medicine*, I, 75; Victor Hugo Paltsits, "New Light on 'Publick Occurrences,' America's First Newspaper," in American Antiquarian Society *Proceedings,* LIX (1950), 80–81.

[11] "Salem Town Records, Town Meetings," *loc. cit.*, LXVIII (1932), 315; "Journal of John Pike," *loc. cit.*, 44; John Wentworth to Jeremy

Ten years elapsed before smallpox returned to the colonies. It was reintroduced by a returning seaman who brought the infection to Stonington, Connecticut, where it took at least four lives. Fortunately the outbreak was localized, and New England was spared for another year. In the summer of 1702 the disease broke out anew in Boston and coursed through the town during the winter, not wearing itself out until well into the spring of 1703. An accompanying attack of scarlet fever added to the difficulties confronting the citizens. In December, evidently the peak month of the epidemic, Cotton Mather wrote in his diary: "More than four-score people were in this black Month of *December*, carried from this Town to their long Home." Mather's family suffered heavily; three children and a maid were all seized with the infection within the space of a month.[12]

The figures vary as to the actual mortality from smallpox, but it was apparently around three hundred. Since the population of Boston in 1700 was approximately seven thousand, the outbreak, in relation to some of the others in this period, was not too severe. The presence of scarlet fever which also took its toll complicates the problem of determining the actual smallpox fatalities. As was the usual practice during epidemics, the General Court moved the place of its November meeting from Boston to Cambridge to avoid the danger of infection. Other than to Salem Village, where a fast was ordained because of smallpox deaths, the infection does not appear to have spread beyond the city. However, the Boston outbreak coincided with an attack in

---

Belknap, Portsmouth, March 10, 1774, in *Belknap Papers*, Massachusetts Historical Society *Collections*, Ser. 6, IV (1891), 47.

[12] Frank Denison Miner and Hannah Miner (eds.), *Diary of Manasseh Minor* (n.p., 1915), 42–46; Webster, *History of Epidemic Diseases*, II, 53; *Diary of Cotton Mather*, *loc. cit.*, VII (1681–1708), 451.

Canada which was estimated to have killed one fourth of the inhabitants of Quebec.[13]

Although an occasional case shows up in the diaries of the period, no serious epidemic seems to have occurred in New England between 1702 and 1721. The records of the town of Providence, Rhode Island, in July, 1716, mention the smallpox "that hath bin and is now in ye Towne." Samuel Sewall expressed a typical colonial attitude toward the contagion when he noted in 1718 that "Dr. Clark says the Small pocks is in Town. Capt. Sargent of Newbury, his daughter, has it in Charter-Street. The Lord be Merciful to Boston!" [14] Fortunately, either Dr. Clark was wrong, or the quarantine methods already in force proved effective, for the records make no other reference to smallpox in this year.

Boston's second major epidemic of the eighteenth century struck the city in April, 1721. Dr. William Douglass wrote to Cadwallader Colden that the infection came from Barbados and was restricted to a few cases on the waterfront until June when it "broke loose generally." For the next few months business was at a standstill. All intercourse was shunned, and the streets were deserted with the exception of wagons carrying the dead and of a few doctors and nurses visiting the victims. Late in September the selectmen had to make provision for boats to bring wood into the city because the regular boatmen refused to enter, and the Boston *Gazette* reluctantly conceded that 110 deaths had occurred

[13] John Hayward, *A Gazetteer of Massachusetts* (Boston, 1847), 41; Douglass, *British Settlements*, II, 395–99; "John Marshall's Diary," Massachusetts Historical Society *Proceedings*, XXI (1884–85), 156; Heagerty, *Four Centuries of Medicine*, I, 68.

[14] *The Early Records of the Town of Providence*, 21 vols. (Providence, 1897), XIII, 5; *Diary of Samuel Sewall*, 1700–1714, in Massachusetts Historical Society *Collection*, Ser. 5, VII (1882), 207.

and that "upwards of Fifteen Hundred [persons were] well Recovered of that Distemper." [15]

The mortality figures starkly depict the ravages of this scourge. In the spring of 1722 the selectmen of Boston ordered a complete investigation of the outbreak. The final report showed that of 10,670 people in Boston, 5,980 were infected and 844 subsequently died. Douglass, writing in 1722, estimated that there were about 6,000 cases of which 899 were fatal—a figure slightly higher than that given by the selectmen, but in general corroborative. He added that, of the inhabitants who remained in town but who had not previously been infected, only about 700 escaped the disease. Twenty years later he estimated the population of Boston to have been around 12,000 at the outbreak of the disorder. His figure is supported by all contemporary evidence.[16] Therefore, one half of the town fell victim to the malady; and of these, over 14 per cent died—a ratio of one in seven.

The mortality rate was high for large-scale smallpox epidemics in colonial America; yet it compares favorably with the 18 to 40 per cent fatalities reported for outbreaks

[15] For a short account of the 1721 outbreak, along with a discussion of variolation, see Reginald H. Fitzgerald, "Smallpox, Boston, 1721," in *Johns Hopkins Hospital Bulletin*, XXII (1911), 315–27; Sparks (ed.), "Letters from Dr. William Douglass to Dr. Cadwallader Colden of New York, *loc. cit.*, 166; *Boston Record Commissioners*, VIII (Boston, 1883), 154; Thomas Amory to Francis Holmes, Boston, October 23, 1721, in Business Letterbook of Thomas Amory, Amory Papers, Manuscript Division, Library of Congress; Boston *Gazette*, No. 96, September 18–25, 1721.

[16] Douglass, *British Settlements*, I, 530–31; Thomas Hutchinson, *The History of the Province of Massachusetts-Bay . . .*, 3 vols. (Boston, 1767), II, 273; "Letters from Dr. William Douglass to Dr. Cadwallader Colden of New York," *loc. cit.*, 167. Boylston, *An Historical Account of the Smallpox Inoculated*, 39–40, gives a total of 5,759 cases by natural means, of whom 844 died, and 244 cases by inoculation, with 6 deaths; Boston *News-Letter*, No. 943; February 19–26, 1722, lists a total of 5,889 cases resulting in 844 deaths.

in English towns and cities. As already noted, variolation served to minimize the effects of subsequent epidemics in the colonies, and the fatality rate tended to decline.

Unfortunately for New England, smallpox was not confined to Boston. The refugees who fled from Boston probably carried the infection to the neighboring towns, causing a series of outbreaks. The diary of the Reverend William Homes of Martha's Vineyard records that the pestilence prevailed at Sandwich in the fall of 1721. Samuel Sewall, Jr., mentioned deaths from the infection in Cambridge, Roxbury, Brookline, and Medford in 1721–22. Cotton Mather spoke of smallpox in Cambridge in June, 1721, and later in Marblehead, in January, 1722. In Connecticut the legislature felt it necessary during 1722 to pass two laws bearing on smallpox. One sought to prevent the spreading of the disease, the other exempted physicians and chirurgeons from military duty. These measures may have been precautionary, but it is probable that at least a few cases of the disease prevailed in the colony. Nor did Rhode Island escape, although the outbreak there seemingly was a minor one. An article in the Boston *News-Letter* in June, 1721, declared that Rhode Island was free of the infection but that twenty cases were quarantined two miles from Newport.[17]

During the next eight years smallpox apparently disappeared from the New England colonies, reappearing again in 1730 when Boston was scourged by its third smallpox epidemic of the century. Douglass stated that the plague

[17] "Diary of Rev. William Homes of Chilmark, Martha's Vineyard," in *New England Historical and Genealogical Register*, L (1896), 157; *The Letter-Book of Samuel Sewall* in Massachusetts Historical Society *Collections*, Ser. 6, II (1888), 301–304; *Diary of Cotton Mather, loc. cit.*, 1709–1724, 600 ff.; Packard, *History of Medicine*, I, 168–69; Boston *News-Letter*, No. 906, June 22–26, 1721.

was imported from Ireland late in 1729. The first notice of the disease in the local newspapers was an announcement in the *New England Weekly Journal* on October 27 that the ministers would turn the coming Friday into a day of fasting and prayer because of the danger from smallpox. In the succeeding issues for November and December the *Journal* and the selectmen united in proclaiming that Boston was free of the disease—with the exception of two or three mild cases now recovering in the hospital.[18] In this they were following the customary policy of denying emphatically the presence of contagions until the outbreak became too self-apparent. At such a point the newspapers would fall discreetly silent until the worst was over, when they could assert that the city was now clear of the infection—excepting, of course, a few cases "now upon recovery."

On January 12, 1730, the Boston *Gazette* and the *Journal* both indignantly denied the "several Reports [which] have been made relating to the Small-Pox by some Ill-minded Persons," and concluded that "at this Day, thro' the Goodness of GOD, we cannot understand that there is One Person that keeps their Bed for that Distemper in the whole Town." Having thus dismissed the matter, the papers said nothing further, although in March a series of notices in the *Gazette* informed the public that the Court of Probates of Wills, the Inferior Court of Common Pleas, and the Court of General Sessions would temporarily be moved from Boston because of smallpox.[19]

In May President Benjamin Wadsworth of Harvard

[18] Douglass, *British Settlements*, II, 396–97; *New England Weekly Journal*, No. 136, October 27, No. 140, November 24, No. 141, December 1, No. 143, December 15, 1729.

[19] *New England Weekly Journal*, No. 147, January 12, 1730; Boston *Gazette*, No. 529, January 5–12, No. 536, March 9–16, No. 538, March 23–30, 1730.

notified the public through the press that since smallpox had ceased in Cambridge, the students were ordered "forthwith [to] repair to the college." The worst may have been over in Cambridge, but in Boston the weekly burials continued to average close to forty until August 17, when the number fell off sharply to eight and remained relatively low for the rest of the year. By October 12 the *Journal* reported that the town was clear of the infection and that those who had fled to the country were now returning. As a matter of fact, however, the disease lurked in town for another year: even as late as November of 1731 the selectmen conceded the presence of one or two cases.[20]

As was the case with previous major epidemics, life in Boston came virtually to a standstill—not at all surprising in view of the fact that the best estimates placed the casualties at about 4,000 cases and 500 deaths. The case mortality rate of about one in eight, or 12.5 per cent, was only slightly lower than for the epidemic of 1721–22, but variolation was still in an experimental stage.

If we may assume that the town's population at this time was around 14,000, 25 to 30 per cent of the inhabitants fell victim to the disorder during the outbreak. A large percentage of the sick were children born since the previous epidemic. Dr. Timothy Cutler of Boston stated that he alone of his family had escaped the infection, and the Boston papers mentioned one family in which the father and five of six children died within a twelve-day period.[21]

[20] *New England Weekly Journal*, Nos. 163–84, May 4–October 12, 1730; Boston *Gazette*, Nos. 619–20, November 1–15, 1731.

[21] Douglass estimated the population of Boston to be 11,000 in 1720, and 15,000 in 1735, "Account of Burials and Baptisms in Boston," in Massachusetts Historical Society *Collections*, Ser. 1, IV (1795), 213–16; Hayward, *Gazetteer of Massachusetts*, 41; Timothy Cutler to Secretary, Boston, February 2, 1730, in S.P.G. MSS., A22, fpp. 141–43; Boston *Weekly News-Letter*, No. 179, May 28–June 4, 1730.

Neighboring towns, too, were affected: at least one death occurred in Medfield; fifty-seven cases were reported in Windham; five out of seven cases in one part of Norwich, Connecticut, proved fatal; and a correspondent from Chatham declared that smallpox was raging among the Indians and that "not so much as one has yet escaped." The disease must have been restricted to Massachusetts, however, since the governor of Connecticut proclaimed a day of thanksgiving in October, 1730, "for the Preservation of the Inhabitants of this colony, from the spreading of that infection which has so much Distressed a Principal part of the neighboring province." [22]

For a few years smallpox lay dormant, with the exception of an outbreak at Wallingford, Connecticut, where fifty or sixty cases caused fourteen deaths in the spring of 1732. The island of Martha's Vineyard was next to pay toll to smallpox, for an epidemic occurred in the winter of 1737–38. The towns of Chilmark and Edgartown bore the brunt of the attack which struck seventeen adults and twenty-six children, leaving twelve dead in its wake. The following summer, smallpox appeared in Newport, Rhode Island. In June eleven deaths were reported and it was not until July 20 that an official statement proclaimed the epidemic at an end. As of that date, sixty-seven cases had resulted in seventeen deaths.[23] In these three epidemics the case fatality rate averaged above 25 per cent—a high figure for the colonies.

[22] *The Weekly News-Letter*, No. 198, October 1–8, No. 200, October 22–29, 1730; *New England Weekly Journal*, No. 163, May 4, No. 177, August 11, 1730; "Diary of William Homes of Chilmark, Martha's Vineyard," *loc. cit.*, 163; Boston *Weekly News-Letter*, No. 1400, November 19–26, 1730.

[23] Boston *Weekly News-Letter*, No. 1477, May 11–18, 1732; No. 1838, June 7–14, No. 1844, July 19–26, 1739; "Diary of William Homes of Chilmark, Martha's Vineyard," *loc. cit.*, 164; Boston *Gazette*, No. 942, January 23–30, 1738.

Only two smallpox outbreaks affected New England in the succeeding twelve years: a minor attack at Portsmouth, New Hampshire, and a more severe one at Harwich, Massachusetts. The Portsmouth epidemic was serious enough, however, to cause the justices to adjourn the General Sessions. Two weeks later a sum of money was voted to build a house of quarantine for those infected, indicating only a few cases. The epidemic was probably seaborne, for the provincial records of New Hampshire for the 1740's make many references to vessels quarantined because of smallpox.[24]

In the case of Harwich a group of local seamen caught the disease in Philadelphia and on their return home in March spread the infection throughout the town. Benjamin Bangs mentions nine deaths from the disease in his diary and noted on July 28 that an "abundance of people die with it and [it] is spread all over the place."[25]

In an article written in 1780, Thomas Pownall, a former governor of Massachusetts, wrote of "a great depopulation by small-pox and war" which had occurred in Massachusetts from 1742 to 1751.[26] When he looked back thirty years, Pownall may well have confused his dates. No evidence of smallpox has been found in this period in Boston nor in any other part of New England, except for the two outbreaks mentioned above. Boston was free from the disease from 1731 to 1751, except for three or four isolated

[24] Nathaniel Bouton (ed.), *Provincial Papers, Documents and Records Relating to the Province of New Hampshire . . .*, 7 vols. (Concord, 1867–73), V (1871), 8, 98, 113, 124, 507, 512–13. (Hereinafter cited as *Documents and Records of New Hampshire.)*

[25] Diary of Benjamin Bangs, 1742–1765, Massachusetts Historical Society MSS., March 24–July 28, 1747.

[26] F. B. Dexter, "Estimates of Population," in American Antiquarian Society *Proceedings*, N.S., V (1887), 27.

cases in March, 1745. Pownall's statement has been quoted widely but it is incorrect if it implies that smallpox prevailed during all or any considerable part of this time. True, the New Englanders suffered greatly from the war and concomitant Indian troubles, but smallpox was no problem until its reappearance in Boston in 1751.

In this year smallpox was brought into Boston by a ship from London, which landed at the adjacent port of Chelsea. The epidemic resulted in the deaths of over one fifth of the town's population, and then moved on to the neighboring city. By January, 1752, cases appeared in Boston, and for the next three months the Boston papers repeatedly denied that the disease had reached epidemic proportions. Each week the selectmen reluctantly conceded a few cases, but firmly assured the people that the quarantine measures were keeping the disease under control.[27] As usual, the newspapers in conjunction with the selectmen deliberately played down the seriousness of the situation in order to maintain normal business relations with adjacent towns.

By the end of March the papers gave up the struggle and henceforth paid little attention to the outbreak. Except for an occasional notice of the removal of the courts from Boston, or the public advertisement by the town council of Newport, Rhode Island, increasing tenfold the fine for persons failing to observe proper quarantine on coming from Boston or neighboring towns, the newspapers gave no hint that a major epidemic was in progress. Inoculation may have backfired on this occasion, since a local physician maintained that the turning point which led to an intensification of the

[27] Henry R. Viets, *A Brief History of Medicine in Massachusetts* (Boston and New York, 1930), 65; Douglass, *British Settlements*, II, 397–98; Boston *Post Boy*, Nos. 890–99, January 13–March 16, 1752; Boston *Weekly News-Letter*, No. 2590, February 13, 1752.

outbreak occurred when "inoculation was let loose" on March 23.[28]

The epidemic, like its predecessors, completely disrupted the normal activities of the town. The Reverend Roger Price wrote in April, 1752: ". . . the small pox is broke out in Boston in a violent manner after two and twenty years absence, it has occasioned almost a total Stagnation of trade So that half the houses and shops in town are shut up and the people retir'd to the country." A letter from Braintree written in April described the town as crowded with refugees from the Boston epidemic. The writer, the Reverend E. Miller, mentioned the fact that there had been no smallpox in Boston for over twenty years. He added that the current estimates placed the number of cases at thirteen thousand or fourteen thousand. The Reverend Thomas Smith of Falmouth said of Boston in the same month, "All business is laid aside in the town. The streets desolate, many of the shops shut up, and the people universally spend their time to attend to the sick." [29] At this time, April, 1752, the records of the court of probate were moved from Boston to Dorchester. The notice of removal stated that the judge would hold sessions on alternate Fridays to transact the business of the country towns and Boston so as "to prevent as far as may be, the Small-Pox being communicated from the Town to the Country. And the Inhabitants of the Town of Boston are desired to use all possible Precautions against bringing the Infection in their apparel, Papers, or by any other Means, as one of the officers

[28] Boston *Post Boy*, No. 903; April 13, 1752; Boston *Weekly News-Letter*, No. 2598, April 9, 1752; Douglass, *British Settlements*, II, 397–98.

[29] Roger Price to Secretary, Boston, April 3, 1752, in S.P.G. MSS., B20, fp. 46; E. Miller to Secretary, Braintree, New England, April 7, 1752, *ibid.*, B20, fp. 56; William Willis (ed.), *Journals of the Rev. Thomas Smith and the Rev. Samuel Deane* (Portland, 1849), 148.

of the Court is liable to the Distemper." The danger remained great throughout the spring and summer, and it was not until September 21, 1752, that a notice appeared in the Boston *Weekly News-Letter* announcing the return of the records to Boston.[30]

Excellent statistical information is available for learning the extent of the epidemic. The Reverend Mr. Miller's claim of 13,000 or 14,000 cases was far too high. A clergyman of Boston, the Reverend Thomas Prince, in an article in the *Gentlemen's Magazine* in 1753, claimed that out of a total population of 15,684 smallpox seized 5,545; another 2,124 were inoculated with it, and of these, 569 died. Douglass gave a set of figures for the period from January to July only slightly less than those of Prince, which covered the entire epidemic, and which coincides with the report of the selectmen of Boston published on July 30. Other statistical records tend to confirm the data given by Prince and Douglass.[31]

Prince showed how difficult it was to avoid the contagion during major epidemics. Of the people living in Boston in 1751, 5,998 had had smallpox previous to the outbreak. In the course of the epidemic another 7,669 either caught it or were inoculated. Of the remainder, 1,843 fled to the country, and only 174 of those left in town who had not previously been infected escaped the disease. Prince probably got the latter figure from the Boston *Weekly News-Letter* which stated that as of July 30 only 174 persons were still exposed, the majority of whom were infants

[30] Boston *Weekly News-Letter*, No. 2599, April 16, No. 2620, September 21, 1752.

[31] Thomas Prince to Editor, Boston, undated, *Gentlemen's Magazine*, XXIII (1753), 413–14; Douglass, *British Settlements*, II, 397–98; Boston *Weekly News-Letter*, No. 2614, July 30, 1752; Willis (ed.), *Journals of Smith and Deane*, 148 n.

born since the beginning of the epidemic.[32] In the light of these statistics, the general fear and consternation aroused by the appearance of even a single case need no further explaining.

It is a little surprising, in view of the foregoing, to find a Boston correspondent writing of the epidemic on July 22, "but upon the whole 'tis allow'd that the Smallpox never was so favorable on Boston before."[33] And even more so to learn that his statement was correct: the death rate among the smallpox victims was considerably lower than in previous outbreaks. Assuming that all deaths occurred among those infected by normal exposure, the 5,545 cases and 569 fatalities give a ratio of about one in ten. This mortality rate represents approximately a 20 per cent decrease over the one-in-eight ratio for the epidemic of 1731.

The disease apparently did little damage outside of Boston, despite the exodus of hundreds of refugees, some of whom must have carried the infection. Records of surrounding towns speak of the epidemic in Boston but say nothing of the infection in their own localities. However, the *Pennsylvania Gazette* reported in April that the contagion was in Concord and other Massachusetts towns.[34]

It was generally agreed that smallpox came to New England by sea. The endemic nature of the disease in most English cities and ports and its prevalence in the West Indies, another major trading area for New England, lend credence to this supposition. The occurrence of the disease at infrequent intervals and its appearance in ports further prove the point. Provincial records constantly refer to ships

[32] Thomas Prince to Editor, Boston, undated, *loc. cit.;* Boston *Weekly News-Letter*, No. 2614, July 30, 1752.

[33] Joseph Greenleaf to Robert Treat Paine, Boston, July 22, 1752, Robert Treat Paine Papers, Massachusetts Historical Society MSS.

[34] *Pennsylvania Gazette*, No. 1224, May 28, 1752.

quarantined because of smallpox, and in the General Assembly of Rhode Island, Stephen Hopkins, a deputy from Newport, reported

> unto this assembly, that in and near said town, for some time past, there hath been, and still is carried on, a considerable trade by sea, whereby the small pox of late hath been very often brought into said town; and as there is no pest house in that section of the colony for the receiving such infected persons, there is very great danger of the distemper's spreading; which (should it happen) would be of fatal consequences to this colony.

A sum of £600 was voted for the building of a pesthouse subsequent to the above resolution. Between 1721 and 1752 constant fear of smallpox epidemics prompted the Rhode Island provincial assembly to pass seven acts in an effort to curb the outbreaks.[35] This action was true of the other colonies, all of which passed numerous laws of a similar nature. In general, the quarantine measures and the recourse to pesthouses worked fairly effectively in New England.

In the seven or eight years following the Boston epidemic of 1751, smallpox practically disappeared from New England, despite the fact that Canada in 1755 underwent the worst epidemic in its history. The relative isolation of New England from the other sections of North America carried at least some advantage. In 1753 a few cases developed in New London, Connecticut, and at least four deaths occurred when the disease was brought in from New York. One of the victims was buried in a pasture almost before her body was cold. Joshua Hempstead related in his

[35] John R. Bartlet (ed.), *Records of the Colony of Rhode Island and Providence Plantations in New England*, 10 vols. (Providence, 1860), V, 338–39. (Hereinafter cited as *Records of Rhode Island.)*

diary that "Nathanael Coit & the widow Hobbs buryed her. they drew the Coffin with long Ropes on the ground etc." [36]

Four years later the infection again plagued New London and gained a minor foothold in Portsmouth, New Hampshire, and in Falmouth, a small town in what is now Maine. In July the Reverend Thomas Smith of Falmouth wrote in his journal of "a clamoring by some of the town against me for visiting Mrs. Cox, who has broke out with the small pox, when I did it at the desire of the Justices and Selectmen." He added that several families had already moved away for fear of the malady. His notation, and the account of the burial in New London, show the feeling of dread inspired by smallpox among the New Englanders. The following year Hampton, New Hampshire, suffered a minor attack. The provincial legislators urged the selectmen of the town to take immediate steps against the spread of the infection.[37] In cases such as these, however, the local authorities rarely needed prompting.

In 1760 smallpox appeared sporadically throughout New England. The occasion was the return of soldiers from army camps, where smallpox, dysentery, and typhus were fast decimating the provincial forces which had been mustered into service against the French. The diaries and journals of New England troops repeatedly tell of sickness and death. One soldier claimed that smallpox kept breaking out with every change of the moon and that two out of every three infected with the contagion succumbed. Another stated that smallpox victims were carried out of camp daily.

[36] *Diary of Joshua Hempstead of New London, Connecticut, 1711–1758*, in New London County Historical Society *Collections*, I (1901), 597–600.

[37] Willis (ed.), *Journals of Smith and Deane*, 172; Bouton (ed.), *Documents and Records of New Hampshire*, VI (1872), 674–75.

With this scourge rife in the military forces, where terms of enlistments were short and desertion frequent, it was inevitable that returning soldiers would serve as carriers of the infection, as Dr. Benjamin Gale testified when he wrote to Huxham: "During the late war, the smallpox was brought into divers towns, in this and other colonies, by the return of our soldiers (employed in his majesty's service, in the pay of New England Colonies) for winter quarters, and by seamen employed in our navigation to the British Islands in the West Indies, where small pox was universally present." [38]

The colonies of Connecticut, Rhode Island, and Massachusetts all experienced outbreaks in 1760. From Stamford, Connecticut, the Reverend Ebenezer Dibbler wrote that the disease had already proved fatal to one of his children. The infection was present in Cambridge and Harwich, Massachusetts, in November and December, and a number of deaths occurred from smallpox in Newport, Rhode Island. The towns of New Casco and Stroudwater near Falmouth were also affected.[39]

Outbreaks of smallpox continued into 1761. The legislative records of New Hampshire indicate its presence in the parish of Brintwood in February and of Portsmouth in March, the latter outbreak forcing the legislature to change its meeting place. The following month the legislature

[38] "Journal of Captain Jenks," Massachusetts Historical Society *Proceedings*, XXV (1889–90), 386; "Journal of Sergeant Holden," *ibid.*, XXIV (1887–89), 403; Benjamin Gale to Dr. John Huxham, May 23, 1765, in *Philosophical Transactions*, LV (1765), 193–204.

[39] Ebenezer Dibbler to Secretary, S.P.G. MSS., B23, Pt. 1, fpp. 221–24; Diary of Benjamin Bangs, November 19–December 13, 1760; "Diary of Dr. Nathaniel Ames," in *Dedham Historical Register*, I (1890), 187; "Deaths in Newport, Rhode Island, 1760–1764," in *New England Historical and Genealogical Register*, LXII (1908), 287; Willis (ed.), *Journals of Smith and Deane*, 187.

agreed to reimburse the selectmen of Newmarket, Greenland, Kingstown, and Stratham for the care of soldiers infected with the sickness. From Boston it was reported that smallpox "has broak out in many places in this Town & [it is believed] . . . it will spread." The selectmen acknowledged a few cases in January but announced that the city was free of the disorder on April 1. Additional deaths from smallpox occurred in Salem, Brookfield, and Harwich during this same year.[40]

Outbreaks of smallpox seem to have subsided between 1761 and 1764. One death occurred in Branford, Connecticut, in February, 1763, and earlier the Reverend William Smith wrote that the presence of the disease had compelled him to retire from Weymouth into the country. By 1764 the disorder reappeared in several towns. As usual, Boston was the chief sufferer. The town had been relatively free from smallpox for about twelve years, and it was expected that the disease would run its usual course. The townspeople remembered the previous outbreak only too well, and the news of smallpox in town precipitated a mass exodus. Describing it to William Martin, James Gordon wrote in March: "Of the first 12 or 13 persons seiz'd with it, ten or eleven of them died of it, being chiefly adults; the town was greatly alarmd. A great panick seized every body, either for themselves, their children, or relations that had not the distemper before. All those whose condition or cir-

[40] "Journals of the House," in Bouton (ed.), *Documents and Records of New Hampshire*, VI (1872), 764, 788–89; Elizabeth Fitch to Henry Lloyd, in Dorothy C. Barck (ed.), *Papers of the Lloyd Family of Lloyd's Neck, New York*, 2 vols. (New York, 1927), II, 591–92, in New-York Historical Society *Collections*, LX (1926–27); Boston *Weekly News-Letter*, No. 2948, January 1, No. 2961, April 2, 1761; *Green and Russell's Boston Post Boy and Advertiser*, No. 195, May 11, 1761; George Francis Dow (ed.), *The Holyoke Diaries, 1709–1856* (Salem, 1911), 48–49.

cumstances of life would admit of it hurried away into the country with their goods & furniture, etc."[41]

The courts adjourned to Cambridge or other towns, and the selectmen of Boston set guards around the infected houses, permitting no one to enter or leave them. Strict penalties had been enforced against the practice of inoculation, one of the chief methods by which the plague was spread. Despite all these precautions, Gordon was forced to conclude, ". . . but vain is human [effort to prevent] the Acts of Divine Providence." About the time that Gordon wrote, the Reverend Thomas Smith recorded in his journal, "The guards at infected houses in Boston are removed, the people finding they can stop the spreading no longer."[42]

In spite of this grim report, the epidemic exacted a lighter toll than had been expected. A large proportion of the population had been exposed during the previous outbreak of twelve years earlier, and when the authorities relaxed the prohibition against inoculation early in February, literally thousands turned to it. The Reverend Thomas Smith made a note of it in his diary, and the Gordon and Lloyd family letters both mention the inoculation of their children. Benjamin Gale discussed its use in a letter to Dr. John Huxham, stating that mercury, used in conjunction with inoculation, had proved successful, as only 5 out of the 3,000 inoculated in Boston had succumbed. In July, 1764, at the end of the epidemic, the selectmen of Boston announced that of the 4,977 persons who had undergone variolation, 46 had died. Since Boston's population was between

[41] Boston *Weekly News-Letter*, No. 3087, February 17, 1763; "Diaries of William Smith," in Massachusetts Historical Society *Proceedings*, XLII (1908–1909), 469; James Gordon to William Martin, Boston, March 9, 1764, *ibid.*, XXXIII (1899–1900), 389.

[42] James Gordon to William Martin, *loc cit.*; Willis (ed.), *Journals of Smith and Deane*, 198.

15,000 and 20,000, one third to one fourth of the townspeople must have resorted to the practice.[43]

In addition to those inoculated, 699 inadvertently caught the infection, which resulted in 124 deaths. These fatalities plus the 46 from inoculation give a total of 170 casualties. A record of births and deaths in Boston kept by the Reverend Ezra Stiles places the death toll from smallpox at 150,[44] a figure which ties in fairly closely with other estimates. Accepting the highest number of 170 deaths and relating it to the population figure of between 15,000 and 20,000, one can see how favorably this epidemic compares with the previous ones. In 1721, for example, 900 deaths had occurred in a population of less than 12,000.

Concurrent with the Boston outbreak, smallpox spread extensively throughout New England. Across the Charles River in Cambridge the fear of smallpox drove 649 persons to inoculation, a mass operation conducted with considerable success—only two deaths resulted. Of the 38 natural cases there, 4 proved fatal, giving a case fatality rate of almost 11 per cent. Smallpox was blamed specifically for 9 deaths in Newport, Rhode Island, in 1764, but unfortunately, in the majority of cases no record was made as to the cause of death and probably smallpox prevailed to a greater extent than the figure indicates. Even if it represents all

[43] Willis (ed.), *Journals of Smith and Deane*, 202; James Gordon to William Martin, *loc. cit.;* Henry Lloyd, II, to Joseph Lloyd, Boston, March 30, 1764, in *Papers of the Lloyd Family*, II (1927), 625–54; Benjamin Gale to Dr. John Huxham, May 23, 1765, *loc. cit.; Massachusetts Gazette and Boston News-Letter*, No. 3150, July 5, 1764; Boston *Post Boy and Advertiser*, No. 359, July 2, 1764; *A Century of Population Growth* (Washington, 1909). Hayward, *Gazetteer of Massachusetts*, 41, gives Boston a population of 15,520 in 1765. R. R. Wilson (ed.), *Burnaby's Travels through North America* (New York, 1904), 132, gives the population in 1759 as between 18,000 and 20,000.

[44] "Births and Deaths in Newport, R. I., 1760–64," in *New England Historical and Genealogical Register*, LXIII (1909), 56–57.

deaths from smallpox, using a conservative ratio of one death to every eight cases we must conclude that approximately seventy or eighty persons were infected. Chatham, Falmouth, Medfield, Norton, Freetown, Middleborough, and several other towns endured minor outbreaks in 1764. At Martha's Vineyard the people resorted to extensive inoculation when cases of smallpox developed.[45] The widespread use of inoculation must have contributed to the dispersion of the infection throughout New England, and certainly the hundreds of refugees fleeing from Boston furthered the process.

By the end of 1764 the New England colonies had recovered from the effects of smallpox brought back by the soldiers. No major epidemics occurred for almost ten years, although a number of small ones developed in Boston and other towns. John Rowe, a Boston merchant, recorded a few cases of smallpox in the city in 1769, 1771, and 1774, but added that a general inoculation accompanied each flare-up of the infection. The attack he mentioned in 1769 was also noted by a clergyman who commented that "it is thought in a little time it will be harryed thro by Inoculation." The newspapers listed a few cases in July, August, September, and October, but apparently few deaths ensued. Outside of Boston a few cases occurred in Newburyport and Providence in 1769, but all places suffered only lightly.[46]

[45] *Boston Post Boy and Advertiser*, No. 358, June 25, 1764; "Births and Deaths in Newport, R. I., 1760–1764," *loc. cit.;* "Description of Chatham," in Massachusetts Historical Society *Collections*, Ser. 1, VIII (1802), 151; *Massachusetts Gazette and Boston News-Letter*, No. 3127, January 26, 1764; New York *Mercury*, No. 647, March 26, 1764.

[46] "Diary of John Rowe," in Massachusetts Historical Society *Proceedings*, XXX (1895–96), 59; Anne Row Cunningham (ed.), *Letters and Diary of John Rowe, Boston Merchant, 1759–1762, 1764–1779* (Boston, 1903), 189, 290; John Lathrop to Mr. Baldwin, Boston, September 4, 1769, Simon Gratz Collection, American Clergy, Pennsylvania Historical Society, MSS.; *Massachusetts Gazette*, No. 402, August 10, No. 408, August 24, No. 412,

During 1771 a few cases were reported in Boston and in a small town in Connecticut, and during the winter of 1771–72, Newport, Rhode Island, was thrown into a turmoil by a minor outbreak. The major issue was the question of inoculation, on which the town was almost evenly divided. Ezra Stiles recorded that the town voted on the matter many times, frequently reversing itself.[47]

Both Salem and Marblehead were subject to smallpox in 1773. One church record in the former town lists 17 deaths from the disorder, a fact which would indicate 80 to 90 or more cases. The selectmen of Marblehead issued a statement in September declaring the town clear of the infection, but in Salem new cases were still developing in November.[48]

New London, Connecticut, and Newport, Rhode Island, were threatened by smallpox in 1772–73, but in both cases the authorities were able to prevent the infection from reaching epidemic proportions. However, by 1774 the contagion was widespread, with cases reported in Boston, Cambridge, Charlestown, Ipswich, and other towns.[49] The movement of troops and other preparations for the coming

---

September 7, 1769; *Massachusetts Gazette and Boston Weekly News-Letter*, No. 3446, October 19, 1769; Boston *Chronicle*, No. 96, May 25–29, No. 108, July 6–10, No. 114, July 27–31, No. 115, July 31–August 3, No. 124, August 31–September 4, No. 130, September 21–25, 1769.

[47] *Massachusetts Gazette and Boston Weekly News-Letter*, No. 3522, April 4, 1771; Ezra Stiles Diary, 1770–1775, entries for October 27, 1772, January 27, 1773, Force Transcripts, Manuscript Division, Library of Congress.

[48] "Description of Salem," in Massachusetts Historical Society, *Collections*, Ser. 1, VI (1800), 276–77; Boston *Evening Post*, No. 1981, September 13, 1773; *Massachusetts Gazette and Boston Weekly News-Letter*, No. 3657, November 4, 1773.

[49] Boston *Gazette and Country Journal*, No. 953, July 12, 1773; No. 982, January 31, No. 985, February 21, 1774; Newport *Mercury*, No. 720, June 22, No. 735, October 5, 1772; *Massachusetts Gazette and Boston Post Boy and Advertiser*, No. 859, January 31–February 7, 1774.

conflict disrupted all attempts to isolate the disease, and by April 40 or 50 cases were present in Boston and reports of the disease poured in from all quarters. The outbreak of hostilities in 1775 marked the beginning of a new wave of smallpox and a repetition of the events of the French and Indian War.

The Middle and Southern Colonies

Smallpox appeared in the middle and southern colonies in the seventeenth century and remained a health menace throughout the eighteenth. While New England suffered only periodically, New York, New Jersey, and Pennsylvania were rarely without a visitation during any five-year period, and especially was this true after 1730. That the southern colonies were not affected quite so much can be attributed to their scattered population and comparative isolation from the other sections of the country. Virginia suffered the least from smallpox, and South Carolina the most. Charleston, an important seaport and commercial center like Boston and New York, was the victim of seaborne epidemics.

Not only was there an exchange of smallpox between the English colonists and the Indians, but the red man served as an intermediary in epidemics between the settlers of the Atlantic seaboard and the French in Canada. The normal course of smallpox seems to have been northwest from New York into the Great Lakes region and the St. Lawrence Valley. On other occasions the disease began in Canada and progressed southward into the middle and southern colonies. Constant warfare between the British and their Indian allies and the French and their supporters served to distribute the infection far and wide. New England, for geographic reasons, suffered less from this smallpox traffic.

Closer contacts with the Indians were responsible in part for the greater frequency of the disease outside of New England, since the Indians were much more susceptible than the whites. And it is very likely that the disease gained virulence when transferred from the Indians to the colonists —particularly during military campaigns. Reciprocity in smallpox was a constant element in Indian-colonial relations.

In the colonial period no hard and fast boundaries separated Canada and the American colonies. French missionaries, traders and explorers, Indians of many tribes, and land-hungry British all ranged the Ohio Valley and the other Trans-Appalachian areas. Hence the same epidemics struck American colonists, Canadians, and Indians alike, and in many instances it is impossible to determine which group was infected first. To complete the picture of smallpox in the middle and southern colonies, an accompanying account of the disease among the Indians—who in turn were affected by the French in Canada—is essential.

The disease was an Indian exterminator in all the Americas. A recent medical history estimates that the introduction of smallpox into Mexico in 1519 wiped out three and a half million Indians. What was true of South and Central America held good for North America as well. The scenes of smallpox ravages depicted by the Jesuits are indeed harrowing. An outbreak among the Iroquois in 1663 "wrought sad havoc in their villages and . . . carried off many men, besides great numbers of women and children; and as a result their villages [were] nearly deserted, and their fields only half-tilled." In 1679, Count de Frontenac, terming smallpox the "Indian Plague," described its effect upon the Iroquois. "The Small Pox desolates them to such a degree," he wrote, "that they think no longer of Meeting nor of Wars, but only of bewailing the dead, of whom there is already an immense number."[1]

All early accounts from the English settlements, too, tell of serious inroads in the Indian population. In 1667, a sailor infected with smallpox landed in what is now Northampton County, Virginia, and passed the disorder on to members of the local tribes, who "died by the hundred." So devastating was the attack that "practically every tribe fell into the hands of the grim reaper and disappeared, the only exception being the Gingaskins."[2]

In 1679–80 whites and Indians alike suffered heavily from a major smallpox attack. A visitor recorded in October, 1679, that all the people he saw "had more or less children sick with the small pox, which, next to fever and ague, is the most prevalent disease in these parts, and of which many have died." In one house "there were two children lying dead and unburied, and three others sick, and . . . one had died the week before." The disease spread to the neighboring Indians with equally disastrous results, and they in turn may have passed it on to the southern tribes, since a number of them were reported to have "gone south to war against the Indians in Carolina beyond Virginia."[3]

[1] Ashburn, *Ranks of Death*, 83–85; Heagerty, *Four Centuries of Medical History*, I, 27; Count de Frontenac to the King, Quebec, November 6, 1679, in O'Callaghan (ed.), *Documents Relative to Colonial History*, IX (1855), 129.

[2] Thomas B. Robertson, "An Indian King's Will," in *Virginia Magazine of History and Biography*, XXXVI (1928), 192–93.

[3] Henry C. Murphy (ed. and trans.), *Journal of a Voyage to New York, 1679–80*, in *Memoirs* of the Long Island Historical Society, I (New York, 1867), 129, 277; Bartlet B. James and J. Franklin Jameson (eds.), *Journal of Jasper Dankaerts, 1679–80*, in *Original Narratives Series* (New York, 1913), 239.

An outbreak among the French settlers in 1685 may have had repercussions on the English colonies. While no general epidemic developed, Increase Mather mentioned that there was smallpox in Boston in 1685–86, and William Byrd recorded in August of the latter year that his family and two of his Negroes were ill with the contagion, which, he claimed, had been brought from Gambia. A month later four of Byrd's Negroes were dead and twenty more sick, but apparently this outbreak was confined to the Byrd plantation.[4]

Smallpox prevailed generally throughout North America from 1688 to 1691. Whether the disease originated in the French or English settlements is not clear; possibly both regions were infected independently. In any case the hostilities of King William's War spread the infection generally. Both forces suffered as a consequence, since smallpox showed no partiality when Europeans fought each other, and on more than one occasion well-planned military campaigns were defeated by this unseen enemy. In 1690, according to Frontenac, the English, allied with the Mohegans and Iroquois, planned an assault on Quebec but were foiled by an outbreak of smallpox. When the British and Mohegan emissaries, still bearing the marks of smallpox, were sent to the Iroquois, they were accused of bringing the plague. Subsequently the Iroquois became contaminated and about three hundred died. The rest then refused to join the expedition.[5]

Again in 1690, Father Michel De Couvert reported to Frontenac from Quebec that "a malady which was prevalent among the English having communicated itself to the

[4] "Letters of William Byrd," in *Virginia Magazine of History and Biography*, XXV (1917), 128–38.

[5] Count de Frontenac to the Minister, December 12, 1690, in O'Callaghan (ed.), *Documents Relative to Colonial History*, IX (1855), 459–61.

Loups, and some of them having died, the Loups laid the blame upon the English." As a result, the English abandoned the campaign. The next year Father Millet, another Jesuit, related that the British sent two armies against Quebec and that "smallpox stopped the first completely, and also scattered the second." [6]

Reports from the English side confirmed the essentials of the French account. Robert Pike wrote to Governor Simon Bradstreet of Massachusetts in September, 1690, that he wanted to attack the French but that the condition of his Indian allies prohibited his doing so. "The small pox haue Carryd away some," he reported, "& divers of more of them have been . . . sick." In November the Governor ascribed the failure of the expedition to "God's anger," which, he stated, "hath appeared against us in the loss of so many of our friends . . . by the contagion of the small Pox, Fevers and other killing distempers. . . ." [7]

The province of New York bore the brunt of the smallpox attack in the English colonies. According to an account written in 1692, "The Country is generally healthy tho' 2 years ago ye Small Pox which was very mortall especially to grown people . . . took away a great many." Major General Winthrop, in his journal of marches in the vicinity of Albany during these years, often mentioned the presence of smallpox among the troops and in the towns through which they passed. Naturally the contagion was passed on to the Indians. Robert Livingston reported the deaths of an entire group of Dovaganhae Indians who had come to Albany to

[6] Father Michel De Couvert to Count de Frontenac, Quebec, 1690, in Reuben G. Thwaites (ed.), *Jesuit Relations and Allied Documents*, 73 vols. (Cleveland, 1896–1901), LXIV, 7. (Hereinafter cited as *Jesuit Relations.)*; *ibid.*, 97–98.

[7] *Documentary History of the State of Maine*, in Maine Historical Society *Collections*, Ser. 2, V (1897), 138, 168.

trade in 1691.[8] In short, whether engaged in trade or in warfare, the Indians' susceptibility to smallpox steadily reduced their numbers.

When Jamestown, Virginia, underwent an epidemic in 1696, the assembly recessed to escape the infection. During the following two years, smallpox appeared in South Carolina, causing a mortality high for the colonists, and as usual, higher for the Indians. The governor and council of the province wrote to the Lord Proprietors in March, 1698, "We have had the small pox amongst us nine or ten months which hath been very infectious and mortal. We have lost by the distemper 200 or 300 persons." The next month, another letter reported some mitigation of the severity among whites but continued disaster for the Indians. A neighboring tribe, probably the Pemlico Indians, was completely destroyed. Its extermination was described in 1707 by John Archdale, whose account subsequently was copied by John Oldmixon and other eighteenth-century writers.[9]

In 1702 smallpox was again prevalent in New York province but in a mild form. Lord Cornbury wrote to the Lords of Trade in the summer of 1702, "The small pox is very much here, but except that the Province is very healthy." This somewhat optimistic note scarcely would have been sounded in the face of a serious smallpox epi-

[8] Charles Lodwick's Account of New York, transcription in New-York Historical Society MSS.; "Journal of Major General Winthrop's March from Albany to Wood Creek, July to September, 1690," in O'Callaghan (ed.), *Documents Relative to Colonial History*, IV (1854), 193–96; Robert Livingston, Albany, N. Y., June 4, 1691, *ibid.*, III (1853), 778.

[9] Philip Alexander Bruce, *Institutional History of Virginia in the Seventeenth Century*, 2 vols. (New York and London, 1910), II, 487; McCrady, *History of South Carolina*, 198, 308; John Archdale, "A New Description of that Fertile and Pleasant Province of Carolina," in Bartholomew R. Carroll (ed.), *Historical Collections of South Carolina*, 2 vols. (New York, 1836), II, 462–535. The account by John Oldmixon in his *British Empire in America* is identical with Archdale's.

demic. The governor later reported smallpox among the River Indians near Albany; he also declared that hundreds of people had been carried off by the scourge in Canada.[10] As a matter of fact, the death total in Quebec was around three thousand. It is very likely that here again the Indians served as a channel of communication between the valley of the Hudson and the St. Lawrence Basin.

Aside from a minor outbreak in Virginia and a more serious one in South Carolina, there is little evidence of smallpox from 1703 to 1715. William Byrd, who recorded two cases which occurred in Virginia in 1711, illustrated the prevailing fear of the disease. No one would go near one of the victims, and the other "died of the smallpox, for want of attention." This somewhat ruthless treatment does seem to have been effective in preventing the spread of the infection. Charleston, South Carolina, suffered greatly from sickness during the winter of 1711–12. Commissary Gideon Johnston, the S.P.G. representative in South Carolina, wrote on November 16, 1711 that "Never was there a more sickly or fatall season than this for the small Pox, Pestilential ffeavers, Pleurisies, and fflux's have destroyed great numbers here of all sorts, both Whites Blacks and Indians, and these distempers still rage to an uncommon degree"; but he did not state which disease took the greatest toll. The following March the Boston *News-Letter* reported many deaths from "Small-Pox & Pestilential Feavers" at Charleston, adding that the epidemic was about over.[11]

[10] Lord Cornbury to the Lords of Trade, New York, May 18, 1702, in O'Callaghan (ed.), *Documents Relative to Colonial History,* IV (1854), 958–59; *id.* to *id.*, June 30, 1703, *ibid.*, 996–97, 1061.

[11] L. B. Wright and Marion Tinling (eds.), *The Secret Diary of William Byrd of Westover, 1709–1712* (Richmond, 1941), 361, 366, 370; Commissary Gideon Johnston to Secretary, South Carolina, November 16, 1711, in S.P.G. MSS., A7, fpp. 383–84; Boston *News-Letter,* No. 412, February 25–March 3, 1711.

The return of the disease after a long absence usually meant a severe attack, and the outbreak that struck the middle and southern colonies in 1715 was no exception. Starting in New York and New Jersey, smallpox ran its course through all the English colonies during the next seven years. One Ellis, a schoolmaster at Burlington, New Jersey, made the first mention of it when he wrote to the S.P.G. in 1715 that his school had been "very much disorder'd, by reason of that Contagious Distemper, the Small pox with wch. God hath been pleased to Visit us all this last Sumer in and about our inhabitants and is now very brief among us here in Town." In September, an S.P.G. missionary wrote from Perth Amboy, New Jersey, that he had just recovered from a severe attack. A year later, Cadwallader Colden wrote to Hugh Graham that smallpox had been "Epidemicall" during the summer in New York and that scarcely any had avoided the infection. At the same time, a missionary working among the Indians in western New York related that "The Small Pox has been much among ye Indians here this last Summer & swept off a great many of ym & now it is got among ye Other Nations beyond us, & Die as many there with it." [12] Smallpox continued to plague the Indians throughout 1716 and 1717, few of them in the Northwest escaping it.

An indication that smallpox reached Canada is given in a report of a conference between the French and Indians. M. de Vaudreuil, who transmitted an account of the meeting to the French government in October, 1717, mentioned that

[12] Rowland Ellis to Secretary, New Jersey, *c.* 1715, in S.P.G. MSS., A12, fp. 165; Edward Vaughan to Secretary, Perth Amboy, N. J., September 2, 1715, *ibid.*, A11, fp. 124; Cadwallader Colden to Hugh Graham, October, 1716, in Copy Book of Letters, Cadwallader Colden Papers, New-York Historical Society MSS.; William Andrews to Secretary, Fort by Mohawk Castle, October 11, 1716, in S.P.G. MSS., A12, fp. 136.

the disease was prevalent among some of the Iroquois. Earlier that year Governor Hunter of New York had held a conference with the representatives of the Five Nations at Albany. In his opening address to them he expressed sympathy "for the loss that has happened by the Small Pox to the brethren, or any of your friends and allies." Not one Christian family in Pennsylvania had escaped smallpox, he told them, and it was still raging in the Jerseys. Apparently hoping to drive home a moral lesson, he pointed out that "we Christians look upon that disease and others of that kind as punishments for our misdeeds and sin, such as breaking of covenants & promises, murders, and robbery, and the like." The Indians were not overly impressed and replied that they intended to dispatch someone to "Canistoge, Virginy, or Maryland" to find out who had been sending the contagion and to prevent them from so doing.[13]

The following year, 1718, Charleston, South Carolina, suffered an outbreak during the summer, although there is little evidence of its extent. A "Malignant fever," which proved fatal, accompanied the smallpox. In December, Cadwallader Colden again mentioned the presence of the sickness in New York and claimed that it was increasing in virulence.[14] The contagion plagued New England for the four succeeding years, but the middle and southern sections remained free of the disease from 1718 to 1730.

[13] M. de Vaudreuil to the French Government, October 24, 1717, in O'Callaghan (ed.), *Documents Relative to Colonial History*, IX (1855), 877; Governor Hunter's reply to the Five Nations at the Conference at Albany, N. Y., June 13, 1717, reported by Robert Livingston, Secretary of Indian Affairs, *ibid.*, V (1855), 485–86; Indian reply to Governor Hunter, New York, June 13, 1717, *ibid.*, 487.

[14] Thomas Hassell to Secretary, St. Thomas Parish, Charleston, S. C., October 11, 1718, in S.P.G. MSS., A13, fpp. 241–45; Cadwallader Colden to Hugh Graham, New York, December 7, 1718, in Copy Book of Letters, Colden Papers.

A particularly virulent form of smallpox affected Boston, New York City, and Philadelphia in 1730–31. It ran its course in Boston during 1730 and did not affect the middle colonies until January, 1731, when it appeared widely in the provinces of Pennsylvania, New Jersey, and New York. Philadelphia suffered from January to April. By the time this city was free of the scourge, cases began developing in New York, but here the epidemic did not reach its peak until September and October.

A private correspondent writing from Philadelphia in January, 1731, declared that smallpox was a major problem and had already "proved Mortall to many." In February the *American Weekly Mercury* devoted the front page of one issue to an article on smallpox by the great Sydenham, explaining that "in this present dreadful Mortality of the Small-Pox, We imagine this treatise may be acceptable to the generality of our Readers." A month later a newspaper account stated that the contagion was still raging, with but few houses escaping it. A list of burials in Philadelphia from February 23 to March 18 shows a total of one hundred, indicating that smallpox was exacting a heavy toll; and Burlington, New Jersey, prohibited all fairs "by reason of the great Mortality in *Philadelphia*, and other parts of *Pennsylvania*, where the Small-Pox now violently rages." [15]

New York City managed to avoid a serious outbreak until the end of summer. A few cases occurred earlier, but it was the end of August before any notice was taken of the sickness. "Here is little or no Business, and less Money," wrote one resident on August 30; "the Markets begin to grow very thin; the Small-Pox raging very violently in

[15] Mrs. John Hill to Dr. Colden, Philadelphia, January 31, 1731, in *Colden Papers*, VIII (1937), 196–97; *American Weekly Mercury*, No. 582, February 16–24, No. 593, April 22–29, 1731; New York *Gazette*, No. 283, March 22–29, 1731.

Town, which in a great measure hinders the Country People from supplying this Place with Provisions. . . . The Distemper has been a long time very favourable, but now begins to be of the confluent kind, and very mortal." The death toll from the disease rose steadily in the ensuing weeks. In the two weeks from September 27 to October 11 a total of 138 persons died in New York of smallpox. Fortunately the peak was reached soon after that, and the number of victims began to taper off. President Rip Van Dam in a report to the Lords of Trade, which included a census covering ten counties in New York as of November 2, explained that "since the taking of said list I believe neer eight hundred are lost by the small pox, and daily more dying." Inasmuch as he reported a population of only 50,242, the 800 deaths represented a serious loss to the colony. His estimate of the dead was confirmed by the New York *Gazette*, which reported in mid-November:

> In the Month of August last the Small Pox began to spread in this city, and for some Weeks was very favorable, and few died of this Distemper, but as soon as we observed the Burials to increase, which was from the 23rd of August, in our Gazette, No. 305 we began to incert weekly, the Number both of Whites and Blacks that were buried in this City, by which account we find, that from the 23rd of August to this Instant, which is two Months and 3 weeks, there was buried in the several burying Places of this City, as follows, viz.

Whites in all	478
Blacks in all	71
Whites and Blacks in all	549[16]

[16] Boston *Weekly News-Letter*, No. 1441, September 2–9, 1731; New York *Gazette*, No. 310, September 27–October 5, No. 311, October 5-11, No. 316, November 8–15, 1731; President Rip Van Dam to the Lords of Trade, New York, November 2, 1731, in O'Callaghan (ed.), *Documents Relative to Colonial History*, V (1855), 929.

An estimate based on Van Dam's population figure of 8,622 for New York City shows that 7 per cent of the residents were lost in approximately three months, and at least one half of the population fell sick with the infection. The loss of life in the city was much higher, both numerically and proportionally, than in the province at large. In the fall of 1731 President Van Dam had considerable difficulty getting enough members of the house or council to perform the necessary business of the province because, he explained, the disease raged "especially in the City." [17]

During 1732–33 the contagion continued to ravage the provinces, although the number of cases dropped off sharply in New York City. In February, 1732, the *American Weekly Mercury* reported sixty-eight smallpox deaths in Albany and twenty-two at Kingston; from other sources, too, it is evident that the infection was steadily working its way through the middle colonies. In the lower counties in Pennsylvania an observer wrote later in the year that "the Living are scarce able to bury the Dead, whole Families being down at once, and many die unknown to their Neighbours." [18]

Inoculation was practiced on a large scale and no doubt performed its double function of both preserving from and spreading the sickness. An S.P.G. missionary in New Jersey wrote, "Soon after my Removal to Burlington that deplorable distemper ye Small Pox raged among the people and Spread farr and Near, that for Six Months & Up-

[17] President Rip Van Dam to the Lords of Trade, September 11, 1731, in O'Callaghan (ed.), *Documents Relative to Colonial History,* V, 924.

[18] *American Weekly Mercury,* No. 632, February 1–8, No. 676, December 7–12, 1732; *Pennsylvania Gazette,* January 18–25, 1732, quoted in W. A. Whitehead *et al.* (eds.), *Documents Relative to the Colonial History of New Jersey,* 30 vols. (Newark, 1880——), Ser. 1, XI (1894), 271 (hereinafter cited as *Documents Relative to New Jersey History).*

wards ye Congregation was very Small, partly by the mortality that followed that infection and the fears that ye generality of ym were under of going abroad, Even to ye Publick worship of God." He ended on the hopeful note that the contagion was abating and his church was again beginning to fill up.[19]

A month later, in August, the widow of a missionary reported that her husband, the late rector of the parish at Jamaica, Long Island, had just died and that she and her five children had all been visited with smallpox. The next year, 1733, the Reverend Thomas Standard mentioned the presence of the infection at Westchester, New York, stating that it had been brought there from the West Indies; but the accuracy of his statement is doubtful in view of the widespread prevalence of the disease in the American colonies. In any case Standard found some consolation in the thought that the smallpox had "occasioned some grown People, allarm'd with the sense of their danger to offer themselves for baptism." [20]

By 1732, if not sooner, smallpox had reached the Indians. M. de Beauharnois declared in a letter written in October that the disease was ravaging the Senecas and other Iroquois. The following year, 1733, Governor William Cosby of New York offered condolences to the Five Nations for the "great mortality among you by the small pox." A virulent epidemic among the Indians in Canada during the winter of 1732–33 drove many of them into British territory, arousing considerable alarm among the frontier settle-

[19] Boston *Weekly News-Letter*, No. 1463, February 3–10, 1732; Robert Weyman to Secretary, Burlington, N. Y., July 12, 1732, in S.P.G. MSS., A24, fpp. 165–66.

[20] Mrs. Poyer to Secretary, Jamaica, Long Island, N. Y., August 23, 1732, in S.P.G. MSS., A24, fpp. 177–78; Thomas Standard to Secretary, East Chester, N. Y., November 4, 1733, *ibid.*, B1, fpp. 30–32.

ments.[21] The Indians in the Northwest were also decimated at this time. So far no statistics have been found as to the ravages of the malady among the Indians, but the Indian susceptibility to the infection, coupled with its widespread distribution, must have produced some grim results.

From 1733 to 1737 the colonies were given a respite from smallpox. In March of the latter year Williamsburg, Virginia, underwent a mild siege, which fortunately affected only a few families. William Byrd, writing to Sir Hans Sloane in August, 1737, sent him a "certain" cure for smallpox. The "cure" consisted of copious draughts of water "that had stood two days upon tar." So effective was this preventive that after a few drinks, one could not take smallpox even by inoculation. In his letter Byrd remarked that, although smallpox was not common in Virginia, it had "raged lately very much in Barbados and South Carolina." [22]

The outbreak in South Carolina mentioned by William Byrd increased in virulence in the two succeeding years. In July, 1738, an S.P.G. missionary described the outbreak as "very Mortal." In September the general assembly of the province was called into session to deal with the pestilence then raging in Charleston. However, in this month the peak was reached and thereafter the number of cases sharply declined, prompting the *South Carolina Gazette* to publish a summary of the casualties. Up to the end of September 1,675 had been infected by natural means, and 295 of these

[21] M. de Beauharnois to Count de Maurepas, October 15, 1732, in O'Callaghan (ed.), *Documents Relative to Colonial History*, IX (1855), 1035–37; *ibid.*, V (1855), 963; Letter to David Dunbar, Boston, September 17, 1733; *Belcher Papers*, in Massachusetts Historical Society *Collections*, Ser. 6, VI (1893), 367.

[22] *Pennsylvania Gazette*, No. 429, February 24–March 3, 1737; William Byrd, II, to Sir Hans Sloane, Virginia, August 20, 1737, in *William and Mary Quarterly*, Ser. 2, I (1921), 198.

had succumbed. In addition, another 437 were inoculated, of whom 16 died.[23] The fatality rate among the natural cases of about 18 per cent, although not unusual for smallpox, was relatively high for the colonies.

The population of Charleston in 1738 is not known, but the town did not reach eight thousand until 1760. An estimate made in 1748 placed the number of houses at six hundred. Allowing a ratio of eight or nine people per house would give Charleston about 5,000 inhabitants in 1748. The town could scarcely have had more than five thousand people and probably had fewer in 1737–38. Hence the total of over twenty-one hundred cases represents almost half of the population. Further, the statistics presented in the *Gazette* do not give the full picture; for as late as January, 1739, an S.P.G. missionary in Charleston reported that the contagion was still in the city and had "carreyed off many people" in the country.[24]

The disease was communicated to the Indians with disastrous results. The Cherokees were devastated, losing half their number in 1738 alone. Unable to explain this catastrophe, the Indians accused the English of poisoning them and threatened to trade with the French. Only by careful diplomacy was this contingency avoided.[25]

In 1736–37 Philadelphia was the scene of an epidemic which "prov'd mortal" to many of its residents. The in-

[23] Lewis Jones to Secretary, St. Helen's, S. C., July 17, 1738, in S.P.G. MSS., B7, fpp. 258–59; McCrady, *History of South Carolina,* 310; *South Carolina Gazette,* No. 245, October 5, 1738.

[24] *A Century of Population Growth,* 11; John Harris, *A Complete Collection of Voyages and Travels,* 2 vols. (London, 1748), II, 277; Thomas Hassell to Secretary, St. Thomas, Charleston, S. C., January 15, 1739, in S.P.G. MSS., B7, fp. 242.

[25] "A Treaty Between Virginia and the Catawbas and Cherokees, 1756," *loc. cit.;* Newton D. Mereness (ed.), *Travels in the American Colonies* (New York, 1916), 239. Captain James Oglethorpe met a delegation of Indians in September, 1739, and managed to allay their suspicions of the English.

habitants resorted to inoculation, apparently with considerable success. The following year New York City was the victim. Cases were first reported in November of 1738, and the infection remained in town until the fall of 1739. Lieutenant Governor George Clarke noted in April that nine of the twenty-seven members of the house of representatives had not acquired immunity to the disease and were greatly disturbed by its appearance in town. Clarke, at the lawmakers' request, moved the house to Greenwich, but this action did not satisfy the frightened legislators. Upon further address, he was forced to adjourn the meeting until the end of August.[26]

By the middle of August it was evident that the epidemic was waning. The mayor officially announced that as of August 18 the cases numbered 1,550 and that 16 of these were still active.[27]

Smallpox subsided in 1739 and did not reappear in the middle colonies until 1745. In November, Governor George Clinton of New York was compelled to adjourn the assembly for a fortnight. The infection lingered in the province for many months. During the winter of 1746–47, New York City and surrounding towns suffered heavily from its ravages. In February, 1747, the S.P.G. was notified that its missionary on Staten Island had died during one of the smallpox attacks "that have raged very much in this Province for many Months past." Soon the contagion spread to the Indians. A message of condolence was

[26] *Gentlemen's Magazine*, VIII (1738), 55; *A Journal of the Life and Travels of Thomas Chalkley*, *Friends Library*, II (1835), 418; *American Weekly Mercury*, No. 914, June 30–July 7, 1737; Boston *Gazette*, No. 982, November 6–13, 1738; New York *Gazette*, No. 683, December 4–11, 1738; Lieutenant Governor George Clarke to the Lords of Trade, New York, April 18, 1739, in O'Callaghan (ed.), *Documents Relative to Colonial History*, VI (1855), 140.

[27] New York *Gazette*, No. 718, August 13–20, 1739.

dispatched by the governor of Canada to the Onondagas for their sufferings from smallpox in the preceding fall and winter.[28]

New Jersey was too close to New York to escape any epidemic in the latter province. From Perth Amboy, William Skinner, an S.P.G. missionary, explained to the Society that the decrease in his congregation was due in part to a smallpox epidemic "which had proved very mortal here last winter."[29]

The disease gradually moved south, affecting Maryland during 1747. In June the Maryland legislature excused the absence of a number of assemblymen when it was learned that rumors of smallpox in Annapolis had frightened them away. From Dover in Kent-on-Delaware, Thomas Bluett wrote in January, 1748, that a general fast was in progress, occasioned, among other things, by the heavy toll from smallpox. The same month, "malignant smallpox" seriously affected Cecil County, Maryland. The governor of Virginia was unable to call a meeting of the assembly in the early months of 1748, since smallpox was coursing through Williamsburg, the only town suitable for such a gathering. Except for a few cases in Hampton in 1751, Virginia was free of the disease for the next four years.[30]

[28] Governor George Clinton to the Lords of Trade, New York, November 11, 1745, in O'Callaghan (ed.), *Documents Relative to Colonial History*, VI (1855), 286–88; Colonel William Johnson to Governor Clinton, Mount Johnson, N. Y., May 7, 1747, *ibid.*, 360–62; Stokes, *Iconography of Manhattan*, IV, 593; Church wardens and vestrymen to Secretary, Staten Island, N. Y., February 24, 1747, in S.P.G. MSS., B14, fp. 176.

[29] William Skinner to Secretary, Perth Amboy, N. J., July 15, 1747, in S.P.G. MSS., B15, fpp. 239–40.

[30] Journal of the General Assembly at Annapolis, June 5, 1747, William Hand Brown *et al.* (eds.), *Archives of Maryland*, XLIV (1925), 526; Thomas Bluett to Secretary, Dover in Kent-on-Delaware, January 4, 1748, in S.P.G. MSS., B16–17, fpp. 251–52; John R. Quinan, *Medical Annals of Baltimore, from 1608 to 1880* (Baltimore, 1884), 12; Sir William Gooch to the Provincial Council of Pennsylvania, Williamsburg, Va., March 7,

The disease became general the following year in New York, New Jersey, and the Northwest. The general assembly of New York was prorogued in March, 1752, as a result of a smallpox outbreak in New York City, and the infection lurked in the town for many months. As late as October new cases were still developing, although one of the papers declared hopefully, "We are assured, that there are now very few Families in this City, but what either have, or have had the Small-Pox, and that we have good Reason to hope the City will soon be clear of that Distemper." [31]

Perth Amboy, New Jersey, also was affected by this same epidemic and suffered heavily. William Skinner wrote in July, "The Small Pox hath raged in this poor Place most of the winter and almost hitherto, so that by the Death of some and the Flight of others we have lost many." In the Northwest, an outbreak occurred among the Miami Indians and spread through much of the Great Lakes region. M. de Longeuil reported to the French government in April, 1752, that smallpox had deprived him of the active support of the Miamis in his struggle with the English. He added that the malady had reached Detroit and the "Beautiful" (Ohio) River and was "ravaging the whole of that Continent." [32]

Three years later, in 1755, the sickness reappeared. This time, contrary to its usual custom, it began in Canada and

---

1748, in *Colonial Records, Minutes of the Provincial Council of Pennsylvania*, 10 vols. (Harrisburg, 1851–52), V (1851), 221 (hereinafter cited as *Colonial Records of Pennsylvania)*; "Diary of John Blair," *William and Mary Quarterly*, Ser. 1, VIII (1899), 16.

[31] New York *Gazette Revived in the Weekly Post-Boy*, No. 478, March 16, No. 507, October 16, 1752.

[32] William Skinner to Secretary, Perth Amboy, N. J., July 9, 1752, in S.P.G. MSS., B19–20, fpp. 229–30; M. de Longeuil to M. de Rouille, April 20, 1752, in O'Callaghan (ed.), *Documents Relative to Colonial History*, X (1858), 246.

then moved south into New York. For years afterward Canadians were to refer to 1755 as the year of the great smallpox epidemic. The plague did not wear itself out until late in 1757, having swept through both French and Indians by that time. According to the official French records, smallpox had appeared among the Senecas in October, 1755. In the following June, a French dispatch from Canada described the Indians on the borders of Acadia and New England as still hostile to the English but added that "unfortunately, they have not as yet been able to go on the war path, having been afflicted by the smallpox in all their villages." Two months later a French official wrote of his difficulty in marshaling the Indians against the English because of their fears of the infection "at Niagara, Prequ' Isle and Fort Duquesne." The sufferings of the Indians were duplicated by those of the French settlers. In July, 1755, the French governor wrote, "Small-pox prevails in the cities and in the rural districts; few houses are exempt from it." Another letter dated November, 1756, mentions the terrible ravages of this plague throughout the colony.[33]

Smallpox was as violent in the American colonies in 1756 as in Canada. Serious epidemics broke out in a number of localities. In July the disease was reported to be raging in Philadelphia, and Governor Charles Hardy of New York, in a letter to the council at Elizabeth Town, New Jersey, listed measures taken to prevent its spread.[34]

[33] Heagerty, *Four Centuries of Medical History*, I, 74; Report of the Conference between M. de Vaudreuil and the Seneca Indians, October 1, 1755, in O'Callaghan (ed.), *Documents Relative to Colonial History*, X (1858), 345; Dispatches from Canada, June 4, 1756, *ibid.*, 408; M. de Vaudreuil to M. de Machault, Montreal, August 8, 1756, *ibid.*, 435–38; *id.* to *id.*, July 25, 1755, *ibid.*, 324; *id.* to *id.*, November 6, 1756, *ibid.*, 496.

[34] Sir Charles Hardy, Governor of New York, to Council at Elizabeth Town, N. J., July 26, 1756, in Whitehead *et al.* (eds.), *Documents Relative to New Jersey History*, Ser. 1, XVII (1892), 49, 53–54.

The governor of Pennsylvania declared to his council in December that despite his orders, nothing had been done to help the miserable conditions among the soldiers and that the rising tide of infection among the King's forces threatened to engulf all Philadelphia. Other than a small group who resorted to inoculation, few persons escaped the disorder there. Nor was the disease restricted to the city, for the Indians in the interior also were afflicted.[35]

The following April Governor Denny of Pennsylvania wrote that the malady was relaxing its grip on Philadelphia but was widespread in Lancaster. The outbreak in Lancaster was not too severe, for the governor's council held a meeting there in May. The Indians' susceptibility to this scourge precluded any possibility of their avoiding so extensive an epidemic: hence it is not surprising to find that in May, 1757, the governor's council in Pennsylvania granted presents and extended condolences to the Indians for their heavy losses from the disease.[36]

Like Pennsylvania, the province of New York endured an extensive outbreak. Dr. Samuel Johnson, president of King's College, and his family were reported to have fled New York City because of smallpox. The appearance of this plague in Albany, according to one writer, frightened the provincial troops more than the appearance of Montcalm himself could have done. It was found necessary to garrison the town entirely with British troops and discharge all the colonial soldiers except one regiment raised in New York.

[35] Governor of Pennsylvania to Council at Philadelphia, December 15, 1756, in *Colonial Records of Pennsylvania*, VII (1851), 358; Records of the Meeting with the Indians, Philadelphia, April 2, 1757, *ibid.*, 517; Cecil K. Drinker, *Not So Long Ago: An Analysis of Philadelphia from the Diary of Elizabeth Drinker, The March of Medicine* (New York, 1940), 74.

[36] Governor Denny to Croghan, Philadelphia, April 6, 1757, in *Colonial Records of Pennsylvania*, VII (1851), 473; "Minutes of the Council at Lancaster," May 21, 1757, *ibid.*, 546.

By November the disease was reported in Niagara and the surrounding posts, affecting both whites and Indians. The death of James Wetmore, an S.P.G. missionary at Rye, New York, in May, 1756, is another indication of the wide distribution of the infection throughout the province.[37]

The smallpox continued to flare up sporadically in most if not all the middle colonies and the Great Lakes region well into 1757. A French official in Canada reported in July that he had heard the disorder was plaguing the English at Forts George and Lidius. General Montcalm noted that a number of "Upper Country Indians" were "dying from smallpox caught from the English on the expedition against Fort William Henry." In April a conference between the Indians and the English at Philadelphia was disrupted when a number of Indian representatives fell victim to smallpox. Soon the infection spread to the other Indians and they decided to return home immediately.[38]

An epidemic in Annapolis, Maryland, during this same winter of 1756–57 delayed the convening of the assembly for five months. In January, Governor Horatio Sharpe wrote that he expected the assembly to meet in Annapolis, "unless the News of our having the Small-Pox in this Place should deter them." A week later only fourteen of the burgesses had arrived in town, the others remaining away

[37] Alexander Colden to Cadwallader Colden, New York, November 14, 1756, in *Colden Papers*, IX (1937), 162–64; John Marshall, *A History of the Colonies Planted by the English on the Continent of North America* (Philadelphia, 1824), 303–304; Report of the Conferences with the Indians at Fort Johnson, November 22, 1756, in O'Callaghan (ed.), *Documents Relative to Colonial History*, VII (1856), 240; Gideon Johnston to the Archbishop of Canterbury, *c.* 1757–58, *ibid.*, 440.

[38] M. de Vaudreuil to M. de Moras, Montreal, July 12, 1757, in O'Callaghan (ed.), *Documents Relative to Colonial History*, X (1858), 579–80; M. de Montcalm to M. de Paulmy, Montreal, April 18, 1758, *ibid.*, 698–700; Report of the Conferences with the Indians at Philadelphia, April 4, 1757, in *Colonial Records of Pennsylvania*, VII (1851), 517.

for fear of infection. Since twice this number was necessary for a quorum, no business was transacted. In February, Sharpe reported that the assembly was again postponed for this same reason. Finally on May 29 he wrote that the assembly had convened at Baltimore, since the smallpox "continued to rage in Annapolis." [39]

Minor outbreaks of smallpox troubled the middle colonies from 1758 to 1760. Unquestionably the movements of the British and provincial troops spread the infection. Another probable source was the general use of smallpox inoculation. As has been pointed out, variolation was beneficial in checking the ravages of the disease when used with caution, but its indiscriminate use could produce more harm than good. The letters and diaries for these years indicate that inoculation was practiced with more energy than discretion. Cadwallader Colden furnished a long description of the inoculation of one of his sons, a youth of exceedingly frail health, who fortunately managed to survive. The Drinker family, who faithfully recorded the effect of smallpox in Philadelphia, reported that they had all escaped the sickness through this method. As in New England, ministers took the lead in popularizing the practice. Colin Campbell, the S.P.G. missionary at Burlington, New Jersey, wrote to the Society in December, 1759, that he had inoculated all five of his children, and thereby set an example for his congregation.[40] In general the middle and upper classes recognized the value of variolation, though

[39] Governor Horatio Sharpe to Robert Dinwiddie, Annapolis, Md., January 22, 1757, in Brown *et al.* (eds.), *Archives of Maryland*, VI (1888), 519–20; Sharpe to Major Alexander Prevost, January 28, 1757, *ibid.;* Letter from Governor Sharpe, May 29, 1757, *ibid.*, IX (1890), 5.

[40] Cadwallader Colden to Dr. Bard, Flushing, N. Y., July 5, 1758, in *Colden Papers*, V (1921), 234–47; Elizabeth Drinker's Diary, 1758–1775, Pennsylvania Historical Society MSS.; Colin Campbell to Secretary, Burlington, N. J., December 20, 1759, in S.P.G. MSS., B24, fpp. 151–53.

they probably increased the danger of smallpox among the rest of the population by using it.

The smallpox epidemic that drove Samuel Johnson out of New York City in 1756 either remained until 1758 or broke out anew, for in the latter year Lieutenant Governor James De Lancey of New York recorded that "the Assembly met in the outward of this City to avoid the small pox." In October of the following year Dr. Johnson wrote from the city, "I thank God, I seem to have a very firm health; but my condition here is very precarious, chiefly by reason of the small pox, being obliged now, (already a second time) to retire on account of it." From Stamford, New York, John Lloyd wrote a few weeks later that the sickness was "very bad this Season." [41]

In December Colin Campbell reported from New Jersey that the disease had "made dreadful havock . . . among thousands of white people and Indians when taken in the natural way." Meanwhile, the city of Philadelphia was still not free of the disease. Elizabeth Drinker wrote in her diary on October 24, 1759, that the daughter of a friend was ill with the smallpox "which she has taken in the natural way: and to most who take it Naturally (at this time) it proves mortal." A few deaths from smallpox occurred in Virginia in 1758 and in Bladensburg, Maryland, during 1759.[42]

The Indians in Georgia and South Carolina were decimated by smallpox in 1759–60. A report from Georgia pub-

[41] Lieutenant Governor James De Lancey to the Lords of Trade, New York, January 5, 1758, in O'Callaghan (ed.), *Documents Relative to Colonial History*, VII (1856), 341; Samuel Johnson to Archbishop Becker, New York, October 10, 1759, *ibid.*, 404; John Lloyd to Henry Lloyd, Stamford, N. Y., November 17, 1759, in *Papers of the Lloyd Family*, II (1927), 574–75.

[42] Colin Campbell to Secretary, Burlington, N. J., December 20, 1759, in S.P.G. MSS., B24, fpp. 151–53; Elizabeth Drinker's Diary, 1758–1775; Joseph Ball, Notes to Accompany Letterbook, Joseph Ball MSS., phototranscript in Library of Congress; Quinan, *Medical Annals of Baltimore*, 13.

lished in August, 1759, states that Savannah was exercising all precautions against the introduction of the disease; that Augusta was free of it; and that it had almost disappeared from among the Chickasaws. On December 15 the *South Carolina Gazette* commented editorially: "It is pretty certain that the Smallpox has lately raged with great Violence among the Catawba Indians, and that it has carried off near one-half of that nation, *by throwing themselves into the River,* as soon as they found themselves ill—This Distemper has since appeared amongst the Inhabitants of the *Charraws* and *Waterees,* where Many Families are down; so that unless special care is taken, it must soon spread thro' the whole country." Over a month later a correspondent in Augusta wrote: "The late accounts from Keowee are, that the Small-Pox has destroyed a great many of the Indians there: that those who remained alive, and have not yet had that Distemper, were gone into the Woods, where many of them must perish as the Catawbas did." During the ensuing months smallpox continued its inexorable progress through the Indian tribes. On August 13 the *Pennsylvania Gazette's* correspondent in Augusta wrote: "We learn from the Cherokee country, that the People of the Lower Towns have carried smallpox into the Middle Settlement and Valley, where that disease rages with great Violence, and that the People of the Upper Towns are in such dread of the Infection, that they will not allow a single Person from the above named Places to come amongst them." In October the *Gazette* noted that the "Cherokees had brought the Small-Pox into the Upper Creek Nation." [43]

Smallpox, after striking the Indians, occasionally re-

[43] Boston *News-Letter,* No. 3021, August 2, 1759; *South Carolina Gazette,* No. 1321, December 15, 1759; *Pennsylvania Gazette,* No. 1625, February 14, No. 1654, September 4, No. 1662, October 30, 1760.

turned to the settlers with renewed virulence. This may have been the case in 1760, when Charleston and the surrounding settlements experienced one of the worst epidemics in the colonial period. In 1759, Governor Henry Lyttleton of South Carolina led an expedition against the Cherokees, which was concluded by the Treaty of Fort St. George late in the fall. Just as the treaty was signed, smallpox, which had been ravaging a nearby Indian village, broke out in the governor's camp. The result has been vividly described by Dr. Alexander Hewat, a contemporary historian: "As few of his little army had ever gone through that distemper, and as the surgeons were totally unprovided for such an accident, his men were struck with terror, and in great haste returned to the settlements, cautiously avoiding all intercourse one with another, and suffering much from hunger and fatigue by the way." [44]

More than likely the returning soldiers carried the infection to Charleston and the other white settlements, since the *South Carolina Gazette* reported on January 12, 1760, that smallpox was prevalent both in the city and in the country.[45] Charleston had been free of smallpox for over twenty years, and this absence probably served to increase the severity of the outbreak.

Added to the problems incident to the epidemic were those stemming from a series of bloody Indian uprisings. A letter from Charleston dated February 4 described the Indian troubles and added that "our Distress is great, and greatly aggravated by the Small Pox, which spreads amongst us. Some Thousands are now under Inoculation, and many taken down in the natural Way; of the latter a pretty large Proportion have died." A report from one of

44 Carroll (ed.), *Historical Collections of South Carolina*, I, 452.

45 *South Carolina Gazette*, No. 1326, January 12, 1760.

the frontier forts asserted that two thirds of the garrison were incapacitated by smallpox. In the meantime Charleston was resorting to inoculation on a mass scale: by the beginning of March it was estimated that around twenty-five hundred persons had used this preventive. In an account dated March 20, the correspondent of the *Pennsylvania Gazette* pictured realistically the effects of the double calamity:

Tis to be presumed that you will naturally expect some News relative to the present situation in this Colony, which you will, in a few words, when I assure you, that no Description can surpass its Calamity.—What few escape the Indians, no sooner arrive in Town, than they are seized with the Small-Pox, which generally carries them off; and, from the Numbers already dead, you may judge the Fatality of the Disease. Of the white Inhabitants 95; Acadians 115; Negroes 500, were dead two Days ago, by the Sexton's Account. About 1500 white Inhabitants, 1800 Negroes, and 300 Acadians, have had the Distemper, and chiefly by Inoculation.[46]

On April 19 the *South Carolina Gazette* claimed the epidemic was over, but the announcement was premature, for smallpox remained in Charleston for some months after April. From Augusta a correspondent noted on April 30, "The last Boats from Savannah and Charlestown brought us the Small-pox, which it is expected will soon be all over this Place." [47]

The population of Charleston in 1760 was approximately 8,000. No exact count of the number of smallpox cases was made, but a description of South Carolina published in

[46] *Pennsylvania Gazette,* No. 1628, March 6, No. 1632, April 3, No. 1663, April 10, 1760.

[47] *South Carolina Gazette,* No. 1340, April 19, 1760; *Pennsylvania Gazette,* No. 1639, May 22, 1760.

1763 mentioned in connection with the Indian wars an outbreak of smallpox among both Indians and white soldiers in the spring of 1760, and added that "no less than 4,000 then lay ill in Charles-town." On April 19 the *South Carolina Gazette* estimated the cases at 6,000 and the deaths up to date at 730; and it must be borne in mind that the *Gazette* probably minimized the effect of the outbreak in order to encourage trade.[48] The *Gazette's* conservative estimate of 730 fatalities meant that over 9 per cent of the population died during the epidemic. The *Gazette* did not state how many were inoculated, but undoubtedly the number was high. It is probable that less than 5 per cent of those inoculated died; therefore the case fatality rate among those infected naturally may have reached a new peak for colonial smallpox epidemics.

In addition to the major outbreak in South Carolina and Georgia, scattered epidemics were reported all the way to Canada in 1760. In Cecil County, Maryland, smallpox prevented the congregation of St. Stephen's Parish from holding their annual meeting on Easter Monday for the election of vestrymen. The Moravians at Bethlehem, Pennsylvania, reported over fifty cases of a mild form of smallpox, and in April, Richard Charlton, an S.P.G. missionary on Staten Island, wrote that smallpox had been present throughout the winter, "chiefly in the Inoculating way," but was now almost gone. One of the victims on the island was the Society's schoolmaster, who died that spring.[49] Charlton's re-

[48] *A Century of Population Growth*, 11; *South Carolina Gazette*, No. 1340, April 19, 1760; "A Short Description of the Province of South Carolina," in Carroll (ed.), *Historical Collections of South Carolina*, I, 528.

[49] Petition from the Rector and Vestrymen of St. Stephen's Parish, Cecil County, Md., July 8, 1760, in "Proclamations and Acts of the General Assembly of Maryland, 1764–1765," in Brown *et al.* (eds.), *Archives of Maryland*, LIX (1942), 508; Peter Boehler to Jacob Rogers, Bethlehem, December 29,

mark about inoculation illustrates its increasing use and emphasizes again the dangers inherent in its indiscriminate application.

Meanwhile in the western part of New York and on the Canadian border the disorder was scourging provincial troops. Sickness was rife, and the rapid turnover from desertion, medical discharges, and short-term enlistments spread smallpox, typhus, and other diseases far and wide. Almost without exception the recurrent theme in the diaries of the soldiers was their constant fear of smallpox—apparently a greater danger than enemy action. New England troops were particularly susceptible, and it was the return of these men carrying smallpox which made the malady so prevalent in New England for the next four or five years.

One contemporary diarist, a Sergeant Holden, has recorded the reactions of his New England regiment in the face of a smallpox epidemic. In May, 1760, the men pitched camp below Albany but were forbidden to enter the town because of the prevalence of smallpox. On May 26, several smallpox victims were hospitalized, and as summer wore on, the outbreak intensified. On September 26, he reported that "Men [are] carried out of Camp with Smallpox More or less Every Day." Four subsequent entries in the diary speak for themselves:

> Sept. 27 A very sickly time in Camp.
> Sept. 29 A very Sickly & Dying Time.
> Oct. 10 Men Die Very fast in the Hospital.
> Oct. 15 A Sickly Time & Many Die.[50]

1760, in Ferdinand J. Greer Collection, American Clergymen, Pennsylvania Historical Society MSS.; Richard Charlton to Secretary, Staten Island, N. Y., April 10, 1760, in S.P.G. MSS., B3, fpp. 159–60; *id.* to *id.*, June 21, 1760, *ibid.*, fpp. 161–62.

[50] "Journal of Sergeant Holden," *loc. cit.*, 390, 403.

Smallpox, however, was not entirely to blame, for typhus—and probably dysentery too—were complicating military life.

On September 14 Captain Jenks, another New England diarist, noted that "Our men break out fast with the smallpox. I am greatly afraid it will spread in the army altho all the care we have taken to prevent it." His worst fears were realized, for smallpox raged with increasing violence.[51]

A Pennsylvania soldier in Fort Ontario accused his officers of failing to take proper precautions against the infection. On July 25 he wrote that the soldiers were apprehensive, for "near 20 have it in the Fort; and ye Principal Officers are very careless about it." When one victim was reportedly buried less than a foot underground, it was asserted that the men could "smell the infection." [52]

Little evidence has been uncovered as to the extent of smallpox among the Indians in the Great Lakes and Ohio Valley regions in these years. However, since it was devastating the tribes to the south and was widespread in both French and British armies, it is doubtful that they could have avoided it.

In 1762 minor outbreaks occurred in New York City and Philadelphia. The threat of smallpox reportedly caused the New York assemblymen to rush through their business with undue haste, and in Philadelphia Elizabeth Drinker noted in her diary on October 15 that "The Small Pox [is] in Town and proves very mortal." [53]

[51] "Journal of Captain Jenks," *loc. cit.*, 379.

[52] Journal of Benjamin Pomroy, 1758–1768, Pennsylvania Historical Society MSS.

[53] Cadwallader Colden to the Lord Commissioners for Trade and Plantations, New York, June 12, 1762, in *The Colden Letter Books*, 2 vols. (New York, 1877–78), IX (1876), 212–14, in New-York Historical Society *Collections;* Elizabeth Drinker's Diary, October 26, 1762.

A petitioner to the house of burgesses in Virginia requested compensation for medical supplies sent to the regimental hospital during this year.[54] However, the regiment may not have been in Virginia at this time, and in any case smallpox was widespread in the colonial armies.

The following year South Carolina was again visited by smallpox. The outbreak was described as the "most favorable kind ever known here."[55] Since the major epidemic of three years previously must have reduced the number of nonimmunes to negligible proportions, it is logical that the casualties were light in 1763.

The years 1764–65 saw smallpox flaring up sporadically among the Indians from South Carolina to New York. On July 30, 1764, the New York *Mercury* stated that "Smallpox has gone among the Creek Indians & carried off great Nos. of them." The following spring the *Pennsylvania Gazette* reported that fifteen hundred Choctaws and three hundred Chickasaws had died from the infection. Cornelius Bennett, an S.P.G. missionary among the Indians in the vicinity of Mohawk Castle, explained to the Society that the dangers from smallpox had compelled him to return to Boston. The notorious lack of enthusiasm of the S.P.G. missionaries for remaining among the Indians may have caused Bennett to overrate the danger. However, he did write the following year that he was ready to return to the Indians—an indication that his concern over smallpox may have been justified. In January, 1765, smallpox was reported among the "Shawnese" Indians.[56]

[54] Petition of the House of Burgesses, November 23, 1764, in Kennedy (ed.), *Journals of the House of Burgesses of Virginia*, 1761–65 (Richmond, 1907), p. 275.

[55] *South Carolina Gazette*, No. 1490, February 5, 1763.

[56] New York *Mercury*, No. 666, July 30, 1764; *Pennsylvania Gazette*, No. 1901, May 30, 1765; Cornelius Bennett to Secretary, Boston, September

A widespread epidemic occurred in Maryland in the spring of 1765, when no less than seven counties reported cases. In Annapolis the presence of the infection in March gave the governor, who was quarreling with the house of delegates, an opportunity to delay the legislative meeting until the fall. In May a correspondent reported that the town was still not free of the infection, although it was present in only sixteen or eighteen families and appeared to be on the wane.[57]

Apparently the report was too optimistic, for the representatives petitioned the governor to prorogue the house in December on the grounds that "The Unhappy circumstances of the small Pox being in town and One of our Members now Dead of that disorder will . . . make it impossible for us to keep a sufft. number together to compose a House longer than this Day or Tomorrow." [58]

Smallpox struck Williamsburg, Virginia, early in 1768. In March the president and masters of the College of William and Mary voted £50 to a local doctor for his attendance upon those ill with the disease at the college.[59]

Apparently the contagion remained in Virginia throughout the following winter. That its virulence may have been the result of unrestricted inoculation is evidenced in a petition of May, 1768, addressed to the house of burgesses. The petition set forth "the destructive Tendency of Inocu-

12, 1765, in S.P.G. MSS., B22, fpp. 130–31; Heagerty, *Four Centuries of Medical History*, I, 43.

[57] Boston *Post Boy and Advertiser*, No. 401, April 22, 1765; *Massachusetts Gazette and Boston News-Letter*, No. 3184, February 28, No. 3195, May 16, 1765; Address of the House of Delegates to Governor Horatio Sharpe, December 13, 1765, "Proclamations and Acts of the General Assembly of Maryland," in Brown *et al.* (eds.), *Archives of Maryland*, LIX (1942), 230–31.

[58] Brown *et al.* (eds.), *Archives of Maryland*, LIX (1942), 251.

[59] "Journal of the Meetings of the President and Masters of William and Mary College," in *William and Mary Quarterly*, Ser. 1, V (1896), 15.

lation with Small-Pox; and therefore pray[ed] that no such Practice may be allowed in Virginia." In November, though a committee to investigate variolation resolved to reject the petitions of "divers inhabitants" who urged the prohibition of inoculation, it decided to accept one which favored its regulation.[60] By doing so Virginia was conforming to the usual colonial practice.

Philadelphia was attacked by smallpox several times in the ten years from 1765 to 1775, and it is not at all unlikely that inoculation served to keep the infection circulating. Elizabeth Drinker mentioned deaths from smallpox in the years 1765–66, 1769, and 1773. In the latter year the Philadelphia Bills of Mortality show that over three hundred smallpox deaths occurred. "As the chief of them were the Children of poor People," a newspaper account stated, "a Number of Gentlemen in that City have formed a Society for innoculating the Poor, free of Expense to them, and are providing a Fund for that Purpose." [61]

Other than Philadelphia the only Pennsylvania town to suffer from the disease was Reading. A report from Philadelphia dated December 19, 1768, declared: "We hear from Reading, in berks County, that the small pox rages with great violence in that town, having carried off near sixty children, in less than two months." [62]

Aside from the one outbreak in Philadelphia in 1773, the disease was kept in check from 1770 to 1775. A few isolated cases may have occurred, but, as in New England, the period was the lull before the storm.

[60] Petition of the House of Burgesses of Virginia, May 11, 1769, in Kennedy (ed.), *Journals of the House of Burgesses of Virginia*, 1766–69, p. 203; *ibid.*, November 18, 1769, p. 269.

[61] Elizabeth Drinker's Diary, August and December, 1765, February, 1766, June and December, 1769, February, 1773; *Massachusetts Gazette and Boston Post Boy and Advertiser*, No. 861, February 14–21, 1774.

[62] *Massachusetts Gazette*, No. 337, December 19, 1768.

Quarantine Laws and Pesthouses

The seriousness of smallpox attacks and the obviously contagious nature of the disease led to a whole series of legislative measures, all of which aimed at isolating the sick. Practically all the colonies early enacted laws requiring ships from infected ports to await ten to twenty days' quarantine. In general these measures were administered adequately and served to reduce outbreaks of smallpox, yellow fever, and other epidemic contagions. As early as 1647, vessels entering the harbor of Boston from the West Indies were compelled to observe quarantine. Pennsylvania passed an act around 1700 to prevent ships with sick aboard from coming into the colony.[1]

The records of New Hampshire clearly indicate the necessity for such measures. In 1738 the journals of the house refer to a vessel in quarantine because of smallpox. The minutes of the council mention a ship at Portsmouth isolated for twenty days in 1744 for the same reason. A vessel from the West Indies with smallpox aboard was quarantined for ten days in July, 1747. In 1749 a boat from Jamaica was placed under similar restrictions when the infection was found among the crew.[2] These instances are only a few of the many that can be cited to show the danger inherent in trading with endemic smallpox areas. In consideration of the relatively low number of major smallpox outbreaks in New England, one must conclude that the quarantine laws worked fairly effectively.

[1] Henry E. Sigerist, *American Medicine* (New York, 1934), 37; Viets, *History of Medicine in Massachusetts,* 44; Packard, *History of Medicine,* I, 173–74.

[2] "Journals of the House," in Bouton (ed.), *Documents and Records of New Hampshire,* V (1871), 8; "Records of the Council," *ibid.,* 98, 113, 124.

A second group of laws endeavored to isolate individual cases within the colonies. One of the earliest of these attempts took place in Virginia in 1667. The "Colonel and Commander" of Northampton County, acting as health officer, issued a proclamation warning all families infected with smallpox to allow no member "to go forth their doors until their full cleansing, that is to say, thirtie dayes after their receiving the sd. smallpox, least the sd. disease shoulde spreade by infection like the plague of leprosy . . . such as shall no-things notice of this premonition and charge, but beast like shall p[re]sume to act and doe contrarily, may expect to be severely punished according to the Statute of King James in such case provided for their contempt herein; God save the King." [3]

Massachusetts passed a series of laws dealing with infectious diseases. In 1699 the general court created "An Act to prevent the spread of infectious sickness." Two years later another measure provided "for those sick with contagious diseases." During the smallpox epidemic of 1730–31 a law was passed by the general court which sought "to prevent persons concealing the small pox and requiring a red cloth to be hung out in all infected places." And in 1742 an amendment extended this requirement to all infectious diseases. A few years later the magistrates were given the power to send those suffering with contagious infections to the quarantine hospital on Rainsford Island.

These measures are typical of many passed by Massachusetts and the other colonies. A slight variation was provided by Connecticut which passed "An Act to prevent the small-pox being spread in this colony by pedlers, hawkers, [and] petty chapmen." The influx of Germans and Scotch-

[3] "Northampton County Records, 1655–1658," quoted in Bruce, *Institutional History of Virginia*, II, 17–18 n.

Irish led Pennsylvania to enact many laws specifically covering "infected" immigrants in addition to the general laws affecting those sick with contagious disorders.

The last method used by the governing authorities to control infectious diseases was the building of quarantine hospitals. Probably the earliest one was built by Massachusetts. The appropriation was made in 1717 and the hospital was built on Spectacle Island the following year, and subsequently transferred to Rainsford Island. The legislature of New Hampshire voted £112 in June, 1747, to build a "pesthouse" for smallpox victims. Rhode Island granted £600 for a like institution in 1751, and three years later South Carolina followed suit.[4] The medical treatment was of little value to the victims. However, it was little, if any, worse than could be expected from the physicians of the time. Although the hospitals were of little benefit to those infected with smallpox, they did serve to isolate cases and so to protect the community.

All colonies passed laws dealing with epidemic diseases, but Massachusetts appears to have been the most advanced both in the number and in general enforcement of the regulations. Hence it is not surprising that Massachusetts, closely followed by the other New England colonies, was most successful in meeting the threat from smallpox.

An Evaluation

The problem of correlating the epidemics of smallpox in the various sections of North America presents

[4] Viets, *History of Medicine in Massachusetts*, 44; Packard, *History of Medicine*, I, 167; "Journals of the House," *loc. cit.*, 512–13; Bartlett (ed.), *Records of Rhode Island*, V (1860), 338–39; Packard, *History of Medicine*, I, 177.

considerable difficulties. Usually the disease was brought into the colonies from the British Isles or the West Indies. Since smallpox was endemic in these areas, there were few limitations on its importation. The peripheral development of North America and the lack of land transportation limited the disease largely to water-borne commerce. Hence, when the diseases were passed from one colony to another, they were likely to enter through the ports. Geographical features tended to isolate New England, and distance combined with a sparse population did the same for the Carolinas. The ports of Boston, in New England, and Charleston, in South Carolina, were the chief focal points of infection and took the heaviest casualties from disease. The essential difference between the two sections was that Charleston was the only good port in the Carolinas, whereas New England had an abundance of excellent harbors. Consequently, smallpox appeared with greater frequency in New England. Fortunately the strictly administered quarantine laws were of some aid in preventing serious outbreaks.

The central colonies, extending from New York as far south as Virginia, represented a continuous belt of population with considerable commercial and social intercourse. The whole region was connected with the Northwest, since communication lines reached up the Hudson Valley from New York. The Indian nations constituting the buffer between the French and English were in contact with the whites through trade and war and so served as carriers of smallpox and other diseases.

Some conception of the prevalence of smallpox can be gathered from the fact that in the one hundred years from 1675 to 1775 the infection was absent from the colonies for as long as five years on only two occasions. The longest intervals between outbreaks naturally occurred in New England and the Carolinas. Both of these regions were free from the scourge for almost twenty years on one occasion. In the central colonies the infection disappeared for ten years only once, from 1719 to 1730. Particular localities often remained unaffected for almost a generation but smallpox could usually be found in some section of North America.

Little correlation is apparent between the years of major epidemics in England and those in America. Smallpox was at its worst in England in 1721–23, 1740–42, and 1766–67. During the first period the colonies were free of the infection except for an outbreak in Boston, and it is definitely established that the Boston epidemic of 1721 was imported from the West Indies rather than England. The other two periods occurred two or three years after general attacks in America, and even allowing for slow transportation, any connection is doubtful.

A comparison of the course of smallpox in England with its history in the colonies does lead to one generalization. Smallpox first became a serious problem in England in the latter half of the seventeenth century and grew steadily worse during the eighteenth, tapering off slightly for the last twenty years of the century. In the colonies the infection increased in extent and virulence up to the 1760's and then dropped off sharply, whereas the peak was still to be reached in England. The increasing use of variolation mitigated the worst effects of smallpox in the colonies at a time when the sickness was still a rising threat to British health. Although the incidence of smallpox increased in America around the mid-century, it was never as high as in England. For example, the London Bills of Mortality show that the deaths from smallpox were over fifteen hundred annually for seventy-one years during the eighteenth century. In thirteen of these years the smallpox fatalities exceeded three thousand. Since the total number of deaths in London from all causes averaged between fifteen and thirty thousand, smallpox was both a serious and perennial menace. The Bills of Mortality for Liverpool, Manchester, and other British towns present a similar picture. In the latter half of the century the mortality rate from smallpox in Glasgow exceeded that of London. The death rate during outbreaks in the colonies was relatively high, but the relief between epidemics affected statistics favorably. Hence the total number of smallpox deaths in America for a twenty-five- or fifty-year period averages a relatively low annual figure as compared with England.

The endemic nature of smallpox in nearly all major European cities raises the question as to why this was not the case in American urban areas. One of the more obvious explanations is density of population. New York, Boston, and Philadelphia were smaller than London and other large European cities; yet smallpox was endemic in English towns such as Chester where the population ranged from 10,000 to 15,000. Another reason, and possibly a better one, is the higher standard of living in America. During the years of the Napoleonic wars, when much money was spent and wages were higher than ever before in England, the general health showed a marked improvement, and smallpox declined along with other diseases. The end of the war and the ensuing depression brought a return of epidemics. Variolation, the greatest check to smallpox in the eighteenth century, was beyond the means of the English working class, but this did not hold true for America. The abundance of land, which kept wages high in the urban regions of the colonies, also served to promote the general health. Higher wages among lower-income groups invariably mean more and better food, a fact which may account for the failure of smallpox to establish itself permanently anywhere in the American colonies.

Much has been made of the disfigurement caused by smallpox. The scars resulting from this pestilence have been a favorite theme of many historians who have had occasion to mention the disease. One or two classic advertisements for runaway bonded servants or slaves stating that the runaway was "not pockmarked" [1] have been seized upon and passed from writer to writer as proof that a face without smallpox pits was almost the exception rather than the rule. The previously quoted passage by Macaulay lays too much emphasis upon the disfiguring effects of smallpox and undoubtedly has been a definite factor in promoting the general impression that pitted faces were universal.

The best study of the question was made by Charles Creighton, who showed convincingly that the incidence of pockmarked faces in the late seventeenth century had been greatly exaggerated. From December, 1667, to June, 1674, the London *Gazette* published 100 descriptions of persons wanted, such as runaway apprentices and servants who had robbed their masters. Creighton examined these advertisements and found that only 16 of the runaways had pockmarks. Four of these were Negroes and 2 were boys, one who had lately "had the smallpox," and the other who was "newly recovered of the smallpox." Creighton concluded that 12 out of 100 (excluding the Negroes) was about a normal ratio for London. He pointed out that during the seventeenth century a very high percentage of adults, who would be more likely to retain permanent scars, were attacked. As final proof he quoted the opinions of prominent

[1] Major, *Disease and Destiny*, 104.

contemporary physicians, all of whom dismissed the danger of pitting.[2]

Of the eighteenth century, when smallpox was at its height, Creighton asserted: "I have found nothing in the medical writings of the 18th century, nor in its fiction or memoirs, to show that pockpitting was more than an occasional blemish of the countenance. At that time most had smallpox in infancy or childhood, when the chances of permanent marking would be less."[3]

In the American colonies, where the prevalence of smallpox was never comparable with that in London, disfigurement from smallpox was even less likely. It is true that the relative incidence of smallpox among adults was higher in eighteenth-century America than in England. But it is also true that a larger percentage of colonists escaped the infection completely. The concept of the widespread appearance of pockmarked faces in England has been carried over into the colonies. The case of George Washington, who actually contracted the malady while visiting Barbados in 1751, is often used to support this theory. Yet an examination of colonial records gives little indication that pockmarked faces were common. Undoubtedly, many bore the scars of smallpox, but they never constituted more than a small minority. Pitting is characteristic of a certain texture of skin, and in the American colonies many who would have been subject to it probably escaped the disease altogether. It is safe to say that in the colonies, as in England, the extent of pockmarked faces has been exaggerated.

Smallpox had a direct effect upon education in the colonies both for good and evil. Lack of higher educational

[2] Creighton, *History of Epidemics*, II, 453–56.
[3] *Ibid.*, 456–57.

facilities compelled the colonists to visit England in order to complete their education. Unfortunately, many of those who did so fell victims to smallpox or other diseases and never returned. The dangers inherent in journeying to England were one of the chief complaints of the Church of England ministers, who could not be ordained in the colonies.[4] From this high mortality among American travelers abroad came the development of institutions of higher learning, such as the College of William and Mary. Francis Louis Michel, a French visitor to the college in 1702, found that "There are about forty students there now. Before it was customary for wealthy parents, because of the lack of preceptors or teachers, to send their sons to England to study there. But experience showd that not many of them came back. Most of them died of smallpox, to which sickness the children of the West are subject." A student commencement speaker at the college on May 1, 1699, emphasized the needless risks incident to attending school in England. He pointed out that students so doing first exposed themselves to the dangers of climate and smallpox in England, and then had to readjust themselves to the "seasoning" in Virginia on their return.[5] The threat of smallpox in England was a decided stimulus to the development of colleges in the colonies.

On the debit side, many of the young and able colonists were lost by smallpox while completing their education in the mother country. In the colonies, schools were

[4] In a letter dated London, 1743, Nathaniel Whittaker complained to the S.P.G. that on coming to England he had caught smallpox and was in need of help. Many such appeals were made to the Society. See S.P.G. MSS., B13, fpp. 43–44.

[5] William J. Hinke (ed.), "The Journey of Francis Louis Michel, 1701–1702," in *Virginia Magazine of History and Biography*, XXIV (1916), 23–26; *William and Mary Quarterly*, Ser. 2, X (1930), 325–26.

disrupted by smallpox outbreaks.[6] In England, where most children were infected in the preschool ages, this situation was not so likely to occur. On the credit side, the incidence of smallpox in the colonies was relatively low, and only in times of major epidemics were the schools affected.

It is difficult to determine the actual economic cost of smallpox or to measure its interruption of normal life. Even a mild outbreak was enough to prevent the provincial legislatures from functioning efficiently—if they convened at all. Repeated complaints were made by the governors of their inability to get a quorum or of members hurrying the business at hand because of fears engendered by the presence of the contagion. The governor of New York and New Jersey wrote in 1716 that he was afraid he would not be able to get a quorum of either the council or the assembly at Burlington, New Jersey, because smallpox was threatening. President Van Dam had similar trouble in New York City in 1731, and reported that some of the "Councellors" refused to enter the city, and that many of those who had arrived were already leaving from fear of the infection. Governor George Clarke of New York was compelled to adjourn the house of representatives in April, 1739 until the following August for the same reasons.[7] Similar instances recur only too frequently in colonial records.

The disruption of legislative activity by smallpox was essentially an American phenomenon. In England and on the Continent, where smallpox was a disease of childhood,

[6] Instances of this nature have been cited earlier. See Rowland Ellis to Secretary, Burlington, N. J., *c.* 1716, in S.P.G. MSS., A12, fp. 165.

[7] Governor Hunter to the Lords of Trade, New York, November 12, 1716, in O'Callaghan (ed.), *Documents Relative to Colonial History*, V (1855), 481; President Rip Van Dam to the Lords of Trade, New York, September 11, 1731, *ibid.*, 924; Lieutenant Governor George Clarke to the Lords of Trade, New York, April 18, 1739, *ibid.*, VI (1855), 140.

local and national governments were unaffected. Long intervals between epidemics, which were sometimes spaced a generation apart, meant a high incidence among adults in the American colonies. The presence of smallpox aroused fear and consternation among all groups, therefore, and this anxiety presented almost as much of a problem to the governing authorities as the casualties from the disease itself.

The descriptions, previously quoted, of Boston, New York, Charleston, and other American cities during smallpox epidemics show that most economic activities were almost paralyzed. This collapse must have worked hardship on the individual members of the community. The merchant in Boston, for example, who was forced to close his business for many weeks and who may have lost one or more members of his family during the epidemic, unquestionably suffered a severe setback. The same can be said for the families of the thirteen men who died from smallpox in Roxbury, Massachusetts, in 1721. When these instances are multiplied a thousandfold, the result cannot be dismissed lightly. Yet the colonies were predominantly agricultural, and the urban areas constituted a small percentage of the population.

From an economic standpoint the destruction caused by smallpox among the Indians more than compensated for any damages done to the colonists. The elimination of certain tribes and the decimation of many others greatly facilitated colonial expansion. Indirectly, smallpox saved both lives and property which would otherwise have been expended in warfare with the Indians.

The depletion of manpower was a most serious loss in the colonies, where vast resources awaited development. On the other hand, a high birthrate replaced losses and doubled the population about every twenty-three years. And it must be borne in mind, too, that the relative loss of life in America was well below that in England and on the Continent. Smallpox was a costly disease in America; yet it was not destructive enough to cripple the economic development of the country.

CHAPTER III

Diphtheria and Scarlet Fever

The study of diphtheria is one of the most profitable adventures in American medical history. Considered a new disorder, it did not attract the attention of the medical profession until the occurrence of a virulent outbreak in New England during 1735–36. Mild attacks occurred earlier, but it was not until then that the disease assumed its fatal form.

Unfortunately, at that time it was impossible to distinguish between diphtheria and scarlet fever, and the inadequate diagnoses of the colonial era make it extremely difficult for the present-day student to draw a clear line of differentiation between them. Adding to the difficulty is the fact that both these infections were in a process of evolution and had not taken their present forms. Creighton, writing in the early 1890's, when the miasmatic theory was still the explanation for most contagious diseases, held that scarlet fever and diphtheria were not separate and distinct diseases in the eighteenth century and hence could not be traced separately.[1] From the standpoint of the medical practitioner of his time he was correct; but he did not know that diphtheria is caused by a baccillus, whereas scarlet fever

[1] Creighton, *History of Epidemics*, II, 678.

is a streptococcus infection. On the basis of apparent symptoms Creighton probably was justified in classing the two diseases together, but they were distinct and separate infections, and the failure to distinguish between them must be attributed to the lack of bacteriological knowledge.

The clinical symptoms of diphtheria are fairly distinct: swelling, redness, and tenderness of the throat, followed by the appearance of grayish-white specks or patches and the gradual formation of a yellowish-colored false membrane over all the mucous surfaces of the throat. As this membrane thickens and spreads down the larynx and trachea, breathing becomes increasingly difficult, and in severe cases death results from suffocation. Under certain conditions an acrid fetid discharge, and sometimes bleeding, comes from the nostrils. This latter characteristic early gave the name "putrid sore throat" to diphtheria. Human contact is the chief method of spreading the disease, and its principal victims are children below the age of puberty. Despite the advance of medical science, the infection remains endemic in all European and American countries, reaching epidemic proportions periodically. Many children have a natural resistance and show only the mildest symptoms, usually a slight sore throat and fever, thus preventing a correct diagnosis and adequate quarantine. A small percentage of these cases, on recovering, remain active carriers. Consequently, the infection is perpetuated in the community and passed on to other children.

Contemporary observers confronted with diphtheria and scarlet fever gave them many names: throat disease; throat distemper; throat ail; canker ail; malignant quinsies; putrid, malignant, or pestilential sore throat; malignant croup; cynanche trachealis; angina suffocativa; and malignant angina. These terms are confusing because many of them were applied to other diseases as well. The term "throat distemper," for example, was applied to a number of contagious infections, including diphtheria, scarlatina anginosa, and certain streptococcus infections.

There is little agreement among medical historians as to the origin of diphtheria. Some have claimed that it went back to antiquity, or at least to medieval times. On the other hand, others have held that the disease was still in an early stage of development in the eighteenth century. All authorities agree that the modern form of infection did not appear until 1857, after which it encompassed the globe in the space of two or three years. This evolutionary concept is in accord with the findings of a recent study of microscopic life which maintains that the same laws of heredity apply to lower as well as to higher forms of life.[2]

The first recorded epidemics of throat distemper in the American colonies occurred in 1659. Cotton Mather recorded that "in December 1659, the (until then unknown) Malady of Bladders in the Windpipe, invaded and removed many children; by Opening of one of them the Malady and Remedy (too late for very many) were discovered." Among those who died during this attack were the three children of the Reverend Samuel Danforth of Roxbury, Massachusetts. Their father, who kept the records of the First Church, in a starkly simple entry reported that "the Lord sent a general visitation of Children by coughs & colds, of wch my 3 children Sarah, Mary & Elisabeth

[2] August Hirsch, *Handbook of Geographical and Historical Pathology*, trans. Charles Creighton, 3 vols. (London, 1883–86), III, 73; Howard W. Haggard, *The Lame, the Halt, and the Blind* (New York and London, 1932), 15; R. Hingston Fox, *Dr. John Fothergill and His Friends* (London, 1919), 49–53; Frank MacFarlane Burnet, *Virus as Organism, Evolutionary and Ecological Aspects of Some Human Virus Diseases*, in Harvard University *Monographs in Medicine and Public Health* (Cambridge, 1945), 14, 126.

Danforth died, all of ym within ye space of a fortnight." Whether the infection was scarlet fever—as one medical historian maintained—diphtheria, or another disease is uncertain in view of the limited information available.[3]

Within the next few years several other outbreaks of what may have been throat distemper developed in the colonies, but here again the information is scant. John Josselyn in his description of New England first published in 1673 definitely indicates the presence of contagious throat infections among the English settlers in New England. "They are," he wrote, "troubled with a disease in the mouth or throat which hath proved mortal to some in a very short time, Quinsies, and Imposthumations of the Almonds, with great distempers of colds." In 1686 Virginia suffered an epidemic of sore throats, according to a letter sent to the editors of *Philosophical Transactions* by John Clayton, a minister in that colony, and a "Distemper of sore throats and ffeaver . . . the Like haveing not been knowne in ye Memory of man" brought death to many in New London, Connecticut, in 1689.[4]

In the succeeding years the local records in New England reveal a series of minor outbreaks of "distempers in the throat," and it is evident that diphtheria and scarlet fever were prevalent for many years prior to the major attack in 1735. Another portent of the gathering storm of disease which was to break over the colonies in a few years came from South Carolina in 1724. The Reverend William

[3] Cotton Mather, *Magnalia Christi Americana* . . . (London, 1702), Book IV, 156; Webster, *History of Epidemic Diseases*, I, 193; "Rev. Samuel Danforth's Records of the First Church in Roxbury, Mass.," *loc. cit.*, 87; Packard, *History of Medicine*, I, 97–98.

[4] John Josselyn, "An Account of two voyages to New England," in Massachusetts Historical Society *Collections*, III (1833), 333; John Clayton to Secretary of the Royal Society, Virginia, 1687, in *Philosophical Transactions*, XLI, Pt. 1 (1739–40), 143–62.

Guy of Charleston reported an outbreak of a "Quinzey," which, he stated, was "a Distemper that within a short time prov'd mortal to a great No. of people here." [5]

Eleven years later the first large-scale outbreak of throat distemper began in Kingston, New Hampshire. "About this time, the country was visited with a new epidemic disease, which has obtained the name of the throat distemper," wrote one colonial historian. "The general description of it is a swelled throat, with white or ash-colored specks, an efflorescence on the skin, great debility of the whole system, and a strong tendency to putridity." [6]

The year of the New Hampshire epidemic was long accepted by medical historians as the real beginning of diphtheria. Its extensive nature and high mortality rate made a deep impression upon all observers, both in America and in England. Several pamphlets and many articles were written by physicians and lay observers.[7]

Not one of the first forty victims, most of them children, recovered. The disease did not spread very fast. Beginning at Kingston in May, it reached Hampton by June or July, Exeter, a town six miles from Kingston, and Boston, fifty miles distant, in August. It was not until 1737 that this plague reached the Hudson River.[8]

"In the parish of Hampton-Falls [the disease] raged

[5] Caulfield, *A True History*, 102–103; William Guy to Secretary, St. Andrews, S. C., March 26, 1724, in S.P.G. MSS., B4, Pt. 2, fp. 612.

[6] Jeremy Belknap, *The History of New-Hampshire*, 3 vols. (Boston, 1791–92), II, 118.

[7] William Douglass, *The Practical History of a New Epidemical Eruptive Military Fever, with an Angina Ulcusculosa which prevailed in Boston, New England in the Years 1735 and 1736* (Boston, 1736). Creighton bases much of his account upon this work, which was reprinted in the *New England Journal of Medicine and Surgery*, XIV (1825), 1.

[8] Willis (ed.), *Journals of Smith and Deane*, 82 n.; Timothy Dwight, *Travels in New-England and New-York*, 4 vols. (New Haven, 1821), I, 86–87.

most violently. Twenty families buried all their children. Twenty-seven persons were lost out of five families; and more than one sixth part of the inhabitants of that place died within thirteen months. In the whole Province, not less than one thousand persons, of whom above nine hundred were under twenty years of age, fell victims to this raging distemper." Within one year Hampton Falls lost 210 persons by the infection out of a population of about 1,200, and 95 per cent of the victims were below the age of twenty. Deacon Joshua Lane of Hampton recorded in his journal on July 26, 1735, the deaths of three of his brother's children from a "mortal distemper" which "dreadfully seized their throats in an awful manner." Noah Webster, too, was impressed by its selective nature, declaring, "It was literally the *plague among children.* Many families lost three or four children—many lost all." [9]

Unlike many other contagious diseases which subside after reaching epidemic proportions, the throat distemper continued to break out sporadically in New England for the next few years. In July, 1736, the Reverend Jabez Fitch, a minister at Portsmouth, summarized the deaths caused by throat infection during the preceding fourteen months in fifteen New Hampshire towns. According to his estimate, nearly a thousand persons succumbed to the infection; over 80 per cent were children less than ten years of age.[10]

In 1736–37 the sickness spread further into Massachusetts. A history of Haverhill, based upon the town records, states that in October and November, 1736, the throat dis-

[9] Belknap, *History of New-Hampshire,* II, 120; Caulfield, *A True History,* 15; "Deaths in Hampton, New Hampshire, 1727–1755," *New England Historical and Genealogical Register,* LVIII (1904), 31; Webster, *History of Epidemic Diseases,* I, 233.

[10] Jabez Fitch, "An Account of the Numbers that have died of the Distemper in the Throat . . . in New Hampshire," quoted in Belknap, *History*

temper "swept off" more than one half of the children under 15 years of age. Another account gave a total of 199 deaths from November 17, 1735, to October 6, 1737. Similar statistics were reported for other Massachusetts towns. To cite an example, 75 persons died of the disease in Falmouth by May, 1737. William Douglass mentioned the presence of the scourge at Marblehead in 1736–37 and Malden in 1738.[11]

In February, 1738, Boston papers reported that the "throat distemper" was proving "very mortal" in Marblehead and had brought death to several children in Brain-

---

of New-Hampshire, II, 122. Belknap compiled this chart from Fitch's pamphlet:

TOWNS	*Under 10*	*Between 10 & 20*	*Above 20*	*Above 30*	*Above 40*	*Above 90*	*Total*
Portsmouth	81	15	1		2		99
Dover	77	8	3				88
Hampton	37	8	8	1		1	55
Hampton-Falls	160	40	9	1			210
Exeter	105	18	4				127
New Castle	11						11
Gosport	34	2			1		37
Rye	34	10					44
Greenland	13	2	3				18
Newington	16	5					21
Newmarket	20	1		1			22
Stratham	18						18
Kingston	96	15	1	1			113
Durham	79	15	6				100
Chester	21						21
	802	139	35	4	3	1	984

Though Fitch shows a total of 984 deaths in these 15 towns, Belknap noted that many more children died in the succeeding months of 1736, 13 more in Hampton alone. He estimated the total deaths to be well over 1,000. In another town, Kittery, not included in Fitch's survey, 122 deaths were recorded during this same epidemic.

[11] "Sketch of Haverhill, Massachusetts," in Massachusetts Historical Society *Collections*, Ser. 2, IV (1816), 134; Willis (ed.), *Journals of Smith and Deane*, 84 n.; Douglass to Colden, Boston, Mass., November 12, 1739, in *Colden Papers*, II (1918), 195–200.

tree. In Braintree a number of multiple deaths occurred. A Mr. Vinton lost five grandchildren, three in one family and two in another, "the Parents of whom," reported the Boston *Gazette*, "are now childless by that strange Disease in the throat." Multiple deaths are a good indication that diphtheria rather than scarlet fever was responsible. The Reverend Thomas Smith of Falmouth wrote in his journal on May 1, 1739: "The [throat] distemper is now bad at North Yarmouth. In all seventy-five have died of it in the whole town; forty here and twenty-six in Purpoodock." The coming of summer had little effect upon the outbreak, for he added the following October, "The distemper is still bad at Scarborough. Not one lived that has had it of late." [12]

The year 1740 witnessed a serious outbreak in Massachusetts. The infection appeared first in Roxbury in February and by June had spread to Cambridge, where it proved fatal to, among others, the wife of the president of Harvard, and where it caused the postponement of the July commencement exercises. In the late summer the Reverend William Homes reported from Martha's Vineyard that seven of twelve children infected had succumbed to the attack. In the section of Massachusetts which later formed the state of Maine a reliable estimate placed the death total at about five hundred. With the coming of fall, the disease increased in extent and virulence throughout all Massachusetts. In Sutton one family lost five children during the winter and multiple deaths in families were reported from many towns.[13]

[12] Boston *Weekly News-Letter*, No. 1768, February 2–9, No. 1769, February 9–16, 1738; Boston *Gazette*, No. 943, January 30–February 6, 1738; Willis (ed.), *Journals of Smith and Deane*, 85, 87.

[13] "Diary of Paul Dudley, 1740," in *New England Historical and Genealogical Register*, XXXV (1881), 28; Ebenezer Parkman Diary, January to September, 1740, in American Antiquarian Society MSS.; "Diary of Rev.

Meanwhile the disorder was reaching other sections. Early in 1736 it spread south into Rhode Island, Connecticut, and New Jersey. Both the New York *Weekly Journal* and the *American Weekly Mercury* announced the presence of the sickness in New Jersey, the latter stating in February, 1736: "We are inform'd that at Crosswicks in West-New-Jersey, divers Persons have died lately with a Distemper in the Throat, and that the *Distemper* prevails there." The Reverend Jonathan Dickinson of Elizabeth Town, New Jersey, distinguished between diphtheria and scarlet fever, both of which were apparently ravaging New Jersey.[14]

In February and March the newspapers reported that the throat sickness which had "so long prevailed to the Eastward" was now in western Connecticut. In New London the disease intensified its attack as the summer advanced and did not wear itself out until October. By the following year the infection had spread over half of Connecticut. The attack diminished in 1738 but exacted a heavy toll in 1739. In this year New Haven lost heavily in what was obviously a diphtheria outbreak. One family lost five children within one August week, and as late as the middle of November one of the papers reported: "We have a sorrowful account from New Haven in Connecticut, of the prevailing of the Throat Distemper there, and of the great Mortality thereby, especially among the Children and Youth; whole Families of which have been carry'd off by

William Homes of Chilmark, Martha's Vineyard," *loc. cit.*, 165; Caulfield, *A True History*, 27; David Hall Diary, April 6, 1741, in Massachusetts Historical Society MSS.

[14] New York *Weekly Journal*, February 9, 1736, quoted in Whitehead *et al.* (eds.), *Documents Relative to the History of New Jersey*, Ser. 1, XI (1894), 443–44; *American Weekly Mercury*, No. 839, January 20, 1736; Caulfield, *A True History*, 94–96; Stephen Wickes, *History of Medicine in New Jersey, and of Its Medical Men from the Settlement of the Province to A.D. 1800* (Newark, 1879), 89–99.

the same." By 1740 the deaths from the throat disease in Connecticut ranged around a thousand.[15]

Diphtheria, which had smouldered in New Hampshire in 1738, flared up anew the next year. A correspondent from Hampton reported on March 30, "The awful Distemper in the Throat which some Time ago raged in this Part of the Country, this Month returned again and visited the Family of Mr. Joseph Batchelder, where were Six Children, and carried off Five of them." A recurrence of the infection took the lives of five more of the town's children in the fall of 1741. Hampton suffered ninety-one deaths by the throat distemper from 1735 to 1744, according to a table compiled by a local minister. Since the Reverend Mr. Fitch's summary as of July, 1736, shows only fifty-five, an additional thirty-six must have died in the ensuing years.[16]

From the *Colden Papers* it is apparent that New York, too, was ravaged by the throat disease, but the specific infection or infections cannot be determined. William Douglass in a letter written in May, 1740, expressed the hope that the malady had left Cadwallader Colden's home province of New York. The following year Lieutenant Governor George Clarke wrote that he was glad to hear that the Colden family had "got so well through the throat plague." [17]

[15] *Zenger's Weekly*, February 9, 1736, quoted in Wickes, *History of Medicine in New Jersey*, 25; *American Weekly Mercury*, No. 847, March 16–23, 1736; *Diary of Joshua Hempstead*, 338; Boston *Weekly News-Letter*, No. 1849, August 23–30, No. 1860, November 8–15, 1739; Caulfield, *A True History*, 91.

[16] Boston *Weekly News-Letter*, No. 1829, March 30–April 5, 1739; "Deaths in Hampton, New Hampshire, 1727–1755," *loc. cit.*, 34; Belknap, *History of New-Hampshire*, III, 241–42.

[17] Douglass to Colden, Boston, Mass., May 1740, in *Colden Papers*, II (1918), 204–205; Lieutenant Governor George Clarke to Colden, New York, November 23, 1741, *ibid.*, VIII (1937), 278.

Noah Webster asserted that "ulcerous sore-throat" was general in America in 1742,[18] but he seems to have overlooked the general outbreak in 1744–45 and may have confused his dates.

In 1744–45, the disorder once again prevailed in scattered sections of Massachusetts, New Hampshire, and New York. Hampton, New Hampshire, suffered at least one death from throat distemper in June, 1744, and twelve more the following year. As was usual, eleven of the twelve were children, the other a twenty-seven-year-old woman. A journalist in Falmouth, Massachusetts, reported in November, 1744, that the disease had broken out in Kingston, Exeter, and Stratham, in Massachusetts, with fatal results. A year later Falmouth itself was the victim, for several children "died of the quincy and throat distemper." Joshua Hempstead of Sutton mentioned a number of children's deaths from this same cause from 1743 to 1745.[19]

More than ten years elapsed between the initial outbreak in New England and the first mention of the throat distemper in Pennsylvania. A Philadelphia physician thus described the attack: "In the spring, summer, and autumn, 1746, and during some part of the winter, a disease, since called by the learned Huxham, Fothergill, and others, the Angina Maligna, or the putrid and ulcerous sore throat, prevailed in this and neighboring provinces, and spread itself in mortal rage, in opposition to the united endeavors of the faculty." At the same time, after a brief respite of two years, the disease returned to New England. A history of Kingston, Massachusetts, states: "The throat ail, which prevailed in many places in the years 1747 and 8, severely

[18] Webster, *History of Epidemic Diseases*, I, 237.

[19] "Deaths in Hampton, New Hampshire, 1727–1755," *loc. cit.*, 36, 137; Willis (ed.), *Journals of Smith and Deane*, 116, 122; *Diary of Joshua Hempstead*, 416–50.

visited this town. More than forty persons, mostly children, died. In the family of Thomas Cushman, out of six, four died in eight hours, and were interred in the same grave. That disorder was a violent putrid fever with sore throat, not attended with eruption." [20] The specific point that the sickness was "not attended with eruption" indicates diphtheria and again emphasizes the prevalence of two distinct types of throat infection in New England.

Boston endured a mild outbreak of some form of the infection in 1748, and a number of smaller towns probably were attacked by diphtheria. The Reverend Thomas Smith wrote from Falmouth, "There is an asthmatic quincy prevailing this week among the children, that proves dreadfully mortal." By "asthmatic" Smith was no doubt referring to the difficulty in breathing so characteristic of the throat disease. A month later, November, he recorded the deaths of nine children in the neighboring town of North Yarmouth from what he termed the "canker ail," one of the numerous appellations given to the throat distemper. Another Massachusetts town affected by the outbreaks in 1748 was Pepperell.[21]

The relatively slow progress of the throat disorder has been noted already. South Carolina, which apparently had been free of the disease, was infected in 1750–51 with what was probably diphtheria. Robert Stone, the S.P.G. missionary at Goose Creek, wrote in the spring of 1751 that more deaths had occurred in his parish during his first year and

[20] John Kearsley, "Putrid Sore Throat," in *Gentlemen's Magazine*, XXXIX (1769), 521–23; "A Description of Kingston in Plymouth County," in Massachusetts Historical Society *Collections*, Ser. 2, III (1815), 216; Boston *Weekly News-Letter*, No. 2387, January 14, 1748.

[21] "Diary of John Whiting," in *New England Historical and Genealogical Register*, LXIII (1909), 186; Willis (ed.), *Journals of Smith and Deane*, 133; "Joseph Emerson's Diary," in Massachusetts Historical Society *Proceedings*, XLIV (1910–11), 273.

a half than in the entire ministry of his predecessor. A chief cause for this high mortality was a "Quinsie" which resulted in an inflammation of the throat and lungs so severe, Stone declared, that "They mortify in less than Four & Twenty Hours." [22]

From 1750 to 1755 the throat infection was a constant source of trouble in New England and New York. It killed a number of children in Falmouth in the fall of 1750. An outbreak in Weymouth, Massachusetts, the following summer was particularly severe. A diary kept by the Reverend William Smith lists thirty fatalities from July 12 to October 29. The cause of death was not listed in all cases, but throat distemper was specifically named in twenty-two. Of the thirty who died, twenty-one were children. A neighboring parish, also affected, observed a fast day on November 21.[23] Despite the brevity of the entries in Smith's diary, it presents a moving picture of the suffering and consternation aroused by the loss of so many children.

While Weymouth was undergoing this severe attack, minor outbreaks occurred in New York. From Westchester, Mrs. Peter De Lancey wrote to her parents that she had returned to find her family in good health despite the sickness and death surrounding them. She added that there had been two deaths from throat distemper and that she was praying her children would be saved. In an account of the "throat destroyer" written in 1753, Dr. Colden stated that it had prevailed in the province for several years and was still reappearing. Late in this same year it was present in Boston. A correspondent stated that his daughter was ill

[22] Robert Stone to Secretary, St. James, Goose Creek, S. C., March 22, 1751, in S.P.G. MSS., B18, fpp. 459–60.

[23] Willis (ed.), *Journals of Smith and Deane*, 145; "Diaries of Rev. William Smith and Dr. Cotton Tufts," in Massachusetts Historical Society *Proceedings*, XLII (1908–1909), 459–61.

from "a violent fever and inflammation in her throat," a disorder which had caused many deaths among children in Boston and the surrounding country. The infection continued through the winter, for another writer reported the death of a child of four from throat distemper in April, 1754.[24]

The years 1754–55 saw a great increase in the virulence of the contagion. Of this period Belknap declared: "In 1754 and 1755, it [throat distemper] produced a great mortality in several parts of New-Hampshire, and the neighboring parts of Massachusetts." The church records of Hampton again throw light upon the extent of the pestilence. From January, 1754, to July, 1755, a total of fifty-one persons succumbed to the infection. Of the thirty-four who died in 1754, thirty were children. In the extreme northern section of Massachusetts other outbreaks are recorded. In New Casco, a small town near Falmouth, ten persons died from the disease in the early fall of 1755. The next summer fourteen children were carried off in Saco, an adjacent town. The reporter of these deaths commented upon the prevailing "sickly time" and listed the ills affecting the local towns and villages. In only one town, Saco, was the throat distemper the cause of the trouble. This fact illustrates once again the throat distemper characteristic of moving slowly and flaring up sporadically in scattered areas. Thus, towns within five or ten miles of focal points of infection frequently were unaffected. Webster recorded a very fatal attack of "Angina Maligna" on Long Island in this same year. In

[24] Mrs. Peter De Lancey to Colden, Westchester, N. Y., June 7, 1752, in *Colden Papers*, IX (1937), 11–12; Colden to P. Collinson, Coldengham, N. Y., December 5, 1753, *ibid.*, IV (1902), 418–20; James Gordon to William Martin, Boston, October 18, 1753, *loc. cit.*, 384; Henry Lloyd, II, to Henry Lloyd, Boston, April 17, 1754, in *Papers of the Lloyd Family*, II (1927), 515–16.

one town only two children under the age of twelve survived the epidemic.[25]

Unlike many other diseases, the throat disorder remained dormant during the French and Indian War. After prevailing continuously for twenty years, almost seven years elapsed before the next outbreak. The church records of Salem, Massachusetts, show "a great mortality among children" in the year 1762 which may have been caused by throat disease. In 1763, Haverhill, Massachusetts, reported a return of the pestilence, the first since the initial outbreak in 1736. The attack was mild in comparison with the earlier one and only a few died, despite the large number infected. Josiah Whitney of Brooklyn, Connecticut, wrote to a friend on December 22 that throat distemper had proved fatal to his eldest son. A year later the disease struck at Harwich, Massachusetts, where several families suffered heavy losses.[26]

Philadelphia, which had remained relatively free of the infection for a number of years, experienced a large-scale epidemic in 1763—the first major outbreak in the colonies since 1755. The observer, Benjamin Rush, a competent eighteenth-century medical practitioner, stated that a "malignant sore-throat" carried off many children in the winter of 1763.[27]

Boston, while recovering from a smallpox epidemic, was

[25] Belknap, *History of New-Hampshire*, II, 121; "Deaths in Hampton, New Hampshire, 1727–1755," *loc. cit.*, 137; Willis (ed.), *Journals of Smith and Deane*, 163–68; Webster, *History of Epidemic Diseases*, I, 245; James J. Walsh, *History of Medicine in New York*, 3 vols. in one (New York, 1919), 97.

[26] "Description of Salem," *loc. cit.*; "Sketch of Haverhill, Massachusetts," *loc. cit.*; Josiah Whitney to Dr. James Cogswell, Brooklyn, Conn., December 22, 1763, in Gratz Collection, American Clergymen; Diary of Benjamin Bangs, November 28, 1764.

[27] Rush, *Medical Inquiries*, 2d ed., IV, 372.

attacked by the throat disease in 1765. A letter from a Boston correspondent dated in September declares that it was a "sickly time" among the children, as the "throat distemper prevails amongst them & proves mortal." The disease continued to flare up to epidemic proportions in other Massachusetts towns for the next five or six years. During the winter of 1766–67 Sutton and the surrounding countryside were infected with heavy casualties among a number of families. At Oxford in 1768–69 the disease proved especially fatal. Ebenezer Parkman recorded in his diary on January 17, 1769, that "71 have been buryd in a twelve month. 7 Graves have 2 in each. 3 are to be buryd today." The end was not in sight and the death toll grew steadily in the succeeding months. From March to August an additional thirty-six deaths occurred, and a newspaper correspondent estimated in October that a tenth of the town had died in the course of the outbreak. In one family alone eight members succumbed to the infection. The following year the throat distemper struck Salem and brought death to many of the children.[28]

New York was attacked in 1769 and suffered heavily. Dr. Samuel Bard, a professor of medicine at King's College, wrote an article in 1769 entitled "An Enquiry into the nature, cause and cure of the Angina Suffocative, or Sore Throat Distemper, as it is commonly called by the inhabitants of the city and colony of New-York." His introduction indicates the motive for his work: "I have determined," he wrote, "to attempt the history of a disease which has lately appeared among the children of this city, and which, both

[28] James Gordon to William Martin, Boston, September 10, 1765, *loc. cit.*, XXXIII (1899–1900), 396; David Hall Diary, November, 1766, to March, 1767; Ebenezer Parkman Diary, January 17, 1769; *Massachusetts Gazette and Boston Post Boy and Advertiser*, No. 635, October 16, 1769; "Description of Salem," *loc. cit.*

as an uncommon and highly dangerous distemper, well deserves an attentive consideration." The work is largely technical, but Bard indicates the high fatality rate by citing the case of one of the first families to experience the disorder. All seven children in the family were infected and only four survived the attack.[29] This high mortality ratio probably indicates diphtheria.

Lionel Chalmers in his *Account of the Weather and Diseases in South Carolina* stated that "an *angina* resembling that which is called putrid, appears now and then amongst us, but never *epidemically* that I have observed." He had noticed that it usually affected children under ten or twelve years of age. Despite his statement, he described an epidemic occurring in the fall of 1770 having all the characteristics of the throat disease. The patients had an inflammation in the throat, tonsils, and Eustachian tube: these parts gradually became ulcerated, which sometimes caused a discharge from the nose, a hoarse voice, and an extremely fetid odor. When the infection spread down the glottis, the victim died. In general the attack was restricted to children under fifteen years of age.[30] Chalmers has given us an excellent clinical description of diphtheria and one identical with accounts from New England and the central colonies.

Scarlet fever was definitely identified by Thomas Sydenham as early as 1675, but it was still occasionally mistaken for smallpox and often measles as well as diphtheria.

[29] Samuel Bard, *An Enquiry into the Nature, Cause and Cure, of the Angina Suffocativa, . . .* (New York, 1771), reprinted in the *Transactions* of the American Philosophical Society, 1769–71 (Philadelphia, 1789), I, 388–404.

[30] Lionel Chalmers, *An Account of the Weather and Diseases of South Carolina,* 2 vols. (London, 1776), II, 91, 93, 207.

The main symptoms include sore throat and fever, a violent red rash on the skin, and the characteristic strawberry color of the throat and tongue. In the severe form, scarlatina anginosa, the throat becomes ulcerated as in diphtheria, and the death rate is high.

Although in the latter part of the seventeenth century the disease was mild, heroic measures—purging, vomiting, and sweating—were considered essential in combating it. Sydenham, the exception to this rule, in 1675 recommended confinement indoors, meatless diet, and abstinence from spirituous liquors. It was not until 1703, when seven deaths were attributed to it,[31] that scarlet fever first appeared in the London Bills of Mortality. Scarlatina simplex, or the mild form, was the probable cause of these fatalities.

Referring to scarlet fever for the first time, John Barnard recalled that a British expeditionary force had arrived at Boston in June, 1693, from Martinico bringing with it "a violent malignant distemper, called the scarlet fever." [32] The outbreak was probably yellow fever, and Barnard, writing years after the event, may have substituted a name by then in common usage.

The first definite epidemic of scarlet fever occurred at the time of the Boston smallpox outbreak of 1702. John Marshall claimed that the smallpox "was attended with a sort of feaver called the scarlett feaver." Two deaths from "the fever and sore throat" were recorded in Salisbury about this same time which may indicate a possible spread of the infection. Cotton Mather, who also noted the presence of the disease, recorded in his diary two years later that three of his children were sick with "*Scarlet Feavour*" and that he

[31] Creighton, *History of Epidemics*, II, 680.

[32] "Autobiography of the Rev. John Barnard," in Massachusetts Historical Society *Collections*, Ser. 3, V (1836), 181.

feared the disease was becoming "epidemical." [33] During these years scarlet fever was prevalent in London, whence it may have spread to Boston.

The next major scarlet-fever outbreak occurred in Boston in conjunction with the diphtheria attacks on New England in 1735–36. News of the spreading throat distemper had already reached Boston, and despite their confidence in the local physicians, Bostonians awaited the onslaught of this strange and unaccountable disease with considerable trepidation. Two major smallpox attacks in the past fifteen years had indelibly impressed upon them the horrors of a serious epidemic. William Douglass and Cadwallader Colden, both competent observers, have supplied a good picture of the ravages of the outbreak, which fortunately, proved much milder than was anticipated. Although the first case developed on August 20, no fatalities from the infection occurred until October. During November the number of deaths increased and continued high until the second week in March when they reached their peak. Even in this week, when fatalities were at their height, the total number of burials from all causes rose only from a normal of ten to twenty-four. Douglass estimated that four thousand persons were infected, of whom over one hundred died, and he contrasted this low mortality rate with that of Kingston, New Hampshire, where from one in six to one in three died.

The relatively few fatalities caused many of the people in Boston to doubt that they were suffering from the same disease that had occurred in the other sections of New England. Concerning the mildness of the epidemic, the Boston *Weekly News-Letter* had this to say: "By the Burial it is

[33] "John Marshall's Diary," *loc. cit.*, 156; "Journal of John Pike," *loc. cit.*, 40–52; *Diary of Cotton Mather, 1681–1708*, 507–508.

notorious that scarce any Distemper—even the most favorable which has at any Time prevail'd so generally—has produc'd fewer Deaths."[34]

There were two outstanding differences between the epidemic in Boston and that in the outlying towns. One characteristic of the Boston outbreak was a rash, or erysipelas-like eruption, which appeared in nearly all cases. In the second place, in New Hampshire the disease was almost 100 per cent fatal among the first victims, whereas no fatalities occurred in Boston until the epidemic was well along its course. This mildness continued throughout the entire epidemic and contrasted sharply with the severity of the attacks elsewhere. It seems more than a coincidence that the accounts of throat distemper in the sections where it proved so fatal made no reference to any sort of rash. A letter written by a Boston physician on March 22, 1736, and published in the *Gentlemen's Magazine* stated that the country had been "afflicted with a mortal distemper." The doctor explained that this sickness appeared in two forms: the symptoms of one were "Cankery Ulcers in Glands or throat and mouth, with a glandulous fever," while those of the other were an inflammation in the throat, headache, and an "inflammatory eruptive fever." Three years later William Douglass made a similar observation in a letter to Cadwallader Colden and cited examples of the different forms the disease had assumed in various localities. In Boston and Marblehead in 1736 the infection was characterized by a "military" or "eruptive" fever, and in both towns the disease was mild. On the other hand, outbreaks which occurred in Malden and Marblehead in the two succeeding years

[34] Douglass, *The Practical History of a New Epidemical Fever;* Boston *Weekly News-Letter,* April 29, 1736, quoted in Justin Winsor (ed.), *The Memorial History of Boston,* 4 vols. (Boston, 1886), IV, 539.

were not accompanied by these eruptions and proved extremely fatal.[35] Very evidently, two separate diseases occurred simultaneously—scarlatina in Boston and diphtheria in most of the other localities.

The Boston physicians were completely at a loss to explain the origin or communication of the disease, and in a proclamation issued on April 29, 1736, declared: "As formerly, so now again, after many Months observation, we conclude, that the prevailing Distemper appears to us to proceed from some Affectation of the Air, and not from any personal Infection receiv'd from the Sick, or Goods in their neighborhood." [36] The apparently spontaneous appearance of the throat disease was due in part to the role played by healthy carriers, a fact which was, of course, unknown to the eighteenth-century physicians. The precise method by which the diseases were spread in all instances will never be known; but undoubtedly, since diphtheria and scarlet fever are contact diseases, physicians and ministers who visited the sick, individuals with mild unidentified cases who carried on their normal activities, and healthy carriers all aided in sowing the seeds of infection. Despite some disagreement among medical historians as to the exact nature of the Boston epidemic, the evidence in favor of scarlet fever is overwhelming.[37]

[35] Letter from a physician in Boston, New England, March 22, 1736, in *Gentlemen's Magazine*, VI (1736), 358; William Douglass to Cadwallader Colden, Boston, Mass., November 12, 1739, in *Colden Papers*, II (1918), 196–200.

[36] Boston *Weekly News-Letter*, April 29, 1736, quoted in Winsor (ed.), *Memorial History of Boston*, IV, 539.

[37] Packard, *History of Medicine*, I, 98; James G. Mumford, *A Narrative of Medicine in America* (Philadelphia, 1903), 62; Viets, *History of Medicine in Massachusetts*, 69; Fox, *Dr. John Fothergill*, 49–53; Caulfield, *A True History*, 40; George H. Weaver, "Life and Writings of William Douglass," in *Bulletin of the Society of Medical History of Chicago*, II (1917–22), 229–59.

Newport, Rhode Island, was attacked by what was most likely scarlet fever in the spring of 1736. In June the worst was over, and a newspaper reported: "The malignant Distemper of the Throat, that has been so prevalent and mortal in several Parts of this Land, has been very favorable here, and now through Mercy, very few Persons are afflicted with it, and not one in Fifty that died of it." [38] Although clinical symptoms are lacking, the low mortality rate, coupled with the presence of the disease in Boston at the same time, makes scarlet fever the most likely culprit.

Almost thirty years elapsed before scarlet fever was again identified in the colonies. In 1764 Benjamin Rush reported that the disease was general in Philadelphia. Rush, like many of his contemporaries, clearly distinguished between scarlet fever and diphtheria. The epidemic was relatively mild, but the disease probably remained in Philadelphia for the next few years. It flared up anew in 1769 when an outbreak among the children was reported. The symptoms definitely point to scarlet fever, since the disease was described as rarely fatal and characterized by a sore throat and a rash.[39]

In these same years scarlet fever also was present in the Carolinas. Chalmers, the South Carolina historian, wrote in 1792 that the infection formerly appeared in the spring, "but as it has not occurred in the course of my practice for eighteen years past till lately I believe it not to be a disease of this climate." [40]

In Duxboro, Massachusetts, an outbreak, possibly scarlatina anginosa, proved fatal to many children in 1771. An observer wrote that "This fever seems to differ from what

[38] Boston *Gazette*, No. 859, June 14–21, 1736.

[39] Rush, *Medical Inquiries*, 2d ed., IV, 372; Elizabeth Drinker's Diary, July 14, 1769.

[40] Chalmers, *An Account of Climates and Diseases*, II, 207.

has been usually called the *Scarlet Fever* only in Point of Malignity; the Appearance in those who have it favorably being in all Respects the same." He also noted that although it affected all sections of Duxboro, the surrounding towns remained untouched. New Haven, Connecticut, was ravaged by cynanche trachealis this same year and again in 1773. In the latter year it was fatal to many in New Haven and, in addition, took a heavy toll in East Haven, Connecticut, and Salem, Massachusetts.[41]

Scarlatina anginosa, a form of the throat distemper, was said to be present in Philadelphia in 1774, and cynanche trachealis general in all the northern section of America the next year. Four of the children of Elizabeth Drinker contracted scarlet fever during the outbreak in Philadelphia, but fortunately all recovered.[42]

As was the case during the French and Indian War, throat infections subsided during the Revolutionary period, and did not break out again until 1783. At this time both diphtheria and scarlet fever became prevalent in nearly all the states from South Carolina to New England. In the latter region the infection began in Sandford, York County, New Hampshire, and slowly diffused through most of the towns in the neighboring states.[43] The outbreak was not virulent, and the mortality rate was far below that of previous epidemics. Either the disease itself was less virulent or else some immunity had been engendered in the population.

Shortly after the first violent outbreaks of diphtheria

[41] *Massachusetts Gazette and Boston Weekly News-Letter*, No. 3536, July 18, 1771; Boston *Gazette and County Journal*, No. 849, July 15, 1771; Webster, *History of Epidemic Diseases*, I, 260.

[42] Webster, *History of Epidemic Diseases*, I, 261; Elizabeth Drinker's Diary, May 27, December 12, 1774.

[43] Belknap, *History of New-Hampshire*, II, 121.

and scarlet fever in New England, similar attacks were reported in both France and the West Indies. One LeCat, a French physician, reported that "gangrenous sore throats" caused much trouble among the children in and around Rouen, France, during 1736–37, and an epidemic of sore throats occurred on the island of St. Christopher in the West Indies in the latter year. Although Dr. John Fothergill, the famous English physician, first took note of diphtheria in 1739 and found more cases of it in 1742, England did not suffer from the disease in epidemic form until 1748.[44] In the eighteenth century it seems to have appeared almost simultaneously in Europe and America. In general, it followed the same course; it spread slowly, appeared sporadically, and gradually increased in frequency and extent.

The throat distemper outbreaks pose several interesting problems. Despite the widespread belief among the colonists that they were confronted by a totally new sickness, the evidence is conclusive that both scarlet fever and diphtheria had long existed in at least some sections of the colonies. In view of this fact, why did the initial attacks on New England so often prove fatal? Why was it that New England, whose climate in many respects was more salubrious than that of England or the other American colonies, bore the brunt of the casualties? And even more intriguing, why was it that Boston and certain other sections of New England came through the diphtheria onslaught unscathed?

The simplest explanations for the major epidemics in the 1730's are that the responsible organisms, possibly by

[44] *Philosophical Transactions*, XLIX (1755), Pt. 1, 49–61; "Observations concerning the Cure of most Distempers incident to the Virgin Islands in America," in *Gentlemen's Magazine*, XXII (1752), 73; Fox, *Dr. John Fothergill*, 49–53; John Fothergill, "An Account of the Sore Throat Attended with Ulcers" in Ralph N. Major, *Classic Descriptions of Diseases* (Springfield, 1932), 101–103.

mutation, suddenly had gained virulence, or that the population in the affected areas had undergone a reduction in its capacity for resistance. Very likely both factors played a part in the tragic events.

Neither of these explanations accounts for Boston's freedom from diphtheria. However, this infection has long been known as a frontier disease, and it is significant that at a time when nearly all epidemic diseases centered on Boston, New York, Philadelphia, and Charleston, not one major diphtheria outbreak occurred in any of these cities. One explanation for the prevalence of diphtheria in frontier areas is that the high birth rate tends to increase the percentage of nonimmunes beyond the safety point. But in the colonial period large families seem to have been the order of the day in rural and urban areas alike.

One other possibility presents itself. Smallpox—the scourge of England and many parts of America at this time—seldom assumed such proportions in New England, nor were malaria and yellow fever of much consequence there. Hence the absence of smallpox and certain other selective diseases for long periods of time may have left an open field for diphtheria and scarlatina anginosa: many children who normally would have fallen victim to diseases prevalent elsewhere thus succumbed to diphtheria and scarlatina anginosa in New England.

However, neither of these diseases can be ranked with smallpox and the other major contagions of the colonial period. They were restricted largely to children and were neither so universal nor so virulent as some other sicknesses. It was not until the mid-nineteenth century, when it assumed its present-day form, that diphtheria became a serious threat. Scarlet fever was of even less significance and properly belongs among the minor colonial diseases.

CHAPTER IV

Yellow Fever

One of the most deadly and terrifying of all the infections which ravaged the American coastal cities was yellow fever. Striking suddenly and, to the colonists, in an unaccountable fashion, this pestilence devastated New York, Philadelphia, and Charleston on a number of occasions. Although a number of colonists noticed the connection between the water front and yellow fever and its importation by vessels from the West Indies, they had no inkling of its transmission by mosquitoes. Their inability to account for the spread of the scourge added to the consternation aroused by its high case-fatality rate.

Yellow fever is an infectious tropical disease, transmitted by a specific mosquito, stegomyia fasciata, and probably caused by a filter-passing virus. Its incubation period is short—usually four or five days, and often less. A flushed face, scarlet lips and tongue, and a high temperature are early symptoms. After a few days the temperature falls below normal, and the skin assumes a lemon-yellow tint. Vomiting—first a colorless serum and later an admixture of blood—is a principal symptom, and because the blood vomited is usually partly digested in the stomach and is dark brown or black, yellow fever has been called "black vomit." The amount of blood in the vomit and urine is a measure of the intensity of the attack, for death usually results from the irreparable damage done to the liver and kidneys.

The case mortality is usually high but may vary from 12 to 80 per cent, and an 1893 epidemic in Rio de Janeiro was fatal to 94.5 per cent of those infected. As early as the sixteenth century the disease was notorious among ships in tropical seas. One writer has suggested that the legend of the Flying Dutchman and *The Rime of the Ancient Mariner* may be based on stories of ships stricken with yellow fever and that Francis Drake's loss of a quarter of his men in 1585 may have resulted from this same cause. The contagion also has been given as a possible cause of the Mayan decline.[1]

As it is with many other diseases, the origin of yellow fever is in dispute. One writer has suggested that the virus of the disease is endemic in the jungles of both Africa and America and may break out whenever groups of susceptibles come in contact with it. The more prevalent view is that the infection stemmed from the West Coast of Africa and was brought to this hemisphere by the slave ships. No doubt exists as to the early prevalence of the fever in Africa: five epidemics occurred during the sixteenth century, and the immunity possessed by West Coast Negroes is further proof of its long existence in that area.[2] The consensus is that if the disease did originate in West Africa, it must have been brought to the western hemisphere by mosquitoes bred on board ships. A yellow-fever case which developed shortly after a vessel sailed from the coast would have run its course before the ship reached America. Consequently, the pres-

[1] Burnet, *Virus as Organism*, 95, 98; Major, *Disease and Destiny*, 126.

[2] Burnet, *Virus as Organism*, 95–96; Henry R. Carter, *Yellow Fever, An Epidemiological and Historical Study of Its Place of Origin*, eds. L. A. Carter and W. H. Frost (Baltimore, 1931); Blanton, *Medicine in Virginia in the Seventeenth Century*, 71, 73–74.

ence of mosquitoes, probably bred in water buckets or other containers, was necessary to keep the infection in circulation.

Most authorities agree that the first definitely recognized yellow-fever outbreak in the New World did not occur until well into the seventeenth century. However, by the second half of the century the disease was well established in the West Indies and had moved into Central and South America. A series of yellow-fever epidemics in Yucatan, Barbados, and Cuba in 1648–49 had repercussions in Massachusetts: the General Court, meeting in Boston, established a strict quarantine in March, 1648, for all vessels arriving from the West Indies because of "ye plague or like in[fectious] disease." Apprehension was felt well into the following year, and it was not until May, 1649, that the order was repealed, ". . . seeing it hath pleased God to stay the Sickness there." [3] This incident has been cited as proof of the presence of the disease in the American colonies, but the quarantine measures enacted by the Massachusetts government were purely precautionary. No evidence for even a single case has been found during these years, and the simple fact of quarantine regulations cannot in itself be regarded as evidence of yellow fever.

Despite assertions to the contrary by a number of medical historians, there is no conclusive evidence of yellow fever in North America prior to the last years of the seventeenth century. True, a number of outbreaks earlier in the century could have been yellow fever. For example, in 1618 a "pestilential sickness" was reported to have devastated the Indians in New England so that "the twentieth person is scarce left alive." Contemporary observers reported that the disease turned the bodies of the Indians yellow, and it

[3] Samuel A. Green, "Medicine in Boston," in Winsor (ed.), *Memorial History of Boston,* IV, 532.

has been assumed on this basis that the epidemic must have been yellow fever. The paucity of the evidence and the isolation of the New England Indians from known centers of the infection make this assumption untenable. Whatever the nature of the epidemic, yellow fever can be ruled out. A historian of the Indians on Martha's Vineyard claimed that yellow fever eliminated many of them in 1643 but, for the same reasons as above, this claim seems very doubtful.[4]

New York was attacked in 1668 by an "autumnal bilious fever in an infectious form," [5] but the term "bilious fever" could apply equally to typhoid, dysentery, or several other sicknesses. Had yellow fever been present, the high case mortality and the "black vomit" would certainly have been noticed.

What was probably the first yellow-fever outbreak in North America occurred in 1693 when a British fleet anchored in Boston harbor after sailing from Barbados. "In the Month of *July* a most pestilential Feaver, was brought among us," wrote Cotton Mather, "by the Fleet coming into our Harbour from the West-Indies. It was a Distemper, which in less than a Week's time usually carried off my Neighbours, with very direful Symptoms, of turning *Yellow*, vomiting and bleeding every way and so Dying." The community was much alarmed, Samuel Sewall noted, and "persons [were] generally under much consternation which Mr. Willard [took] . . . notice of in his Prayer." [6] Sewall called the infection "Fever of the Fleet," a relatively meaningless term. However, Mather's description definite-

[4] Webster, *History of Epidemic Diseases,* I, 176–77; "Description of Duke's County Indians on Martha's Vineyard," in Massachusetts Historical Society *Collections,* Ser. 2, III (1815), 90–92.

[5] Webster, *History of Epidemic Diseases,* I, 202.

[6] *Diary of Cotton Mather, loc. cit.* (1681–1708), 166–67; *Diary of Samuel Sewall,* 1674–1700, 379–80.

ly points to yellow fever. The high mortality rate, the rapidity with which death came, the vomiting, and yellow coloring are all clinical symptoms of yellow fever. The yellow-fever mosquito could easily survive the passage from the West Indies in summer, and the masses of soldiers and sailors crammed into the British vessels would supply an ample number of hosts to keep the infection in circulation.

After studying the course of yellow fever in Virginia, Blanton doubted that it existed there during the seventeenth century. He pointed out that once the yellow-fever mosquito was introduced, the way would have been open for additional attacks such as those which occurred in the eighteenth and nineteenth centuries.[7] In view of the long intervals between alleged epidemics and the limited available information, Blanton's conclusions regarding Virginia may well be applied to all British colonies in continental America. At least it can be said that the first epidemic did not occur until the last decade of the century.

In 1699, Charleston and Philadelphia were ravaged by the first definitely identified outbreaks of yellow fever in British America. In both cities the mortality was high, and all normal life was completely disrupted. The devastation in Charleston caused the alarmed governor and council of the colony to report that

> A most infectious pestilential and mortal distemper (the same which hath always been in one or more of his Majesty's American plantations, for eight or nine years last past) which from Barbados or Providence was brought in among us into Charles Town about the 28th or 29th of Aug. last past, and the decay of trade and mutations of your Lordships public officers occasioned thereby. This Distemper from the time of its beginning aforesaid to the first day of November killed in

[7] Blanton, *Medicine in Virginia in the Seventeenth Century*, 72–73.

Charles Town at least 160 persons. . . . Besides those that have died in Charles Town 10 or 11 have died in the country, all of which got the distemper and were infected in Charles Town went home to their families and died; and what is notable not one of their families was infected by them.[8]

The fact that yellow-fever victims who left an infected area did not transmit the disease was a problem which remained to puzzle observers until the discovery at the end of the nineteenth century that the infection was carried by mosquitoes.

Among yellow-fever victims in Charleston were the chief justice, receiver-general, provost marshal, and almost half of the assembly. With half the governing officials ill and the remainder incapacitated from fear of the disorder, the local administration did little to alleviate the general confusion and distress. The most detailed and vivid picture of the epidemic came from a private correspondent who wrote that he found it difficult to describe "the terrible Tempest of Mortality" in Charleston. From the end of August to the middle of November "there died in Charlestown, 125, English of all sorts; high and low, old and young. 37, French. 16, Indians, and 1 Negro." He went on to say that "the Distemper raged, and the destroying Angel slaughtered so furiously with his revenging Sword of Pestilence, that there died (as I have read in the Catalogue of the dead) 14 in one day, Septr. 28th and [the epidemic] raged as bad all October." So many deaths occurred that the dead were simply piled into carts; all business activity ceased for five weeks, and, the writer grimly concluded, nothing was done "but carrying Medicines, digging

[8] Letter from Governor and Council, Charleston, S. C., January 17, 1700, in McCrady, *History of South Carolina*, 309.

graves, [and] carting the dead: to the great astonishment of all beholders."[9]

The news of the disaster in Charleston spread rapidly through the colonies, causing general apprehension. From Boston, Cotton Mather wrote of "the horrible plague of Barbados" which "had made an Incredible Desolation" and had resulted in the death of "all the ministers in Charles-town." Among the dead clergymen was Mather's uncle.[10]

A lack of adequate population statistics for Charleston makes it difficult to determine the percentage of fatalities. The town and colony had been founded less than thirty years before, and the population could not have been very large. An estimate made in 1708 placed the total number of inhabitants of the colony at 9,580. The same year, John Oldmixon estimated about 250 houses and 3,000 persons for the city.[11] On the basis of these latter figures over 7 per cent of the population succumbed to the disorder.

The outbreak in Philadelphia was on a comparable scale with that in Charleston. Isaac Norris, a Philadelphia merchant, referred to it as the "Barbadoes Distemper" and mentioned the vomiting and voiding of blood so characteristic of yellow fever. The disease broke out in August and continued to October 22—the cooler weather in Philadelphia putting an end to it sooner than in Charleston, where it remained until November. As in Charleston, community

[9] Alexander Hewat, *An Historical Account of the Rise and Progress of the Colonies of South Carolina and Georgia*, 2 vols. (London, 1779), I, 142–43; Ramsay, *History of South Carolina*, II, 82; Letter from Hugh Adams, Charleston, S. C., February 25, 1700, in *Diary of Samuel Sewall*, 1700–1714, *loc. cit.*, Ser. 5, VI (1879), 11–12.

[10] Cotton Mather to Mrs. Joanna Cotton, Boston, Mass., August 23, 1699, in Massachusetts Historical Society *Collections*, Ser. 4, VIII (1868), 403–404.

[11] William J. Rivers, *A Sketch of the History of South Carolina . . .* (Charleston, 1856), 231–32; Alexander S. Salley, Jr. (ed.), *Narratives of Early Carolina, 1650–1708* (New York, 1911), 365.

life came almost to a standstill. A Quaker diarist reckoned that "In this distemper had died six, seven, and sometimes eight in a day, for several weeks, there being few houses, if any, free of the sickness. Great was the fear that fell on all flesh! [He] saw no lofty or airy countenances nor heard any vain jesting to move men to laughter.... But every face gathered paleness, and many hearts were humbled, and countenances fallen and sunk, as such that waited every moment to be summoned to the bar and numbered to the grave." At a meeting of the Society of Friends one member publicly offered himself as a sacrifice for the people in the hopes that his immolation would bring an abatement of the infection. But his sacrifice was unavailing: he died of the fever a few days later, and the contagion raged on.[12]

In all, about 220 persons died during the three months of the epidemic. Since the population was around 4,400 at this time, approximately 5 per cent of the people lost their lives.[13] The actual number infected is not known but the evidence indicates a high case-fatality rate.

Three years later yellow fever—or the "American Plague"—attacked New York City. John Bartow, an S.P.G. missionary who arrived in New York on September 29, 1702, found "a very mournfull Town there dyeing near 20 Persons dayly for some Months." During October the town was still "very much visited with Sickness," but in the following month, his fellow missionary was able to re-

[12] Caspar Morris, "Contributions to the Medical History of Pennsylvania," ed. Edward Armstrong, in *Memoirs* of the Historical Society of Pennsylvania (Philadelphia, 1826), I, 353–54; Webster, *History of Epidemic Diseases,* I, 211; Journal of Thomas Story, Minister of the Society of Friends, quoted in Morris, "Contributions to the Medical History of Pennsylvania," *loc. cit.;* Rush, *Medical Inquiries,* 4th ed., III, 95 n.

[13] Webster, *History of Epidemic Diseases,* I, 211; *A Century of Population Growth,* 11; James Mease, *The Picture of Philadelphia* (Philadelphia, 1811), 31. Mease states that the town had about 700 houses in 1700, which indicates a population of around 4,400.

port to the Society that "it has pleased Almighty God to preserve us both in good health all the time Since our Arrivall into America notwithstanding many have been visited with great distempers in diverse Parts which have proved mortall to many in the Town of New York where nearly five hundred persons dyed in the Space of three months, but now thanks to God the place is very healthful." The death toll for the outbreak amounted to about 570 persons. The population of New York City did not reach 8,000 until about 1730 and was probably much lower in 1702.[14] Figuring conservatively, therefore, a tenth of the town's inhabitants were wiped out within three months—a casualty percentage higher than that of the earlier Charleston outbreak.

Although New York was the center of the infection, cases were reported in at least one adjacent town. After he left New York in September, Bartow went to Westchester, which he found "was not wholly free from the Mortal Distemper at New York." [15] It is doubtful that the disease trav-

[14] Webster, *History of Epidemic Diseases*, I, 217; John Bartow to Secretary, Westchester, N. Y., December 1, 1707, in S.P.G. MSS., A3, fpp. 413–22; George Keith to Secretary, New York, November 29, 1702, *ibid.*, A1, fpp. 71–84; Packard, *History of Medicine*, I, 113; Blanton, *Medicine in Virginia in the Seventeenth Century*, 52–55; *A Century of Population Growth*, 11. The author of this latter work states that the population of New York city in 1700 was 4,400 and in 1730, 8,500; President Rip Van Dam submitted a census to the Lords of Trade in 1731 in which he gave the population of New York city as 7,644, New York County, 8,622, and the entire province, 50,242. See President Rip Van Dam to the Lords of Trade, New York, November 2, 1731, in O'Callaghan (ed.), *Documents Relative to Colonial History*, V (1855), 929.

[15] John Bartow to Secretary, Westchester, N. Y., December 1, 1707, in S.P.G. MSS., A3, fpp. 413–22; James Logan to William Penn, Philadelphia, July 11, 1702, in Edward Armstrong (ed.), "Correspondence between William Penn and James Logan and Others, 1700–1750," in *Memoirs* of the Historical Society of Pennsylvania, IX (1870), 134–35. James Logan described a serious outbreak of yellow fever at "York" in 1702, but he probably was referring to the New York epidemic, since yellow fever scarcely could have reached York, Pennsylvania; moreover, the size of the town of York precludes an attack of the proportions he describes.

eled far from the city of New York, and more than likely the victims in Westchester contracted the infection while visiting the larger city.

In 1706 yellow fever returned to Charleston for the second time. "On the 20th of September wee Arrived at Charles Town in Carolina . . . ," reported S.P.G. missionary Gideon Johnston, "which we found visited with a Pestilential Fever very mortal especially to fresh Europeans; My Dear Friend the Reverend Mr. Sam[uel] Thomas your worthy and faithful Missionary died of this Distemper the 10th of October 1706, a great & Surprising loss to me." [16]

In March, 1707, the Lords Proprietors expressed condolences to Sir Nathaniel Johnson for "the loss of Col. Moore, Mr. Howe, and other Worthy persons of our Province, by the late distemper, which we hope is now wholly abated." John Oldmixon classified the epidemic as one of the "raging sicknesses" usually brought from the southern colonies to South Carolina, "as the late Sickness was, which raged A.D. 1706, and carried off abundance of People in *Charles-Town* and other Places." The French and Spanish chose this opportune time to attack the city but were driven off by Governor Nathaniel Johnson, who quartered his troops a half mile from the city to avoid the infection.[17]

Yellow fever also may have been one of the diseases which struck Charleston in 1711. Johnston, the S.P.G. representative, listed "Pestilential ffeavers" among the fatal

[16] Thomas Hassell to Secretary, South Carolina, September 6, 1707, in S.P.G. MSS., A3, fpp. 281–84.

[17] Lords Proprietors to Sir Nathaniel Johnson, Charleston, S. C., March 8, 1707, quoted in Frederick Dalcho, *An Historical Account of the Protestant Episcopal Church in South Carolina* (Charleston, 1820), 75 n.; Oldmixon, *British Empire in America*, I, 515; Carroll (ed.), *Historical Collections of South Carolina*, I, 159–61; Ramsay, *History of South Carolina*, II, 83–84.

sicknesses visiting the town. Forced to work overtime at his calling, he complained to the Society that "three Funeralls of a day, and sometimes four are now very usual and all that I gett by these is a few rotton Glov's and an abundance of trouble day & night." Another resident of Charleston also attributed many of the deaths to the "Malignant Feavers" which were raging at that time.[18]

A few years later another missionary, the Reverend William Tredwell Bull, wrote the S.P.G.: "Mr. Marston, who was formerly Minister in Town removed in the Spring to the Bahama Island and is since dead of a Pestilential Feaver, which raged there and here in Charles Town this fall, we hope it is now over in this Province." At the same time, another minister declared that Charleston had been afflicted all summer with "Small Pox and Malignant ffever the latter of which still continues and have Carryed off great Number of people." [19] The fact that he used the terms "pestilential" and "malignant," and in connection with the West Indies, is good reason for suspecting that yellow fever had again visited Charleston.

A period of ten years elapsed before the next recorded outbreak of yellow fever in Charleston. It was described by one writer as a fatal "Bilious Plague." In the only detailed account of the epidemic Dr. Alexander Hewat recalled that the summer of 1728 was exceedingly hot and that "an infectious and pestilential distemper commonly called the 'yel-

[18] Gideon Johnston to Secretary, S. C., November 16, 1711, in S.P.G. MSS., A7, fpp. 466–77; Thomas Hassell to Secretary, Parish of St. Thomas, S. C., March 12, 1712, *ibid.*, A7, fpp. 498–501.

[19] William T. Bull to Secretary, St. Paul, S. C., November 24, 1718, *ibid.*, A13, fp. 236; Thomas Hassell to Secretary, Parish of St. Thomas, S. C., October 11, 1718, *ibid.*, A13, fp. 241; Walsh, *History of Medicine in New York*, 101. Walsh lists a yellow-fever epidemic in New York and sections of Delaware in 1720. Although this writer has found no evidence of the disease, both areas were subject to it.

low' broke out in town, and swept off multitudes of the inhabitants both white and black. . . . The physicians knew not how to treat the uncommon disorder which was suddenly caught, and proved so quickly fatal. The calamity was so general that few could grant assistance to their distressed neighbors, however much needed and earnestly desired. So many funerals happened every day while so many lay sick, white persons sufficient for burying the dead were scarce to be found." [20] The high case mortality, the rapidity with which the disease took effect, and the use of the terms yellow and "Bilious Plague" all indicate yellow fever.

In 1732 yellow fever again became epidemic in New York and Charleston. In the latter city it began in May and continued until September or October. At the height of the epidemic from eight to twelve whites were buried daily, as well as many Negroes. Practically all business ceased, and because of the excessive number of fatalities, the tolling of bells was forbidden. One of the local physicians diagnosed the disease as yellow fever and asserted it was imported from the West Indies. The Reverend Thomas Hassell, an S.P.G. missionary, wrote to the Society that his congregation had been diminished by the "recent sickness." By December, Governor Johnson was able to report that the province was healthy and "the great sickness that carried off so many last summer over." [21]

[20] Webster, *History of Epidemic Diseases*, I, 230; Hewat, *Historical Account*, I, 316–17; Carroll (ed.), *Historical Collections of South Carolina*, I, 273–74.

[21] Ramsay, *History of South Carolina*, II, 84; John Lining, *A Description of the American Yellow Fever . . .* (Philadelphia, 1799), 5; Currie, *An Account of Climates and Diseases*, 389; Thomas Hassell to Secretary, S. C., November 10, 1732, in S.P.G. MSS., A24, fp. 273; Governor Johnson to Duke of Newcastle, Charleston, S. C., December 15, 1732, in *Collections* of the South Carolina Historical Society (Charleston, 1857), I, 248.

The outbreak in New York was on a much smaller scale than that in Charleston. Webster called it a "malignant infectious fever" and estimated that about seventy persons died. Since the city's population was between 8,500 and 9,000, these seventy deaths represent less than one per cent —a minor loss in those days.[22]

Following these two outbreaks, yellow fever disappeared from the North American continent for about seven years, although Providence, Bahama Island, underwent a particularly severe attack in 1734. An S.P.G. missionary stationed there wrote to the Society on July 3, 1734, that his whole family was dangerously ill with a "raging fever" which had already caused the death of two of his sons. In one month, probably June, twenty-six of the townspeople died, and the Reverend Mr. Smith mentioned that he had buried another thirty-eight since that time. The contagion did not abate until the middle of September, by which time Smith estimated that between one fourth and one fifth of the population had been wiped out.[23]

Two epidemics in Virginia, in 1737 and 1741, have generally been attributed to yellow fever, primarily on the basis of an account written in 1748 by Dr. John Mitchell. Mitchell's description of the symptoms, however, leaves the yellow-fever diagnosis open to suspicion. Some of the main clinical symptoms which attracted the attention of colonial writers—the rapid onset of the disease and the early crisis, which often brought death within 48 to 72 hours —are significantly absent from Mitchell's account. "Almost without exception," in the cases he observed, the crisis did

[22] Webster, *History of Epidemic Diseases*, I, 341; *A Century of Population Growth*, 11.

[23] William Smith to Secretary, Providence, Bahama Island, February, 1734, in S.P.G. MSS., A25, fpp. 212–18; *id.* to *id.*, July 3, 1734, *ibid.*, fpp. 220–25.

not arrive until the fourth day, with death, if it came, occurring on the sixth. Further, Mitchell claimed:

> This Distemper is remarkably contagious, of which we had a better Opportunity to be satisfy'd here in Virginia, where we live in separate and distant Plantations consisting of Numbers of Servants & Slaves; any of whom if the Distemper once seized, there was little Security but Removal. The Distemper spread rather slower than I have observed the Measles or Small Pox to do here. But it spreads faster & rages more violently in the Spring Season, or from Christmas to Whitsuntide than any other Time of the Year; which I have likewise observed in these other Distempers in Virginia.[24]

This statement contrasts sharply with notations of contemporary observers, who nearly all remarked that yellow fever rarely ever spread far from the focal point of infection, usually the waterfront in a port city. In addition, at no time in the colonial period was yellow fever epidemic during the winter months in any of the eastern colonies. The approach of cool weather, even as far south as Charleston, invariably brought relief from yellow fever in October or November, yet Mitchell specifically repeated in another section of his article that it was "the Winter & Spring Season, when the Disease has chiefly raged here."

Significantly, one of Mitchell's fellow practitioners wrote to Dr. John Redman (1722–1808), president of the College of Physicians in Philadelphia, commenting that "the yellow fever in Virginia Described by Dr. John Mitchell Differs from that which appeared in Pensilvania in the Same Period of Time." One particular point of differenti-

[24] Dr. John Mitchell's Acct. of the Yellow Fever in Virginia in 1741–1742, Written in 1748, transcription by Dr. John Redman Coxe, 19–20, in College of Physicians MSS., Philadelphia.

ation which the doctor noted was that in the Philadelphia attacks the sickness was attended by "a very great anxiety [?] with sickness and Pain of the Stomach attended without Exception by Convulsive vomiting which no medicine would scarce relieve. This appeared on the first or second Day but more Commonly on the third when it was Generally fatal by bringing Hiccoughs, Inflammation of the stomach and viscera with a Large Discharge by vomit of a Black [?] Matter like Coffee Grounds, mixed with a Bloody Lymph or Coagulated Blood, which frequently put a period to the Patient's Life tho' Some recovered." [25] This is an excellent picture of one of the chief symptoms of yellow fever and one that Mitchell could scarcely have failed to mention had it been present.

It is possible that the Virginia epidemics—and probably that in Philadelphia in 1762—were outbreaks of dengue, rather than of yellow fever. Dengue, an infection resembling mild yellow fever, is especially hard to differentiate from this contagion in the first stage,[26] and until more substantial evidence than Mitchell's account can be found to support the yellow-fever thesis, the two Virginia outbreaks probably should be classified among the many unidentified colonial epidemics.

Meanwhile, in 1739 Charleston was again the scene of a yellow-fever attack. More than likely the infection was imported from St. Christopher where earlier in the same year a major epidemic had brought death to hundreds. The Charleston outbreak, although severe, was not quite as bad

[25] Dr. Samuel Littitchile to John Redman, Philadelphia [n.d.], 16–18, in Manuscripts Relating to Yellow Fever, College of Physicians, Philadelphia.

[26] Henry R. Carter, *Yellow Fever*, 64–65; Hirsch, *Handbook of Pathology*, I, 57.

as the previous one in 1732. Two S.P.G. missionaries reported their congregations thinned by the many fatalities during the summer; it had been a "Sickly Season everywhere," one of them wrote, "especially in Town, where a Pestilential Fever carried off an abundance of its Male Inhabitants, but, God be praised, it made little Progress in ye Country." [27] The infection seemed to attack Europeans more often than Negroes, which was logical since the slaves, coming from the African West Coast, were more likely to have an immunity to yellow fever. The comment on the failure of the disease to spread far from the city should be noted, for the characteristic limitation of yellow fever to a small locality was frequently observed. What was described as a yellow-fever epidemic broke out in Philadelphia in June, 1741, and did not end until the wet cool weather in mid-October. One of those alarmed by the outbreak was Benjamin Franklin, who, while en route from Boston to Philadelphia, stopped at Burlington, New Jersey, because of the infection and remained there until he was assured that a thunderstorm had cooled the air and eliminated the disorder. The contemporary records include notations on the "12th of the 6th month 1741," that "a malignant yellow fever now spreads much"; and on the "25th of the 7th month 1741," that "many who died of the distemper were persons lively and strong, and in the prime of their time." Another physician, a Dr. Lind, recorded that yellow fever in Philadelphia killed some 200 persons in 1740, but it is possible that he confused his dates, for none of the other accounts make reference to an attack in this year. A much later account of the 1741 outbreak claimed that the disease

[27] Ramsay, *History of South Carolina*, II, 84; Andrew Leslie to Secretary, St. Paul's, S. C., January 7, 1740, in S.P.G. MSS., B7, Pt. 2, fpp. 593–94; Stephen Roe to Secretary, *ibid.*, fpp. 591–92.

was introduced by a shipload of convicts from Dublin and was actually typhus.[28] However, cool weather scarcely would have had an adverse effect upon typhus, and the evidence indicates yellow fever.

The 1741 outbreak in Philadelphia may have come from the Bahamas. A New Providence correspondent reported from there: "There is a Fever now in this Island call'd the yellow which has hitherto carried off every one that has had it. . . . 'Tis attended with a vomiting of Stuff as black as Ink 'til a few Hours before Death: three of the Soldiers in the Fort [showed] Symptoms of it last Night: The Lord help us he only knows where it will terminate." [29] From the correspondence of the S.P.G. missionaries it appears that the contagion was fatal even more often in the Bahamas and West Indies than on the North American mainland.

Two years later yellow fever appeared again in New York City and raged from July to October, 1743. A survey by John Cruger, the mayor, showed a total of 217 deaths from July 25 to September 25, when, he declared, the city was clear of the disease. The population of New York City at this date probably was around 11,000,[30] and on the basis of this figure, the death toll ran only about 2 per cent of the total population—an insignificant figure in colonial days.

One of the victims, S.P.G. missionary Richard Charl-

[28] Rush, *Medical Inquiries*, 4th ed., III, 100; Currie, *An Account of Climates and Diseases*, 390, gives Dr. James Lind's account of the yellow-fever outbreak which killed two hundred persons in Philadelphia in 1740; Webster, *History of Epidemic Diseases*, I, 236; George William Norris, *The Early History of Medicine in Philadelphia* (Philadelphia, 1886), 362.

[29] William Smith to Secretary, New Providence, Bahama Islands, October 26, 1741, in S.P.G. MSS., B10, fp. 402.

[30] Boston *Weekly News-Letter*, No. 2066, November 3, 1743; Webster, *History of Epidemic Diseases*, I, 238; *A Century of Population Growth*, 11.

ton, wrote on September 30 that he had been attacked "in a most violent manner by a malignant (I had almost said a pestilential) fever, which within two Months has carried off a great number here." His sickness prevented him from "venturing to the door in over five weeks," and very nearly ended his career.[31]

Connecticut, too, was affected by this epidemic. A Boston newspaper reported early in October "that the Distemper call'd the Yellow Fever" was proving "very mortal" in some sections of the colony. Since Connecticut vessels plied constantly between the West Indies and New York, it is not at all unlikely that the infection—and possibly the yellow-fever mosquito—landed in Connecticut at this date. In his diary for these years Joshua Hempstead of New London mentioned several instances of local sailors dying from yellow fever contracted either in New York or the West Indies.[32] While a few deaths from yellow fever occurred in Connecticut, it is questionable that the stegomyia fasciata ever got a permanent foothold in the colony, and in all likelihood most of the yellow-fever victims were infected elsewhere.

The lowlands of New Jersey, notorious for their mosquitoes, may have proved a fertile spot for the yellow-fever carriers. Colin Campbell, the S.P.G. minister at Burlington, explained to the Society in May, 1744 that "You would have heard from me last fall were it not that I Sickened in August and was for Six weeks Confined to bed with an Epidemical fever that Raged here and at New York, and Swept away many Suddenly; and I had indeed but Small hopes of

[31] Richard Charlton to Secretary, New York, September 30, 1743, in S.P.G. MSS., B11, fp. 302; *id.* to *id.*, March 26, 1744, *ibid.*, B13, fp. 424.

[32] Boston *Evening Post*, No. 426, October 3, 1743; *Diary of Joshua Hempstead*, 447, 487, 607.

my Recovery, however it Pleased God to restore me to perfect health."[33] If Campbell was correct in his assertion that the Burlington and New York epidemics were the same, then this was one of the few occasions when yellow fever reached epidemic proportions beyond the limits of a major city. Though it was unusual that Burlington, situated many miles from New York, should have received the infection, it could have been brought directly to the town by a ship from the West Indies rather than via New York.

Outbreaks of yellow fever in Charleston and the "bilious plague" in New York were reported in 1745, but both were unquestionably yellow fever. The New York outbreak was so diagnosed by Dr. Colden in the course of an extensive correspondence with Dr. Mitchell of Virginia. He made the point that the fever had broken out in June and commented that it always developed in the dock areas—a fact which he attributed to filthy conditions there.[34]

The Charleston outbreak was a more serious one. Mr. John Fordyce reported to the S.P.G. in November, 1745 that "Charles-Town, is now, & has been for some time past, very much afflicted with a great & Malignant Sickness called the Yellow Feaver, in which they die Suddenly," that business there "can Scarce be transacted," and that "the General Assembly has been Prorogu'd and Adjourn'd several times on account of said Sickness." Fordyce added that a fellow minister was dangerously ill presumably from the fever. "I may Justly say" he added later, "there is Scarce a House or Family, but what some, or more have Died in it." Like most other attacks of the fever, these two outbreaks

[33] Colin Campbell to Secretary, Burlington, N. J., May 26, 1744, in S.P.G. MSS., B12, fpp. 32–33.

[34] Webster, *History of Epidemic Diseases*, I, 239; Cadwallader Colden to John Mitchell, Coldengham, N. Y., November 7, 1745, in *Colden Papers*, VIII (1937), 329–30.

probably originated in the West Indies, for Dr. Rush specifically mentioned the prevalence of the disease in Santo Domingo during this year.[35]

The epidemic in Charleston, however, was further complicated by the presence of other infections. A correspondent wrote in October that the sickness had "carried off vast Numbers of People." Some, he wrote, had died from the "Black Vomit," but a "Nervous" fever and another "more malignant Fever" were also taking a heavy toll, especially among newcomers to the city.[36] The term nervous fever was frequently applied to typhoid, while dysentery and pernicious malaria were perennial problems to the newly arrived settlers in the Carolinas: hence it is possible that all three diseases were assisting yellow fever in winnowing the population of Charleston.

A year later an epidemic fever in Albany, New York, aroused considerable interest. Three of the most outstanding colonial physicians studied the outbreak but were unable to agree on its exact cause. Dr. Mitchell gathered evidence showing that many of the victims turned yellow, but he did not try to determine what the disease was. Douglass unhesitatingly called it yellow fever, but Colden declared it was a nervous fever.[37]

The seriousness of the epidemic was emphasized by Governor George Clinton in an address to the New York general assembly. Speaking of a trip which he had made with Colden the previous July he told the assemblymen that "When we came to Albany that place was afflicted with a

[35] John Fordyce to Secretary, Prince Frederick Parish, S. C., November 4, 1745, in S.P.G. MSS., B12, fp. 258; Currie, *An Account of Climates and Diseases,* 389; John Fordyce to Secretary, Prince Frederick Parish, S. C., April 2, 1746, in S.P.G. MSS., B12, fp. 260; Ramsay, *History of South Carolina,* II, 84; Rush, *Medical Inquiries,* 2d ed., IV, 181.

[36] Boston *Evening Post,* No. 535, November 11, 1745.

[37] Webster, *History of Epidemic Diseases,* I, 239.

contagious Distemper of which many dy'd more perhaps in proportion to the number of people during our residence there of near three months on the publick Service than perhaps has happen'd in this age in North America."[38] Inasmuch as Colden was familiar with yellow fever and was the only one of the three who actually witnessed the outbreak, his diagnosis of nervous fever doubtlessly was the correct one. The nervous or continuous fever of Colden's time is the typhoid of today—a disease much more likely to have prevailed as far inland as Albany.

The following year yellow fever returned to Philadelphia after an absence of six years. A letter from the Pennsylvania council to the proprietor in 1747 reported that a malignant fever had been lurking in town all summer, but fortunately had not been so fatal as the previous outbreak of 1741. The council pointed out that the fever invariably began in the mud and filth around the docks and requested advice and assistance in alleviating this condition. Thomas Penn, the proprietor, countered that there was no necessity for improving the docks because the disease had been traced to the West Indies and was in no way connected with the unsanitary conditions. The connection between yellow fever and the West Indies was not news to Philadelphians, however, and when a vessel from Barbados arrived in September, it was carefully examined. The captain reported the death of one sailor and the recovery of another from what he thought was yellow fever. Although this attack had occurred some twenty days earlier, the council immediately ordered the ship to anchor not less than a mile from the city and forbade the unloading of cargo or passengers until further orders. The council acted wisely for later reports showed

[38] Message of Governor George Clinton to New York General Assembly, November 24, 1746, in *Colden Papers,* III (1919), 289.

a serious yellow-fever epidemic in Barbados at the time.[39]

Following the pattern of the last epidemic in New York, the 1747 Philadelphia infection spread beyond the city and into Delaware. The Reverend Thomas Bluett of Dover, Delaware, reported that yellow fever "of which multitudes died in Phil[a] & many in the lower Countys," had afflicted the province, but fall brought a gradual abatement.[40]

Outbreaks of yellow fever were reported in Charleston in 1745 and 1748, but letters from the S.P.G. missionaries indicate the continued presence of the disease for three successive summers. Levi Durand wrote in the spring of 1747 that "the Lord does yearly visit, sending Pestilential Diseases amongst Men & Beasts, which yearly Sweeps away Numbers of Both." In autumn John Fordyce reported to the Society that "Since I came here, there is not now a Family but what one, two, or more have Died out of it: and Especially most of the Heads which (to my Grief) have very much reduc'd my Congregation." The series of epidemic fevers beginning in 1745 culminated in a severe attack of yellow fever in 1748. Charles Boschi, a missionary stationed near Charleston, called it a "mortal Fever," and informed the Society that his annual letter had been delayed as the "country people" were reluctant to enter the city while the pestilence raged. Ramsay called the infection yellow fever, though a milder attack than that of eight years earlier.[41]

[39] Council at Philadelphia to Proprietors, Philadelphia, 1747, in Samuel Hazard (ed.), *Pennsylvania Archives*, 12 vols. (Philadelphia, 1852–56), Ser. 1, I (1852), 768–69; Thomas Penn to Council at Philadelphia, London, March 30, 1748, in *Colonial Records of Pennsylvania*, V (1851), 244; Minutes of the Provincial Council, *ibid.*, 106.

[40] Thomas Bluett to Secretary, Dover in Kent, Del., January 4, 1748, in S.P.G. MSS., B16–17, fp. 251; Rush, *Medical Inquiries*, 4th ed., III, 100.

[41] Currie, *An Account of Climates and Diseases*, 389; Ramsay, *History of South Carolina*, II, 84; Levi Durand to Secretary, Christ Church, S. C., April 23, 1747, in S.P.G. MSS., B15, fp. 318; John Fordyce to Secretary, South Carolina, October 6, 1747, *ibid.*, B15, fp. 341; Charles Boschi to

Philadelphia must have experienced a mild attack of yellow fever in 1749, for Benjamin Franklin wrote his mother in that year that in addition to a large number of children lost by measles and dysentery, "we have lost some grown persons, by what we call the Yellow Fever;" he added piously that it "is almost, if not quite over, thanks to God who has preserved all our family in perfect health." [42] Though his is the only record of a 1749 outbreak, Franklin had already witnessed two outbreaks of the fever and was not likely to be mistaken. The letter itself indicates the minor nature of the epidemic—a circumstance which may account for the failure of contemporary historians to record it.

Another missionary, who arrived at Charleston in the fall of 1750, reported that "various Kinds of Fevers rage fatally" and that he was shocked by the "prodigious Sickness of the Country." Possibly yellow fever was among the sicknesses but one can only speculate. However, the infection did appear in 1753 and 1755, though little is known of these outbreaks. Only a few cases developed in these years, and yellow fever did not reach epidemic proportions in South Carolina between 1748 and 1792.[43]

Outside South Carolina only one reference is made to yellow fever during the 1750's, and this probably was a mistaken diagnosis. In the spring of 1759 a conference between Sir William Johnson and the Mohawk Indians of

---

Secretary, Bartholomew's Parish, S. C., February 10, 1749, *ibid.*, B16–17, fpp. 345–46; Webster, *History of Epidemic Diseases*, I, 240; Ramsay, *History of South Carolina*, II, 84.

[42] Pepper, *Medical Side of Benjamin Franklin*, 24.

[43] William Langhorne to Secretary, St. Bartholomew's Parish, S. C., March 18, 1751, in S.P.G. MSS., B18, fp. 470; Joseph Ioor Waring, "Medicine in Charlestown, 1750–1775," in *Annals of Medical History*, N. S., VII (1935), 20; Ramsay, *History of South Carolina*, II, 85.

western New York was postponed because "of the sickness or yellow fever prevailing among the Mohawks of the lower Castle."[44] This attack resembled the outbreak in Albany which Colden had classed as nervous fever and which was probably typhoid, although it could easily have been pernicious malaria or some other infection. Yellow fever, however, is the least likely prospect.

A "Bilious infectious fever" was reported in Charleston in 1761.[45] Yellow fever is a possible suspect, but the evidence is scant, and Charleston was plagued by many epidemic fevers.

The last major outbreak of yellow fever during the period of this study ravaged Philadelphia in 1762. A "bilious remitting yellow fever epidemic, prevailed in Philadelphia, after a *very hot summer* and spread like a plague carrying off daily, for sometime upwards of twenty persons." Some cases of the disease were reported in Southwark, and a few sporadic cases were said to have developed the following summer. Dr. John Redman, a contemporary physician who practiced during the epidemic, thought that the infection was brought ashore by a sick sailor and noted that he prescribed for his first patient on August 28. As was usual, he noted, the epidemic was restricted to the water front and ceased with the end of October. The disorder probably originated in the West Indies, for "Bilious plague" prevailed in both Philadelphia and Havana in 1762.[46]

A nineteenth-century medical historian maintained that

[44] "Journal of Sir William Johnson's Proceedings with the Indians," in O'Callaghan (ed.), *Documents Relative to Colonial History*, VII (1856), 378.

[45] Webster, *History of Epidemic Diseases*, I, 250.

[46] Rush, *Medical Inquiries*, 4th ed., III, 44; *ibid.*, 2d ed., IV, 372; John Redman, *An Account of the Yellow Fever as It Prevailed in Philadelphia in the Autumn of 1762* (Philadelphia, 1865), 10–16; Webster, *History of Epidemic Diseases*, I, 251.

Rush gained his method of treatment for yellow fever in 1762 from a manuscript account of a Virginia outbreak in 1741. Whether Rush was familiar with Dr. John Mitchell's manuscript or not, he himself admitted that it was his recollection of yellow fever in 1762 which enabled him to diagnose the disease when it reappeared in a particularly virulent form in 1793. By this time the malady had been absent so long that many of the younger medical men even denied its existence and Rush's opinion was treated with considerable contempt by the majority of the practicing physicians.[47]

Yellow fever seems to have disappeared from British North America for a thirty-year period from 1763 to 1793, though a possible yellow-fever outbreak occurred in Virginia in 1773. However, the fact that the sickness was referred to as a jail fever, introduced into the colony by convicts, suggests that typhus rather than yellow fever was a more likely culprit.[48]

In reviewing the course of yellow fever in colonial America, certain conclusions are immediately apparent. In the first place, the evidence for the existence of yellow fever prior to 1693 is both limited and inconclusive, and a much better case can be developed for the thesis that the entrance of yellow fever into North America dates from this year.

Secondly, the brunt of the yellow-fever epidemics was borne by three cities. Of these three—Charleston, New York, and Philadelphia—the former, Charleston, without question experienced the greatest hardship. Seven major outbreaks ravaged Charleston as compared to four each for the other two cities. Interestingly enough, there is a close correlation between the years of major attacks in all

[47] Elisha Bartlett, *The History, Diagnosis, and Treatment of the Fevers of the United States* (Philadelphia, 1847), 522; Rush, *Medical Inquiries*, 4th ed., III, 44.

[48] Blanton, *Medicine in Virginia in the Eighteenth Century*, 54.

three cities. Apparently yellow fever appeared on the scene around 1700, reached its peak about 1745, gradually diminished in extent and virulence to about 1760, and then disappeared until the end of the century.

The disappearance of yellow fever in the second half of the eighteenth century is a puzzling question. Improved and more rigidly enforced quarantine laws seem an obvious answer until the problem of yellow fever after 1793 is raised. It is scarcely plausible that the quarantine laws were more effective between 1760 and 1793 than after that date. Did the yellow-fever mosquito for some unaccountable reason disappear during these years? This hypothesis, too, is extremely doubtful since even in 1930 a few stegomyia fasciata mosquitoes could be found in certain sections of Virginia.[49] If modern methods of mosquito control cannot eradicate this pest, it is logical to assume that the yellow-fever carrier continued to breed in the many favorable areas along the Atlantic seaboard during the second half of the eighteenth century.

Yellow fever was one of the most dreaded diseases in the affected regions, and certainly individual epidemics took a heavy toll of lives. Nonetheless, the impression left by the graphic and moving accounts of particular epidemics has given yellow fever a more significant place in American medical history than it deserves. Had the stegomyia fasciata adapted itself to all areas in the British American colonies, yellow fever would undoubtedly have ranked with smallpox as a leading cause of death. This adaption did not occur, and yellow fever is well down the list of fatal diseases in eighteenth-century North America.

49 Blanton, *Medicine in Virginia in the Seventeenth Century*, 71.

CHAPTER V

Measles, Whooping Cough, and Mumps

Measles, long considered a children's disease, received little attention from contemporary observers in the eighteenth century. Its relatively low rate of mortality relegated it to a minor role in a day when smallpox and other disorders reduced the population by the hundreds. Yet this sickness was present in epidemic form and was very often fatal. The danger of complications following an attack of measles was noticed by many early writers who commented on the disease. Too often, however, the immediate cause of death was mentioned without reference to the attack of measles which had first weakened the victim. The infection was usually regarded as a comparatively harmless sickness and worthy of mention only in exceptional cases.

Measles ranks with smallpox as one of the most infectious of contagious diseases. Any child coming in contact with the virus is certain to catch it, and few, if any, pass beyond the school age without an attack. Its cause is a filter-passing virus, communicated by human intercourse. The incubation period lasts eight to twelve days followed by the first symptoms: an acute catarrah of the mucous membranes, sneezing, watery discharge from the nose, hoarseness, cough, fever, headache, thirst, and restlessness. On the fourth or fifth day the characteristic eruptions appear, consisting of small dusky red or crimson spots grouped in patches. Of the many types of measles, one is especially malignant. The rash in this variety is less pronounced and is usually a dark purple. Bad hygienic conditions or an absence of the disorder for a long period—conditions illustrated by the Fiji Island epidemic of 1874, which wiped out 40,000 of the estimated 150,000 natives within three months[1]—are prerequisites for a high case mortality.

Although confused with smallpox well into the seventeenth century, measles was identified clearly as early as 910 A.D. by Rhazes. The first London Bills of Mortality issued in 1629 separated measles from smallpox, and it is doubtful that these two diseases were confused in any of the succeeding years, although in the eighteenth century measles was occasionally confused with scarlet fever. An excellent description of the disorder in the Stuart period was made in 1675 by Thomas Sydenham after he had observed the general outbreaks of 1670 and 1674 in England.[2]

The evidence of measles in the seventeenth century is limited, but the disease was present in the colonies and on a number of occasions reached epidemic proportions. As early as 1635 the Jesuits reported a mild outbreak among the French and Indians, and in 1687 M. de Denonville wrote from Quebec that "the King's ships brought the Measles, which have broken out at our Hospital at Quebec and spread everywhere. Very few have been exempt." [3]

[1] Paul William Allen, *The Story of Microbes* (St. Louis, 1938), 244.

[2] "Rhazes, A Treatise on the Smallpox and Measles," in *Medical Classics*, IV (1939), 19–20; Creighton, *History of Epidemics*, II, 633–34; "Selections from the Writings of Thomas Sydenham," in *Medical Classics*, IV (1939), 313–18.

[3] Ashburn, *Ranks of Death*, 90–91; M. de Denonville to M. de Seignelay, Quebec, October 27, 1687, in O'Callaghan (ed.), *Documents Relative to Colonial History*, IX (1855), 354.

In New England the disease became epidemic only twice, but publication in 1677 of Thomas Thacher's *Brief Rule* for the treatment of both smallpox and measles is a possible indication of the continuing presence of the disease. In 1657 John Hull of Boston recorded in his diary that "the disease of measles went through the town," but although few families escaped the infection, "through the goodness of God, scarce any died of it." Subsequently the disease spread to the surrounding communities, where it followed a similarly mild course. The epidemic which troubled the French and Indians in 1687 probably spread south through the other tribes and affected New England in the winter of 1687–88.[4]

The infection may have continued further southward, for Governor Edmund Andros and the council of Virginia issued a proclamation in 1693 appointing a "day of Humiliation and Prayer" because of measles in the province.[5] However, in view of the time lapse it is more likely that the sickness was imported from England.

From 1713 to 1715 a serious measles epidemic harried the American colonies. New England was the first region to suffer, with Boston, the chief city, taking heavy casualties. Apparently the disease appeared in the city late in the summer of 1713 and concluded its course about the end of January, 1714, when the Boston *News-Letter*—possibly optimistically—announced that the town was restored to health. It is evident from contemporary diaries that the death toll was high, but the estimates vary as to the exact number. The most accurate observer, William Douglass, placed the

[4] "Diary of John Hull," *loc. cit.*, 147–81; Ernest Caulfield, "Early Measles Epidemics in America," in *Yale Journal of Biology and Medicine*, XV (1943), 535–36.

[5] *Executive Journals, Council of Colonial Virginia*, I, 285, 292, quoted in Blanton, *Medicine in Virginia in the Seventeenth Century*, 62.

figure at one hundred and fifty.[6] However, his estimate probably did not include the indirect fatalities, *i.e.*, those arising from the complications which so often beset the recuperating measles patient. The Boston bills of mortality indicate that the variance from normal was in excess of Douglass' count; hence one hundred and fifty deaths can be taken as a conservative figure.

The severity of the attack brought forth a number of suggested remedies, at least two of which contained sound advice. In September, 1713, Wait Winthrop of Boston wrote to his son of the many fatalities from measles and advised: "If the measles comes amongst you, it's best to give sage and baum tea, with a little safron, and keep warm and let nature have time to work without too much forcing." Cotton Mather, whose household was devastated by the loss of his wife, maid, and three children in the space of two weeks, was moved to compose the best work by far on measles published during the colonial period. He began by pointing out that although measles was "a Light Malady" in Europe, "in these parts of *America* it proves a very heavy Calamity." He then warned of the dangers of excesses in treatment: "Before we go any farther," he wrote, "Let this Advice for the *Sick*, be principally attended to; *Don't kill 'em!* That is to say, With mischievous Kindness. Indeed," he went on, "if we stopt here, and said no more, this were enough to save more *Lives* than our *Wars* have destroyed."

Mather then proceeded to give an accurate description of the clinical symptoms of the disease, and he made a point of the necessity for complete rest even in the event of a mild case. He noted that "*a Fever*, (perhaps that which they call,

[6] Boston, *News-Letter*, No. 510, January 18–25, No. 517, March 8–15, 1714; William Douglass, *A practical essay concerning the small pox* (Boston, 1730).

the *Pleuritick)* too often follows the *Measles*," and concluded with this warning to the family of the patient, "Let him not be *well too soon*, and throw himself into a Fever, and throw away his *Life*, as many have inconsiderately and presumptiously done." [7] In view of the rigorous bleeding, vomiting, and purging customarily used at this date, it is refreshing to find Winthrop and Mather giving such sound advice. And equally noteworthy is the fact that this advice came from laymen rather than physicians.

Reports of measles came from a number of New England towns in the fall of 1713. Joseph Green of Salem Village mentioned in December that all of his seven children had come through the disease successfully, although some of his neighbors' children were not so fortunate. The same month reports from New London, Connecticut, indicated that the disease had obtained a foothold there. Judging from the records of a local diarist, the first fatalities did not occur until January, and the peak of the outbreak came in April, when Joshua Hempstead recorded, "I was not at meeting. Wee are most of us down with ye Measles." [8] While the majority of the victims were children, enough adults were infected to show that the disease was not endemic in the colonies as was the case in the mother country.

The same winter the infection spread south into New York, New Jersey, and Pennsylvania. In February a New York correspondent reported that "the measles are still among us and have got into the country as far as Burling-

[7] Wait Winthrop to his son, John, Boston, September 6, 1713, in Massachusetts Historical Society *Collections*, Ser. 6, V (1892), 276; James Pierpont to John Winthrop, *ibid.*, 277; Cotton Mather, *A Letter About a Good Management under the Distemper of the Measles, etc.* (Boston, 1739); *Diary of Cotton Mather, loc. cit.* (1709–1724), 255–61.

[8] "Diary of Rev. Joseph Green of Salem Village," in *Historical Collections* of the Essex Institute, X (1869), 103; *Diary of Joshua Hempstead*, 41–44.

ton." The next month a newspaper description of the attack in Philadelphia declared that the measles "was brought hither from Salem in West Jersey, where it proved very Mortal." John Bartow, the S.P.G. missionary stationed in Westchester, New York, excused his neglect of his ecclesiastical duties because "The measles have been Epidemical throughout the whole country this Winter and having not had them myself nor one of my family and the distemper proving very mortal, I declined visiting and baptizing a dying child, if complaint be made I hope the Society will not be offended." [9] Although no statistics are available for the ravages of the infection in the middle colonies, it was evidently on a scale comparable to outbreaks in Boston.

Virginia, which had escaped the outbreak of 1713–14, was not so fortunate three years later. In March, 1717, Colonel Philip Ludwell wrote Francis Nicholson that "The measles hath been epidemicall amongst us this winter, it hath run quick through my family tho' I thank God I have lost none but a young Negro woman, but poor Mr. Berkeley dyed of it as did Jenny Burwell, Mrs. Churchill, Mrs. Page (who was her daughter) Mrs. Corbin & some others." [10] It should be noted that the victims mentioned in the above were nearly all adults—evidence that measles was an infrequent visitor.

In 1729 measles was again widespread in America but generally in a mild or benign form. William Douglass in 1730 claimed that in Boston measles was responsible for only fifteen deaths the preceding year, although a study (based upon an examination of newspapers, church files, and

[9] Boston *News-Letter*, No. 512, February 1–8, No. 518, March 15–22, 1714; John Bartow to Secretary, Westchester, N. Y., April 14, 1714, in S.P.G. MSS., A9, fpp. 131–33.

[10] Colonel Philip Ludwell to Francis Nicholson, Virginia, March 27, 1717, *ibid.*, B4, Pt. 1, fpp. 536–37.

private manuscripts) of burials there shows measles to have been the leading cause of death in 1729. The Reverend Thomas Prince, author of an article published in the *Gentlemen's Magazine* dealing with the vital statistics of Boston, 1701 to 1752, also mentioned the outbreak of 1729,[11] but provided no statistical information.

In New York City, the *Gazette* reported on February 25 that "Many Children in this City, now have the Measles, which are very moderate." Unfortunately, either a concurrent epidemic or the complications ensuing from the measles outbreak added to the woes of the citizens. One of Dr. Colden's correspondents, whose family was hard hit by the New York epidemic, wrote him an anguished letter in March, 1729:

> There was never So great a mortality here Since I came to this place as now. Theres no day but what theres numbers of buryings, Some of the measles but most of the pain of the Side there's hardly a house in town but what had several Sick of the one or the other of these Distempers. Some have half a Score at a time, four of our children have had the Measles two almost quite recovered two Sick as yet . . . we have three children more & three more negroes which we Expect Every day to have them, so you Easyly think the town is in not a little Distress. . . . Our Supreme Court was adjourned by writt under the Seal of the Province for Six weeks because of the Sickness of the town.[12]

The author of the letter later wrote that his wife and

[11] "Account of Burials and Baptisms in Boston," *loc. cit.;* William Douglass, *A practical essay concerning the small pox*, 213–16; Thomas Prince to Editor, in *Gentlemen's Magazine*, XXIII (1753), 413–14.

[12] New York *Gazette*, No. 173, February 18–25, 1729; James Alexander to Cadwallader Colden, New York, March 14, 1729, in *Colden Papers*, I (1917), 276.

four children, along with four of his Negroes, were still sick with the measles and that he thought another Negro was coming down with the infection. Whatever the nature of the second illness, measles was undoubtedly easing its path by draining the community's vitality, for many of the fatalities from measles resulted only indirectly from the disease. The following winter an S.P.G. schoolmaster in Oysterbay, New Jersey, reported that his school had been only sparsely attended, explaining that the presence of measles had disorganized all schools in the vicinity.[13]

During the ten years which elapsed before the next general attack, only one minor local outbreak seems to have occurred. The Reverend Thomas Smith of Falmouth, Massachusetts, recorded that the contagion was prevalent for several months in the fall and winter of 1736;[14] but he was so preoccupied with the devastation resulting from a concurrent throat distemper that he scarcely noticed the relatively mild measles epidemic.

Scattered outbreaks of measles occurred generally in New England, New York, and New Jersey from 1739 to 1741. In the spring of 1739 the presence of the disease in Boston caused a number of its citizens to leave town, some of whom undoubtedly carried the infection with them. By summer other towns in Massachusetts were attacked, and late in the year the disease reached Connecticut. During the winter of 1739–40 journalists in Massachusetts and Connecticut continued to mention additional cases, but like Smith, they were all too concerned with the graver threat of throat distemper to give more than a passing mention

[13] James Alexander to Cadwallader Colden, March 26, 1729, in *Colden Papers*, I (1917), 277; Daniel Denton to Secretary, Oysterbay, N. J., February 17, 1730, in S.P.G. MSS., B1, Pt. 1, fp. 203.

[14] Willis (ed.), *Journals of Smith and Deane*, 85.

to measles.[15] Conceivably, the high fatality rate of the throat distemper may have been due in part to the earlier debilitating attacks of measles.

New Jersey may have been infected about the same time as New England. John Pierson of Salem, New Jersey, wrote to the S.P.G. that he had been very ill with the measles during the spring of 1739. He did not indicate an epidemic, but measles, an extremely contagious disease, rarely appeared as an isolated case. Two years later the people of Winchester, New York, petitioned the S.P.G. on behalf of the Society's schoolmaster, William Forster, who had recently lost his position because his annual report showed so few students for the previous year. The petition explained, "We Certifie That the last ffall the Meazles being in town were a great hindrance to the School." [16] The infection subsided in 1741 and remained dormant for six years.

In 1747–48 measles appeared in widely separated localities in South Carolina, Pennsylvania, New York, Massachusetts, and Connecticut. In South Carolina the sickness in 1747 was "common and fatal; principally by the bowel complaints which followed them." The outbreak in New York, although of a mild nature, spread extensively. Dr. Colden wrote his wife from New York that he was coming home for a visit but could not bring their daughter as she was ill with the measles. He assured the mother that there was little cause for worry, as the danger was very slight, for "tho great Nos. have had it none have been in Danger." Three days later he reported that the crisis had passed. Evi-

[15] Ebenezer Parkman Diary, June, 1739–February, 1740; *Diary of Joshua Hempstead*, 357, 360, 370; "Diary of Paul Dudley, 1740," *loc. cit.*

[16] John Pierson to Secretary, Salem, N. J., May 10, 1739, in S.P.G. MSS., B7, Pt. 2, fpp. 183–84; Petition of Townspeople of Winchester, N. Y., to S.P.G., *ibid.*, B9–10, fp. 153.

dently the New York epidemic persisted throughout the winter of 1747–48. In February Colden's daughter, Mrs. Peter De Lancey, wrote to him that her children were just recovering, and as late as May, Long Island was still under attack.[17]

Measles was just one of the calamities afflicting the congregation of the Reverend Thomas Bluett of Dover, Pennsylvania, who wrote the S.P.G. in January, 1748, that everything from war to a series of "Mortal Sicknesses" had beset the province "& now the Measles is almost universal here." Two months later he described the pulmonary complications which so often prove fatal to those recovering from the measles: "The Sickness that proves so mortal here is a Sort of Pleurisy, most that have not had that are Seiz'd with the Measles, and when they are seemingly on the recovery, are taken with the Pleurisy, which Suddenly carrys them off, so that hardly a day passes but we have account of two, three, or four Deaths and some times more, we have buried in our Church Yard some days one, often two or three." [18] Bluett added that it was almost impossible to estimate the death toll; for many persons were buried on their farms or plantations, while the Dissenters, Catholics, and others had their own burial grounds.

Deaths from measles were reported from New London, Connecticut, in the spring of 1747, and the disease continued to work its way through the town until the fall.

[17] Ramsay, *History of South Carolina*, II, 89; Mrs. Peter De Lancey to Cadwallader Colden, New York, February 10, 1748, in *Colden Papers*, VIII (1937), 351–52; William Smith to Henry Lloyd, Manor St. George, Long Island, N. Y., May 14, 1748, in *Papers of the Lloyd Family*, I (1926), 405; Cadwallader Colden to his wife, New York, June 18, 1747, in *Colden Papers*, III (1919), 213; Cadwallader Colden to John Bard, New York, June 21, 1747, in Colden Papers.

[18] Thomas Bluett to Secretary, Dover in Kent, Del., January 1, 1748, in S.P.G. MSS., B16–17, fp. 251; *id.* to *id.*, March 28, 1748, *ibid.*, fp. 245.

The sporadic nature of the outbreaks is indicated by the fact that Waterbury, Connecticut, was not affected until the winter of 1748–49. Nor did Boston escape the disease. In January, 1748, John Whiting wrote in his diary that "the Mezeals are thick about," and in June he mentioned the presence of a throat distemper, whose path was probably smoothed by the earlier outbreak of measles.[19]

Philadelphia, too, was harried by the widespread infection. In a letter to his mother in October, 1749, Benjamin Franklin rejoiced that his family had remained well despite much illness in town. The "Measles and flux," he reported, had "carried off many children," while a number of adults had fallen victim to yellow fever.[20]

For a second time a ten-year interval separated widespread outbreaks of measles. The next visitation came in 1759 and few regions escaped. The disease was both general and fatal in South Carolina, and Elizabeth Drinker of Philadelphia and Alexander Colden of New York noted its presence in their respective cities during the early part of the year. The infection was restricted to children and was relatively mild.[21]

However, this mildness was not characteristic of the contagion in Fairfield, New Jersey, where Ephraim Harris recalled in his journal "That fatal and never-to-be forgotten year, 1759, when the Lord sent the destroying angel to pass through this place, and removed many of our friends into eternity in a short space of time; not a house exempt,

[19] *Diary of Joshua Hempstead*, 477, 487; Edwards A. Parks, *Memoir of the Life and Character of Samuel Hopkins, D.D.* (Boston, 1854), 55–56; "Diary of John Whiting," *loc. cit.*, 186.

[20] Jared Sparks (ed.), *The Works of Benjamin Franklin*, 10 vols. (Boston, 1839–47), VII, 41.

[21] Ramsay, *History of South Carolina*, II, 89; Elizabeth Drinker's Diary, February 8, 1759; Alexander Colden to his sister, Katherine, New York, April 25, 1759, in *Colden Papers*, IX (1937), 173–75.

not a family spared from the calamity. So dreadful was it, that it made every ear tingle, and every heart bleed; in which time I and my family was exercised with that dreadful disorder, the measles. But blessed be God, our lives are spared." [22] Measles was only part of the troubles in Fairfield, for smallpox and other diseases were also prevalent at the same time.

In the New England colonies the disorder was most extensive in Massachusetts. The first cases appeared in Boston in January, and in the same month the Reverend Thomas Smith of Falmouth (in present-day Maine) noted that "the measles is spreading through the towns in this part of the country." The outbreak increased in intensity during the next few weeks, and in March Smith recorded that many were ill and that several had died from the disorder. The outbreak in Cambridge was most severe in February, according to the diaries of Harvard students, but as late as May John Whiting wrote in his journal that his boys were all ill with the "meazels." With one or two exceptions, however, the outbreaks in 1759 were relatively mild and were comparable to the previous epidemics in 1729. A news item in a Boston paper illustrated the mildness of the attack: "We hear that in the second Parish in Dedham, there have been 260 Persons sick with the Measles this Winter, and but one Instance of Mortality." [23]

The next widespread epidemic did not occur until 1772, when "the measles appeared in all parts of America with

[22] Wickes, *History of Medicine in New Jersey*, 20–21.

[23] Willis (ed.), *Journals of Smith and Deane*, *178*; Dow (ed.), *The Holyoke Diaries*, 20; Jeremiah Belknap Diary in *Ames Almanack*, *1759*, Massachusetts Historical Society MSS.; "Diary for the Year 1759 kept by Samuel Gardner of Salem," in *Historical Collections* of the Essex Institute, XLIX (1913), 4, 8; "Diary of Dr. Nathaniel Ames," *loc. cit.*, 49; "Diary of John Whiting," *loc. cit.*, 190; Boston *Evening Post*, No. 1226, February 26, 1759.

unusual mortality. In Charleston, S. Carolina, died 8 or 900 children." The *South Carolina Gazette* reported on July 30 that the measles which "was introduced here from New York, in March last, has lately proved, and still continues, *very mortal*." The infection was reported to be "frequently fatal in the year 1772; especially when [it] fell on the bowels or lungs." Three years later the disease again reached epidemic proportions in Charleston.[24]

Although measles in previous outbreaks had proved fatal most often in New England, the attack there in 1772–73 was unusually mild. In August Dr. Cotton Tufts, one of the foremost Massachusetts physicians and a founder of the Massachusetts Medical Society, recorded in his diary, "The measles have prevailed in some Parts of the Province for some months past and are at their Height in Boston the latter End of this August; hitherto have been very light." In December Dr. Tufts noted again that "measles spread fast." A correspondent from Waltham, Massachusetts, indicated that the disease was exceptionally mild in that area.[25]

The *Massachusetts Gazette* published an article on the treatment of measles in January, "As the Measles are now very prevalent in most of our Country Towns and the People in general ignorant of the nature of that Disorder and the Method of Cure." The same journal reported in February that two thirds of the people in Weymouth had been sick with the disease, but it had "proved fatal to only 2 persons, one an infant." From Dedham came a report that the infection was also extensive there but that it had pro-

[24] Webster, *History of Epidemic Diseases*, I, 259; *South Carolina Gazette*, No. 1906, July 30, 1772; Ramsay, *History of South Carolina*, II, 89.

[25] "Diaries of Dr. Cotton Tufts," in Massachusetts Historical Society *Proceedings*, XLII (1908–1909), 474, 476; Jacob Cushing to Mr. Williams, Waltham, Mass., December 22, 1772, in Simon Gratz Collection, American Clergymen.

duced no fatal results. From Brookfield, Salem, Sutton, and other Massachusetts towns, too, came similar reports—general infection but few fatalities.[26] However, despite the low case fatality rate, the magnitude of the attack made measles a leading cause of death in Boston in 1772, and the same was probably true of many other New England towns.

In Philadelphia the sickness began in the spring or early summer of 1772 and continued into the following year, when it was attended with an efflorescence about the neck and a "catarrah, which could hardly be distinguished from the measles." [27] Here, too, the disease was mild, but as in New England the infection was general. By the time the measles epidemic was over it had coursed through all of the colonies and few areas had escaped it. One beneficial result was the immunization of the colonial population, with the consequence that measles was one of the few diseases that did not run rampant during the Revolution.[28]

The inadequate medical facilities of the time aggravated the problem of measles and made it a greater threat than it is today. Even so, measles was rarely a major killer disease, and the majority of its victims fell when an attack was followed by other complications, notably pulmonary and bowel infections.

Measles does not appear to have followed any pattern of either increasing or diminishing intensity, although in England deaths from the infection rose steadily in the eight-

[26] *Massachusetts Gazette and the Boston Weekly News-Letter*, No. 3614, January 7, No. 3621, February 25, No. 3631, May 6, 1773; Dow (ed.), *The Holyoke Diaries*, 79; Rev. Nathan Fiske Diary in *Ames Almanack, 1773*, American Antiquarian Society MSS.; David Hall Diary, June 5, 1773; "An Account of Burials and Baptisms in Boston, from the Year 1701 to 1774," *loc. cit.*

[27] Packard, *History of Medicine*, I, 95.

[28] Ernest Caulfield, "Some Common Diseases of Colonial Children," in *Publications* of the Colonial Society of Massachusetts, XXXV (1951), 11.

eenth century.[29] The lack of accurate mortality statistics for measles in America limits generalization, although in the colonial period the disease was usually more often fatal in America than in England and affected a larger number of adults. This greater severity may be ascribed to the lower incidence of smallpox in the colonies. Many children who would normally have been killed by smallpox, had it been endemic in America, fell victim to measles, diphtheria, and other disorders. New Hampshire, which suffered so heavily from recurring attacks of throat distemper during the latter period of this study, was relatively free of measles. Hampton, New Hampshire, where the initial epidemic of throat distemper occurred, showed only four deaths from measles in the forty-one years from 1735 to 1776.[30] Very possibly the presence of one highly selective plague—in this case, diphtheria—may have reduced the toll exacted by other infections.

The incidence of measles among adults in America indicates that, like smallpox, it did not become endemic until late in the colonial period. The intervals between outbreaks

[29] Creighton, *History of Epidemics*, II, 647.

An interesting sidelight to the study of measles in the colonies is found in the correspondence between Cadwallader Colden and Dr. Robert Whytt of Edinburgh. Whytt reported that a Dr. Homes had experimented with a measles inoculation similar to the method used for smallpox. Among the eight or ten patients inoculated, the symptoms had been very mild and the operation apparently successful. Whytt added that a full account of the experiment was in the process of publication by Dr. Homes in a book entitled *Medical Facts and Experiments* and advised Colden to read it. Nothing more is heard of this practice, and it presumably died a natural death. However, a medical dissertation printed in 1793 referred to Homes' experiment and stated that its practice was a "most powerful means of alleviating the common consequences of measles." See Robert Whytt to Cadwallader Colden, Edinburgh, October 27, 1758, in *Colden Papers*, V (1921), 263, and Charles Buxton, *An Inaugural Dissertation on the Measles* (New York, 1793).

[30] Belknap, *History of New-Hampshire*, III, 241–42.

permitted the development of a considerable group of non-immunes.

The prevalence of fatal throat, respiratory, and intestinal infections during measles epidemics indicates that measles was actually a greater problem than the statistics and reports show. The relationship between measles and ensuing disorders was only imperfectly understood, and contemporary reports do not give a full picture of the consequences of this pestilence. This much is certain, measles contributed its share to the high death rate of the period and, as smallpox was gradually placed under control, became one of the leading causes of infant mortality.

Two other childhood diseases, whooping cough and mumps, deserve mention here. Both sicknesses result from specific filter-passing viruses, are usually innocuous, and require little special treatment. The prevalence of the two disorders in the early colonial period must have been slight, since so little record of them can be found. However, by the middle of the eighteenth century both diseases made more frequent appearances and, on a few occasions, were quite troublesome. William Douglass failed to mention either in his discussion of epidemics in Boston during the years of his practice, and only Lionel Chalmers among the contemporary historians deemed either of them worthy of notice.

The earliest reference to whooping cough in the colonies is found in the diary of John Hull of Boston, who recorded in December, 1659, that "in this same month of December, the young children of this town, and sundry towns hereabout, were much afflicted with a very sore whooping-cough: some few died of it." No further mention of whooping cough occurs in the records until 1738, when a whooping cough death was noted in New London, Connecticut, and an epidemic broke out in South Carolina.[31]

Four years later the disease struck the family of an S.P.G. missionary, Jonathan Arnold of Staten Island, New York, who told the Society of "the Long Distresses of my family by reason of the hooping coff [which] are not Easily described; not one escaped, one of my children lies at ye point of Death, another very dangerously ill & my wife not like to live long and I myself have not had a well day this 2 months." Arnold was not exaggerating his plight: the following November he reported the death of his wife and one child from the sickness. The disease is scarcely likely to have been restricted to the Arnold family, but the lack of any further evidence indicates that the outbreak, if it existed, was minor. Another mild outbreak may have occurred in New London, since whooping cough was blamed for the death of a child there in 1746.[32]

In South Carolina, however, the disease was both virulent and widespread. Three epidemics of whooping cough ravaged this colony during the later colonial period, and in each outbreak all age groups were affected and the case fatality rate was—for whooping cough—relatively high. A serious attack in 1738 may have been the first major whooping cough epidemic in the American colonies. The next attack began in January, 1759, and continued until November. At the height of the outbreak the *South Carolina Gazette*, printing a suggested remedy, professed itself "obliged to the gentlemen who generously communicates the fore-

[31] "Diary of John Hull," *loc. cit.*, 190; *Diary of Joshua Hempstead*, 338.

[32] Jonathan Arnold to Secretary, Staten Island, New York, June 18, 1742, in S.P.G. MSS., B9–10, fpp. 180–81; *id.* to *id.*, November 10, 1742, *ibid.*, fpp. 183–84; *Diary of Joshua Hempstead*, 465.

going to the Public thro' our Press; and will thankfully receive any other Recipes or Instructions tending to cure that violent and present reigning Disorder, called the Whooping-Cough."[33]

The last of the South Carolina epidemics, which came only six years later, was naturally much milder than the preceding one. Chalmers, who had witnessed all three outbreaks and who referred to whooping cough as "that dangerous and obstinate complaint," maintained that it was not native to the Carolinas. The epidemics developed when the disease was imported into the colony and on each occasion, he said, "like most other contagious distempers, it did not spare any one, who had not passed through it before."[34]

Whooping cough was present in at least one northern colony in 1738, and in the New England and middle colonies in 1758–59 and 1765–66. Nathan Fiske of Brookfield, Massachusetts, noted in his diary in 1765: "No Sickness excepting Colds & the Chin or Whooping Cough prevails: This last Distemper began last Spring at Boston, & gradually spread over the Country among Children, to some of which it prov'd fatal."[35]

Following the epidemic in 1765–66 whooping cough made at least two other appearances in the colonies prior to the Revolution. In June, 1767, a Philadelphian noted that "one of our neighbr. children [is] dead of the Hooping Cough, almost all the Children in the neighbr-hood bad with it." Three or four years later the infection was again

[33] *South Carolina Gazette*, No. 1287, June 2, 1759; Mabel L. Webber (ed.), "Extracts from the Journal of Mrs. Ann Manigault, 1754–1781," in *South Carolina Historical and Genealogical Magazine*, XX (1919), 132.

[34] Chalmers, *Account of Weather and Diseases of South Carolina*, II, 161–62.

[35] Rev. Nathan Fiske Diary, December, 1765.

widespread in New England and also in Pennsylvania. Diarists in Brookfield and Sutton, Massachusetts, mentioned its presence, and both the *Massachusetts Gazette* and the *Pennsylvania Gazette* published "recipes" for its cure.[36]

Little else needs to be said about whooping cough. The very paucity of material relating to its outbreaks is in itself proof that the disorder aroused little apprehension, and it can be safely relegated to a very minor role among the epidemic diseases of the period.

Mumps, another childhood disease, followed a course similar to that of whooping cough. It appeared only rarely prior to the mid-eighteenth century and intensified its attacks as the colonial period drew to a close. At no time did it occasion any serious trouble. John Marshall was the first to take note of it. "I did not hear of any great matter which happened," he noted casually in his diary in May, 1699, "only we had severall sick with an unusual distemper called the mumps of which some weer bad. But none dyed, that I heard of." [37]

The observant Lionel Chalmers of South Carolina commented that while "serious Quinsies have been mentioned . . . in the years 1744 and 1768, a *quinsy* of that sort which is called the *mumps*, was epidemick amongst us; and it also appeared at other times, but not in so general a manner." [38]

The disease appeared sporadically in all the colonies after 1755 and affected both young and old. An outbreak in Brookfield, Massachusetts, first struck the children and

[36] Elizabeth Drinker's Diary, June 24, 1772; *Massachusetts Gazette and Boston Weekly News-Letter*, No. 3541, August 22, 1771; *Pennsylvania Gazette*, No. 2223, August 1, 1771; Caulfield, "Some Common Diseases of Colonial Children," *loc. cit.*, 38–40; David Hall Diary, May 26, August 18, 1771; Rev. Nathan Fiske Diary, August and November, 1771.

[37] "John Marshall's Diary," *loc. cit.*, 153.

[38] Chalmers, *Account of Weather and Diseases of South Carolina*, II, 99.

then attacked adults, bringing death to several of the latter. In 1767 a similar outbreak in Sutton proved fatal to several young men.[39] Usually children were its chief victims, and even among these the disease rarely proved fatal. Apparently mumps was no stranger to the colonies, but it was inconsequential in comparison with the more virulent epidemic sicknesses of the period.

[39] Rev. Nathan Fiske Diary, March–April, 1755; Diary of Benjamin Bangs, May 8, 1761; David Hall Diary, January 10, 1767.

CHAPTER VI

Respiratory Diseases

In an age when the advantages of fresh air and cleanliness were appreciated by only a few and when dietary deficiencies were the order of the day, it is not to be wondered that the so-called "winter diseases" exacted a heavy toll. The combination of poor food, drafty and badly ventilated houses, and overcrowded housing provided a perfect setting for the development of respiratory infections. Along with ague and fluxes, "pleuritic disorders" were among the chief complaints listed by the S.P.G. missionaries, who blamed their misfortunes on constant exposure to all sorts of weather. However, under colonial conditions exposure to weather was by no means limited to missionaries and ministers, and the sickness among this group only reflects what was undoubtedly the general health conditions of the colonial population.

The problem of diagnosis is particularly difficult in the case of pulmonary disorders. Terms such as pleurisy or "pleuretical disorders" were catch-all phrases for all respiratory diseases. Colonial records are replete with notations of epidemic sicknesses called "pleuretical disorders," "pleurisies," or "peripneumonies," and fatal illnesses were frequently described as "a kind of Pleurisy," or "a sort of Pestilential Pluriticle feaver." Certainly various forms of pneumonia must have reached epidemic proportions on many occasions among a population undernourished from a restricted winter diet.

The definitions of the three main respiratory disorders of this period are all general enough to include a wide range of sicknesses. Though its varied symptoms have led one medical authority to conclude that it is easier to define influenza by stating what it is not, it is a respiratory disease occurring in successive waves. A prolonged debility and nervous depression usually follow an attack, and not infrequently it paves the way for other infections. Pneumonia is a medical term used for an inflammation of the lung itself. Pleurisy refers to an inflammation of or affecting the pleura—the membrane lining of the lungs. Using contemporary colonial descriptions, it is almost impossible for the present-day reader to distinguish between attacks of pneumonia, pleurisy, or influenza, though attacks of the latter usually were common enough for reasonable identification.

Complaints of respiratory disorders were heard from the colonies within a score of years after the first settlement was made. A Virginia report of 1623 explained that "People being enforced to a Continuall wading and wetting of themselves about ye landing of their goods, get such violent surfetts of cold uppon cold as seldome leave them untill they leave to live"; and another colonist wrote of the same year that a "pestilent fever rageth this winter amongst us." Though Blanton classified this outbreak and another "winter fever" in 1635 as respiratory diseases,[1] they may have been something else. "Winter fevers" was a broad term, and many disorders throve in the unsanitary and overcrowded living accommodations of the settlers.

[1] A true answer to a writing of Information presented to his M^{ty} by Capt. Nath. Butler, transcript in Sloane MSS., Vol. 1039, f 92, Library of Congress; Blanton, *Medicine in Virginia in the Seventeenth Century*, 55–56.

The first recorded influenza epidemic in North America occurred in 1647, when John Winthrop recorded:

> An epidemical sickness was through the country among the Indians and English, French and Dutch. It took them like a cold, and light fever with it. Such as bled or used cooling drinks died; those who took comfortable things, for the most part recovered, and that in a few days. Wherein a special providence of God appeared, for not a family, nor but few persons escaping it, had it brought all so weak as it brought some, and continued so long, our hay and corn had been lost for want of help; but such was the mercy of God to his people, as few died, not above forty or fifty in the Massachusetts, and near as many at Connecticut.

John Eliot described the epidemic as "a very depe cold, with some tincture of a feaver & full of malignity & very dangerous if not well regarded by keeping a low diet." In addition to sweeping through the colonies on the mainland, the outbreak extended to the West Indies, where it struck with great severity. An estimated five to six thousand deaths occurred on the islands of St. Christopher and Barbados.[2]

Eight years later an "epidemic catarrh" accompanied by a faint cough passed through New England. In May, 1665, the Reverend Samuel Danforth of Roxbury, Massachusetts, recorded that "God sent an Epidemicall sickness & faintness: few escaped, many were very sick, [and] severall dyed." The mildness of the attack is indicated by the scant attention paid to it by other chroniclers. A similar outbreak occurred in the winter of 1660–61 when John Hull

[2] John Winthrop, *The History of New England from 1630 to 1650*, 2 vols. (Boston, 1825–26), II, 310; Packard, *History of Medicine*, I, 96; Ebenezer Hazard MSS., I, Library of Congress; Webster, *History of Epidemic Diseases*, I, 188; "History of New England," in Massachusetts Historical Society *Collections*, Ser. 2, VI (1817), 531–32.

wrote that "the Lord was pleased to chasten his people with an epidemical cold, which seized not only upon every town, but almost upon every person, though upon the most gently." [3] A few fatalities occurred but these came primarily from a fever and ague which accompanied the cold.

In 1675 influenza was general in Western Europe and may have spread to America, for a "general catarrh" swept the colonies in that year. The following winter the sickness invaded Canada. Father Rafaix, a Jesuit missionary among the Iroquois Indians, mentioned "a general influenza with which God has Chastized those barbarians, and which in one month Carried off more than 60 little children." The disorder was not restricted to children, however, for Father Rafaix added that many adults also had died from the pestilence.[4] He specifically used the term influenza, a common expression in Italy and France long before its adoption by the English.

Massachusetts endured an outbreak of severe "epidemical colds" during the winter of 1678–79. Increase Mather noted that these colds began in October, 1678, and continued throughout the winter. When spring finally brought a cessation of the illness, a public thanksgiving was held in Boston.[5]

An influenza outbreak in England and Ireland in 1688 may have spread to Virginia, for an entry in the Ludwell Papers dated April 19, 1688, noted that a fast was ob-

[3] Webster, *History of Epidemic Diseases*, I, 189; "Rev. Samuel Danforth's Records of the First Church of Roxbury, Mass.," *loc. cit.*, 86; "Diary of John Hull," *loc. cit.*, 197–98.

[4] Creighton, *History of Epidemics*, II, 326–28; Blanton, *Medicine in Virginia in the Seventeenth Century*, 57; Webster, *History of Epidemic Diseases*, I, 203; "Of the Iroquois Missions in the Year 1676." *Jesuit Relations*, LX, 175.

[5] "Diary of Increase Mather," in Massachusetts Historical Society *Proceedings*, XXXIII (1899–1900), 406–407.

served "for ye great mortality" arising from "the Winter distemper." The outbreak was so serious that "the people dyed . . . as in a plague." The local physicians found a remedy in bleeding and evidently they applied the lancet with enthusiasm since "Ld. Howard had 80 ounces taken from him." [6] His survival indicates a mild infection or an admirable constitution—probably both. This Virginia attack does not seem to have affected any of the other colonies.

After a lapse of ten years influenza reappeared, this time in New England. It began in November, 1697, and continued to February, 1698. Boston apparently did not feel the effects of the outbreak until the end of December, when "people in many towns and places began to fall sick of a sore cold attended with a cough and feaver which proved mortal to some." January, 1699, was unusually cold, and "the sickness . . . extended to allmost all familys. Few or none escaped, and many dyed[,] especially in Boston, and some dyed in a strange and unusual manner, in some familys all weer sick together, in some townes allmost all weer sick so that it was a time of distress." Cotton Mather, who was confined to his room for a month, declared that no "man living [can] remember such a time as was hereby brought upon us." [7] Daniel Fairfield of Braintree, Massachusetts, also noted the outbreak and was particularly impressed with the virulence of the disease in certain localities. In Fairfield, Connecticut, one of the towns suffering heavily, seventy persons out of a population of below one thousand died in less than three months.[8]

[6] Creighton, *History of Epidemics*, II, 335–37; "Ludwell Papers," in *Virginia Magazine of History and Biography*, V (1897), 61.

[7] "John Marshall's Diary," *loc. cit.*, 152; *Diary of Cotton Mather*, *loc. cit.* (1681–1708), 247.

[8] Daniel Fairfield, quoted in Webster, *History of Epidemic Diseases*, I, 210.

Eleven years later a "mortal sickness," described as a species of "putrid pleurisy," prevailed in Waterbury, Connecticut, for eleven months; the malady "was so general that nurses could scarcely be found for the sick." Cotton Mather, in his Christmas Eve sermon, told his congregation in dismay that "there has been this Winter, and since our Snow began to fall, . . . a cry raised by the King of Terrors walking his dismal Round thro' the Colony of Connecticut." On March 31, 1712, the Boston *News-Letter* corrected a false impression. "By Misinformation we were lately told," wrote the editor, "that the Distemper in Connecticut had carried off 700 Persons; but [by] last Post from a good hand we are well assured through God's Goodness, that the Distemper carried not off above 250, besides some that Dyed of other Distempers." [9]

Although the northern colonies had the major share of respiratory disorders, those to the south were by no means exempt. In March, 1709, Robert Maule, an S.P.G. missionary in South Carolina, observed that the province was "so very subject to sudden Changes and alterations of Weather as occasions great Colds, and Indispositions, and these frequently terminate in dangerous effects." Prominent among the sicknesses devastating Charleston in 1711 and 1712 were the so-called "Pleurisies," which, according to Thomas Hassell, one of the missionaries, had "proved very Mortall among us & carryed off abundance of our inhabitants." [10] On December 27, 1716, Hassell reported that the clergy

[9] Webster, *History of Epidemic Diseases*, I, 223; Cotton Mather, *Seasonable Thoughts upon Mortality* . . . (Boston, 1712); Boston *News-Letter*, No. 405, January 14–21, 1712.

[10] Robert Maule to Secretary, South Carolina, March 6, 1709, in S.P.G. MSS., A4, fpp. 381–84; Gideon Johnston to Secretary, South Carolina, November 16, 1711, *ibid.*, A7, fpp. 466–77; Thomas Hassell to Secretary, St. Thomas, S. C., March 12, 1712, *ibid.*, A7, fpp. 498–501.

were still unable to meet because of the prevailing sickness. William Bull, one of the few S.P.G. missionaries who seems to have enjoyed perfect health for some years after his arrival in South Carolina, finally caught a "violent cold" in October, 1718, which, he said, "well nigh put an end to my life." [11]

Two years later the Boston *News-Letter* reported that it was a "sickly" time in Virginia and that many persons were dying "of a Fever with a pain in their Side and Breast." [12] Obviously, respiratory disorders played no small part in the sickness and death in the Southern colonies.

The next recorded epidemics of pulmonary diseases occurred in New Jersey and Connecticut in 1728–29. An attack of "pleurisy" struck Penn's Neck, New Jersey, in 1728, and one account states that nearly all the Swedish colonists in the settlement died. Early in the following year John Holbrook, S.P.G. missionary at Salem, New Jersey, wrote the Society that the community had "had a Sickness this Winter (a kind of Pleurisy) that has Carried off a great Number of People & among others one Mr. Windruva a Swedish Missionary that lives not far from me, who died about the beginning of November." Farmington, Connecticut, another town which suffered severe losses at this time, also reported an outbreak of "malignant pleurisy" in 1729.[13] Possibly the illness may have been general in both provinces during the winter of 1728–29, but no record was made except in those towns where the mortality rate was exceptionally high.

[11] Thomas Hassell to Secretary, St. Thomas, S. C., December 27, 1716, *ibid.*, B4, Pt. 1, fp. 323; William T. Bull to Secretary, St. Paul's, S. C., January 3, 1719, *ibid.*, Pkg. VI, American Colonies, No. 6, 1713–1829, fp. 259.

[12] Boston *News-Letter*, No. 830, March 7–14, 1720.

[13] Currie, *An Account of Climates and Diseases*, 103 n.; Wickes, *History of Medicine in New Jersey*, 20; John Holbrook to Secretary, Salem,

This same winter some type of respiratory infection prevailed in South Carolina. The Reverend Francis Varnod declared in April, 1728, that there had been a "great mortality" among the Negroes, which had resulted from "a sort of Pestilential pluriticle feaver." William Day, executor of the estate of the Reverend Richard Ludlam, reported a similar sickness there the following winter. Day, who was responsible for the sale of the Negroes belonging to the estate, was forced to assume the role of doctor on many occasions and apparently was quite familiar with the medical practices of his time. He recorded in his journal on December 11, 1728, that two of the Negroes were very ill with "great Colds." A month later he wrote:

> Having lost two of my own Negroe men this week (with the inflammation of ye Lungs with Scarce any feaver & the blood no ways Pleuritick) & having four or five Negroes now down with it, two of which belongs to the Estate of the Deceased, & others daily falling down am obliged to make use of a Doctor, yt Distemper being now very Mortal amongst both whites & blacks by reason of its different ways of Seizing People & its being so flattening Scarce two being affected alike, & with most all, bleeding which Sydenham prescribes first is here found pernicious, unless the Patient be also vomited, either before or immediately after bleeding.[14]

The Ludlam Negroes underwent the usual rigorous treatment of bleeding, vomiting, purging, and sweating, and Day took full credit for all who survived this cure.

Between 1729 and 1733, influenza had a world-wide distribution, and certainly by 1732–33 the disorder was

---

New Jersey, February 12, 1729, in S.P.G. MSS., A21, fp. 285; Webster, *History of Epidemic Diseases*, I, 230.

[14] Francis Varnod to Secretary, St. George's, S. C., April 3, 1728, in S.P.G. MSS., A21, fp. 63; Journal of William Day, St. James, Goose Creek, S. C., December 11, 1728, *ibid.*, B1, Pt. 2, fpp. 652–53; *ibid.*, January 3, 1729, fpp. 676–77.

general in America. This particular outbreak was said to have begun in North Germany and spread into every country in Europe, subsequently arriving in North America in the fall of 1733.[15] Actually, the infection struck America concurrently with a severe outbreak in England in the winter of 1732–33. It was to this attack that Dr. John Huxham first applied the Italian name of influenza, thus introducing the expression into the English medical terminology.[16]

The first evidence of the new outbreak in America appeared in the Boston *Weekly News-Letter* which noted editorially in October, 1732 that "we hardly ever had a more General Visitation by Colds than now, abundance being confined by reason thereof, and we hear it prevails greatly in the Towns all along to the Eastward, even as far as Casco, few Persons escaping it; tho' we hear the Towns to the Southward, are pretty free from it." A few weeks later, a correspondent in Ipswich reported to the *News-Letter* that "the people here have been almost universally afflicted with the Cold & Cough which has chiefly proved mortal to the Aged among us for within less than a Month, seventeen grown persons have died in the town, among whom were many of the most ancient founders." [17]

[15] Eugene P. Campbell, "The Epidemiology of Influenza," in *Bulletin of the History of Medicine*, XIII (1943), 402–403; Currie, *An Account of Climates and Diseases*, 100–101; Webster, *History of Epidemic Diseases*, I, 232. Webster gives the correct date, 1732. In the *London Medical Journal*, III (1783), 152, an article by a Boston physician describes an outbreak of "epidemic catarrhs" in North America during 1731, but he probably meant the outbreak in 1732.

[16] Campbell, "The Epidemiology of Influenza," *loc. cit.*, 393–94. J. F. Townsend, "History of Influenza Epidemics," in *Annals of Medical History*, N. S., V (1933), 540, claimed that the first use of the word influenza occurred in a 1767 translation from the Latin of Huxham's *De aere et morbus epidemicis*.

[17] Boston *Weekly News-Letter*, No. 1497, September 28–October 5, No. 1500, October 19–26, 1732.

In November reports from New York and Philadelphia showed that similar conditions were prevailing. "The Colds which have infected the Northern Colonies," wrote a Philadelphia correspondent, "have also been troublesome here, few Families having escaped. . . ." A journalist noted of the winter of 1732 that "many people were taken with colds, and many died in both the provinces of New Jersey and Pennsylvania."[18]

In March, 1734, the Reverend Walter Hackett of Newcastle, Delaware, succumbed to what a colleague described as "violent Plurisy." George Ross, another missionary, attributed Hackett's death to his "being seized with a pleurisy a few days before, in his full Strength and vigour. This distemper proved Mortall to many in his parish this last Winter as well as to him." Apparently the southern colonies remained unaffected by the 1732–34 outbreak for the *South Carolina Gazette* reprinted one or two news stories of the epidemic in New England but made no mention of a like attack in South Carolina.[19]

A light influenza attack in 1737 proved as extensive as the one of four years earlier. It began simultaneously on the Continent, in England, Ireland, and the colonies but was milder than the preceding outbreak. The epidemic began in Europe and America in November, but the only specific reference to a respiratory infection in the colonies at this time was made by Thomas Smith of Falmouth,

[18] Benjamin Rush to William Currie, October 7, 1791, in Currie, *An Account of the Climates and Diseases*, 103n.; *American Weekly Mercury*, No. 674, November 23–30, 1732; *A Journal of the Life and Travels of Thomas Chalkley*, 362.

[19] Archibald Cummings to Secretary, Philadelphia, March 22, 1734, in S.P.G. MSS., A25, fp. 238; George Ross to Secretary, Newcastle, Pa., March 22, 1734, *ibid.*, A24, fp. 304; *South Carolina Gazette*, No. 47, December 9, 1732.

Massachusetts, who recorded on November 26, 1737, that "the pleurisy fever prevails and has proved mortal to several in North Yarmouth." Two weeks later he added the statement that "All that had the pleuretic fever have died of it save one." [20]

The exceptionally high fatality rate and the limited area affected by this disease precludes the possibility of influenza. More than likely some form of pneumonia was the source of trouble. It is odd that so little information on the effect of the influenza attack is available. However, the chief criteria by which the American colonists judged an epidemic was the number of ensuing fatalities, and a mild illness, no matter how extensive, was likely to be overlooked. Possibly a more important factor in the obscuring of the influenza attack of 1737 was the rise of diphtheria, which wrought such devastation among colonial children that all attention was riveted upon it.

Beginning in 1747 a series of pulmonary attacks struck various sections of the colonies and culminated in 1749–50 in a widespread epidemic. A surprising number of S.P.G. missionaries fell ill with "pleuretic disorders" in these years, and their correspondence shows the prevalence of the sickness. Late in March, 1747, the Reverend Philip Reading of Apoquiniminck, Pennsylvania, wrote the Society that "the Congregation of St. Anne's at Apoquiniminck, and the Chapel of St. George, have since Autumn last, suffered much by a raging Pleurisy which attacked and proved mortal to many of our members: particularly two successive Church-wardens, four Vestrymen, with others of inferior note, constant and zealous Churchmen, died after a short fit of illness." In June, 1748, missionary Thomas

[20] Creighton, *History of Epidemics*, II, 348–49; Webster, *History of Epidemic Diseases*, I, 235; Willis (ed.), *Journals of Smith and Deane*, 88.

Bluett in Delaware reported that much sickness in his family had resulted in the loss of his youngest child, and that he himself had been sick with "a Violent fit of pleurisie." [21]

The cold months of 1748–49 saw winter sicknesses rampant from South Carolina to Massachusetts. From Narragansett, Massachusetts, the Reverend James Macsparran advised that he had been "seized (among many others) with an Epidemical Distemper," which had kept him from his work for almost a month. A "very mortal pluritick fever" struck three other Massachusetts towns, Truro, Billingsgate, and Plymouth. On Long Island a "malignant pleurisy" worked its way through the population and influenza was epidemic in Elizabeth Town, New Jersey, as well. Two ministers, one at Philadelphia and the other in Lewes, Pennsylvania, informed the Society that they were recovering from severe attacks of "pleurisy." [22]

The Carolinas, too, were affected by these "winter diseases." A respiratory infection resulted in many deaths in Edenton, North Carolina, and left the local S.P.G. missionary in shattered health. From Charleston another minister reported that a severe cold had incapacitated him for over two months.[23]

[21] Philip Reading to Secretary, Apoquiniminck, Pa., March 26, 1747, in S.P.G. MSS., B15, fp. 258; Thomas Bluett to Secretary, Dover in Kent, Del., June 26, 1748, *ibid.*, B16, fp. 255.

[22] James Macsparran to Secretary, Narragansett, New England, January 10, 1749, *ibid.*, B16, fp. 76; Robert Jenney to Secretary, Philadelphia, October 26, 1748, *ibid.*, B17, fp. 332; Arthur Ussher to Secretary, Lewes, Pa., March 26, 1750, *ibid.*, B18, fp. 403; Diary of Benjamin Bangs, January 15, 1749; James Thacher, *American Medical Biography, or Memoirs of Eminent Physicians who have Flourished in America*, 2 vols. in one (Boston, 1828), 52; Benjamin Rush to William Currie, October 7, 1791, in Currie, *An Account of Climates and Diseases*, 103 n.

[23] Clement Hall to Secretary, Edenton, N. C., January 3, 1749, in S.P.G. MSS., B16, fp. 304; Richard St. John to Secretary, Charleston, S. C., February 4, 1749, *ibid.*, B16, fpp. 347–48.

The middle and southern colonies were ravaged by disease the following winter of 1749–50. The *Pennsylvania Gazette* reported hearing "from several parts of the country, of a sickness, which some call the *Winter Fever*, that carries off great numbers. It has been very rife in *Cecil* county, *St. Mary's* county, and on *Kent-Island*: in which last mentioned place, near 40 people have died in a short time." On January 26, 1750, a correspondent in western Virginia wrote that " 'We have had a very severe winter, and a very great mortality among the people: whole families dying almost at the same time.' "[24]

As the spring wore on in New York province Samuel Seabury wrote from Hempstead that among "the little flock at Huntington, their losses have been very Great, by an Epidemic mortal Disease, which thro' the last Winter among many others, Carried off Sundry of the most considerable members of that little Church." "Pleurisies" were among the various illnesses assailing the congregation of an S.P.G. minister at Goose Creek, South Carolina, who wrote of his flock in 1750: "Pleurisies seize them after different Manners. The Pain fixes in some, over ye Eye. In others in ye Side of the Head, and ye like in ye Leg or Arm, which has carried off a great Many Blacks, & Many Whites."[25]

Respiratory infections continued to plague the colonies for the next two or three years. A "pleuritic fever" took many lives at Biddeford, Massachusetts, in January, 1752, and the Reverend Samuel Auchmuty wrote from New York in March of the same year that his health had suffered from a "great cold" caught during the winter. A year later Alexander Colden informed his father that his family in New

[24] *Pennsylvania Gazette*, No. 1105, February 13, 1750.

[25] Samuel Seabury to Secretary, Hempstead, N. Y., March 26, 1750, in S.P.G. MSS., B18, fp. 287; Robert Stone to Secretary, St. James, Goose Creek, S. C., March 22, 1751, *ibid.*, B18, fpp. 459–60.

York City was also sick with "great colds which are common in town." [26]

Some form of pneumonia exacted a heavy toll in the town of Holliston, Massachusetts, in the winter of 1753–54. The pestilence, which ran its course in December and January, was characterized by a high fever, violent pains in the breast, head, or side, and a high mortality—death usually ensuing within three to six days. Of the town's population of about 400 persons, 53 died within 6 weeks. "The sickness was so prevalent, that but few families escaped: for more than a month, there was not enough well to tend the sick, and bury the dead, though they spent their whole time in these services; but the sick suffered and the dead lay unburied; and that notwithstanding help was procured, and charitable assistance afforded, by many in neighboring towns." In many instances the patients appeared to strangle from an inability to expectorate, although among this group, some who had been given up for lost, were saved by "administering oil." [27]

A general outbreak of influenza may have swept through America in either 1757 or 1758, though the evidence of it is limited. In November and December of 1760 a serious pneumonia outbreak of some sort scourged Bethlehem, Connecticut. The victims were "first taken with a Cold, and then a malignant Plurisy set in [which] soon carried them off." The local physician, his wife and two

[26] Willis (ed.), *Journals of Smith and Deane*, 147; Samuel Auchmuty to Secretary, New York, March 26, 1752, in S.P.G. MSS., B20, fp. 138; Alexander Colden to Cadwallader Colden, New York, November 7, 1753, in *Colden Papers*, IX (1937), 134.

[27] "Description of the Town of Holliston," in Massachusetts Historical Society *Collections*, Ser. 1, III (1794), 19; Webster, *History of Epidemic Diseases*, I, 244, claimed that the number of deaths was forty-three instead of fifty-three; Hayward, *Gazetteer of Massachusetts*, 176–77.

children, and a young man staying at his house all died within a short period. The infection around the doctor's house was so great, a neighbor noticed, that when eleven quail alighted in the garden, eight of them immediately died![28]

Influenza definitely broke out in North America in 1761. According to Dr. Thomas Bond, who witnessed the outbreak, it was traced from the West Indies to Halifax, Nova Scotia, where it appeared in the spring. It soon reached Boston and the adjacent countryside, and then spread rapidly through all continental North America "till the month of July, after which it was no more heard of." In the same year Dr. Rush noted its presence in Philadelphia, but, like Bond, he gave no indication of its effect upon the inhabitants.[29]

Many complaints of influenza came from the provincial troops in 1760 and 1761, although this illness was only one of many diseases ravaging the armies. Other evidences of the influenza outbreak are found in the accounts of "epidemical colds." Robert McKean, an S.P.G. missionary in New Brunswick, New Jersey, reported to the Society in October, 1761, that he was just recovering from "an Epidemical Cold," which had affected many in the town. Two months later the Reverend Colin Campbell wrote from Burlington that "many of the old people have died in a manner suddenly by violent pleuretick disorders occasioned by Sudden alterations of the weather here; which runs upon extreams of heats and Cold." Shortly afterwards

[28] Campbell, "The Epidemiology of Influenza," *loc. cit.*, 402–403; Webster, *History of Epidemic Diseases*, I, 246; *Green and Russell's Boston Post Boy and Advertiser*, No. 174, December 15, 1760.

[29] Webster, *History of Epidemic Diseases*, I, 250; Currie, *An Account of Climates and Diseases*, 100–101; Rush, *Medical Inquiries*, 2d. ed., IV, 372.

Campbell himself caught a severe cold which, he said, "well nigh put a period to my life." [30]

Additional reports of the disorder came from a number of localities in Pennsylvania. By spring it had reached Massachusetts, where it was observed and recorded by Dr. Cotton Tufts of Weymouth.[31]

In the latter part of January, 1764, Newport, Rhode Island was affected by some sort of respiratory infection that continued "from January 20 to 30 inclusive 1764 . . . ;" during this period "14 persons [died], of which 6 were buried Feb/ry 1. A nervous pleuretic Disorder being epidemic." [32] The account gives no indication of the exact nature of the infection nor of the case mortality, although the use of the adjective "nervous" may point to influenza.

A recent study of influenza epidemics maintains that the disease reached epidemic proportions in Europe and America in 1767. However, the outbreak in England was so unimportant that it scarcely shows in the London Bills of Mortality and would have been completely forgotten had it not been for a short essay written by an eminent contemporary English physician. A mild attack may have occurred in America, but no indication of it has been found. On the other hand, there is definite proof of influenza in the colonies from 1770 to 1772. In the winter of 1770–71 Philadelphia was ravaged by an influenza epidemic, "An account of which I have preserved in my notebook," wrote a contemporary physician, "and have found it to agree exactly

[30] Robert McKean to Secretary, New Brunswick, N. J., October 5, 1761, in S.P.G. MSS., B24, Pt. 2, fp. 785; Colin Campbell to Secretary, Burlington, N. J., December 26, 1761, *ibid.*, B24, Pt. 2, fp. 158; *id.* to *id.*, June 24, 1763, *ibid.*, B24, Pt. 1, fp. 170.

[31] Webster, *History of Epidemic Diseases*, I, 250.

[32] "Births and Deaths in Newport, R. I., 1760–1764," *loc. cit.*, LXIII (1909), 51.

with the histories of the Influenza in this and other countries." The following winter the malady was epidemic both in Europe and America, and on February 29, 1772, Dr. Cotton Tufts reported that an epidemic cold or catarrhal fever was general throughout Massachusetts.[33]

It is difficult to gauge with any degree of accuracy the effect of respiratory diseases upon the colonial population. Complete descriptions of the clinical symptoms for the hundreds of outbreaks simply do not exist, and even if they did, diagnosis would still involve much guesswork. Respiratory infections attacked on such a broad scale that no count of either the cases or fatalities was possible, but the deaths from any particular epidemic in a given locality did not compare in number with those resulting from smallpox or the other more violent disorders. Yet, influenza, colds, and pneumonia were far more prevalent than were the more fatal diseases. Pulmonary infections were a perennial problem and in the long run killed more than did the spectacular maladies. William Byrd in 1737 wrote of "Pleurisys" that they were "the most fatal of all Diseases in this Clymate amongst the Negros & Poor People." John Tennent in an essay on the pleurisy published in 1742 spoke of it as "being the most fatal Disease that affects the Constitution of the Inhabitants of this County." [34]

Pneumonia constantly weeded out the aged and the ailing. Exposure to weather and inadequate diet made even the most vigorous colonists susceptible to the many respira-

[33] Campbell, "The Epidemiology of Influenza," *loc. cit.*, 402–403; Creighton, *History of Epidemics*, II, 358; Benjamin Rush to William Currie, October 7, 1791, in Currie, *An Account of Climates and Diseases*, 103 n.; Webster, *History of Epidemic Diseases*, I, 258; "Diaries of Dr. Cotton Tufts," *loc. cit.*, 472.

[34] William Byrd to Sir Hans Sloane, Virginia, May 31, 1737; transcript in Sloane MSS., No. 4055, Library of Congress; John Tennent, *An Essay on the Pleurisy* (Williamsburg and New York, 1742), 3.

tory infections, and a contemporary noted that those living on a "fresh nourishing Diet" were not so subject to pleurisy as the "poorer sort of People or Negroes." [35]

The measurement of the economic cost of sickness in terms of lost man-hours is a recent development, but if such a scale could be applied to this period, the cost of pulmonary maladies would probably prove far higher than the more publicized epidemic diseases. Further, if adequate statistics were available, respiratory diseases undoubtedly would rank high on the list of fatal sicknesses which attacked the American colonists.

[35] Tennent, *An Essay on the Pleurisy*, 5.

CHAPTER VII

Agues, Fluxes, and Poxes

Fevers arrived with the early settlers and were a health menace during the entire colonial period. Of all sicknesses mentioned by the colonists, none can compare in frequency with fevers. Often the particular fever can be identified from the description, but in many instances this is impossible. Yellow fever, malaria, dysentery, typhoid, and typhus, which head the list of fevers, are all characterized by a high temperature, but this phenomenon unfortunately is not restricted solely to these disorders.

A survey of colonial records reveals that malaria and dysentery were endemic in all the colonies and that typhoid and typhus appeared occasionally. In the early colonial days malaria and dysentery were widespread in America, although both the incidence and the fatality rates were highest in the southern areas. Typhoid was more frequent in the northern settlements, and typhus troubled only the port cities to which it was brought by immigrant vessels.

The so-called "spotted fever," which may have been cerebrospinal meningitis, also appeared occasionally. Dover, New Hampshire, was subjected to an attack in the winter of 1697–98 of an infection that was described as a "species of inflammatory fever, attacking the brain and ending in typhus which has often proved a terrible scourge in particular parts of America."[1] This may have been nothing but typhus itself, however, for it was sometimes called "spotted fever" too; but neither typhus nor meningitis presented much of a problem in colonial days.

The earliest contemporary accounts reveal the destructiveness of fevers in the colonies. During the first year of the Jamestown settlement, many settlers "were destroyed with cruel diseases, as swellings flixes, [and] burning fevers"[2]—mute evidence of the inadequate diet, and of the presence of dysentery and typhoid.

Two generations later, following the British acquisition of New York, Samuel Maverick wrote Colonel Nicholls that "the flux, agues, and fevers, have much rained both in cittie and country, & many dead, but not yet soe many as last yeare. The like is all N. Engld. over, especially about Boston, where have dyed verry many." A traveler who arrived in Boston in 1671 found "the Inhabitants exceedingly afflicted with griping of the guts, and feaver and Ague, and bloody Flux."[3]

In Virginia, a century after the first settlement was made, European arrivals were still subject to "Fevers, and Agues, the Gripes, and Fluxes [which] are the most common Distempers here, as in the rest of the British Plantations." Nor were the fevers restricted to the warmer climate of the southern colonies. Even in New York, "the months of July Aug. & beginning of September [were] the most sickly months in the year more people being sick

[1] Webster, *History of Epidemic Diseases,* I, 210; Packard, *History of Medicine,* I, 104.

[2] Alexander Brown, *The Genesis of the United States,* 2 vols. (Boston and New York, 1890), I, 168.

[3] [Samuel] Maverick to Col. Nicholls, New York, October 15, 1669, in O'Callaghan (ed.), *Documents Relative to Colonial History,* III (1853), 185; Samuel Abbott Green, *History of Medicine in Massachusetts* (Boston, 1881), 44–45.

and more children dying than in all the rest of the year. The epidemical Diseases [were] intermitting Fevers, Cholera Morbus & Fluxes." But, though "the intermitting Fevers [were] not near so frequent in this Province as in those more to ye Southward, . . . Fluxes [were] more frequent . . . than in Philadelphia." Shortly before the Revolution, "intermittant, nervous, putrid and bilious fevers [were] common in [South Carolina and Georgia], and [proved] fatal to many . . . inhabitants. Young children [were] very subject to worm-fever, which [cut] off multitudes of them." [4]

Malaria

Contemporary accounts of malaria make it one of the most easily identifiable fevers, for the regular alternations of fever and chills early gave the name fever and ague, or intermitting fever, to this debilitating sickness. Different forms of malaria were distinguished by such descriptive appellations as quartan and tertian ague. The infection was no stranger to Europeans: it had long existed both on the Continent and in England, and in the latter country was widely known in the seventeenth century as the Kentish disorder.

In an area inhabited by both the malarial mosquitoes and an infected population, malaria is endemic and flares up annually to epidemic proportions. A seasonal wave of the disease seems to recur every spring and fall without

[4] Thomas Salmon, *Modern History, or Present State of All Nations*, 4 vols. on America (London, 1736–38), XXX, 338; "Cadwallader Colden's Account of the Climate of New York," in O'Callaghan (ed.), *Documents Relative to Colonial History*, V (1855), 692; Carroll (ed.), *Historical Collections of South Carolina*, I, 383.

apparent cause.[5] The term "pernicious malaria" is applied to outbreaks of especial virulence, and undoubtedly many of the severe fever epidemics during the colonial period were in fact this virulent form of malaria.

Like yellow fever, malaria is transmitted by a specific mosquito—a discovery not made until the beginning of the twentieth century. The connection between swampy, low-lying land and fever and ague was widely recognized in the sixteenth and seventeenth centuries; but it led to the development of the erroneous miasmic theory, which maintained that a putrid exhalation arising from stagnant water brought fever to those dwelling in the vicinity.

In the Dutch and French settlements in America malaria took its annual toll. As early as 1659 the vice-director of the Dutch colonies complained that he had been confined to bed for two or three months with a tertian ague. At a Jesuit mission in Canada a malignant fever attacked both whites and Indians in 1684, and "Only one or two of all those who accompanied monsieur the General escaped the attack of a malignant fever, which [kept] all others . . . dangerously sick." The unfortunate Indians pledged all their possessions "in order to have some clothes to cover them in the ague-chill of their fever." There is evidence that the other missions were similarly affected. In this same year, a French envoy to the Five Nations reported that on his arrival at the mission of La Famine, he had "found there tertian and double tertian fever, which broke out among our people, so that more than one hundred and fifty men were attacked by it." [6] The evidences of malaria in 1684

[5] Clifford Allchin Gill, *Seasonal Periodicity of Malaria and the Mechanism of the Epidemic Wave* (London, 1938).

[6] Vice-Director J. Alrichs to the Commissioners of the Colonies on the Delaware River, New York, December 12, 1659, in O'Callaghan (ed.), *Documents Relative to Colonial History,* II (1858), 113; "M. de la Barre's

indicates that the infection was well entrenched in French Canada by this date.

Either the French carried malaria into the Mississippi Valley or the region was already infested with it, for Father Jacques Gravier, who traveled from Illinois to the mouth of the Mississippi River in 1700–1701, frequently spoke of it in his journal. On one occasion, he related, several cases of tertian fever among his companions were cured by means of religious relics. In 1708 he reported that quartan fever was prevalent in Fort St. Louis.[7]

Whether malaria was indigenous to North America or imported from Europe and Africa[8] is still debatable. It was one of the most common complaints in all the English colonies; in most of them its virulence appeared to increase as the eighteenth century progressed except for New England, where the disease steadily diminished and practically disappeared before the Revolution.

Nonetheless, attacks of pernicious malaria in seventeenth-century New England frequently were fatal. A Boston diarist observed in September, 1658, that there was "much sickness in the southern colonies [southern New England],—fevers and agues, of which many died." "In July August and September," wrote Simon Bradstreet of Connecticut in 1668, "these western pts. of the Country wr very sickly, though it pleased god not many dyed. The genll distemper was feaver and ague." A Harvard student in 1683 commented on the death of a fellow student, who

proceedings with the Five Nations," *ibid.*, IX (1855), 242; Jacques Bigot, "Journal of what occurred in the Abnaquis Mission from the feast of Christmas, 1683, until October 6, 1684," *Jesuit Relations*, LXIII, 81, 87.

[7] "Journal of the Voyage of Father Gravier," *Jesuit Relations*, LXV, 103, 105–107; "Father Jacques Gravier upon the Affairs of Louisiana," *ibid.*, LXVI, 125.

[8] Carter, *Yellow Fever*, 69. Carter claims that malaria was brought to the Western Hemisphere by Europeans.

"died at Salem of ye Feaver at [a] time [when] many were visited with ye feaver and ague which was very mortal." Malaria's capacity for disrupting economic life is indicated by a Boston news report in September, 1690, which declared: "Epidemical Fevers and Agues grow very common, in some parts of the Country, whereof, tho' many dye not, yet they are sorely unfitted for their imployments." [9]

Its endemic nature and recurrent epidemic outbreaks make it impossible to trace successive waves of infection. Time and again the presence of intermitting fever, or fever and ague, is noted by contemporary writers, and it is evident that to most colonists the spring and fall flare-ups of malaria were as inevitable as the seasons themselves.

In 1687 the Reverend John Clayton of Virginia listed intermitting fever first among the diseases attacking the English natives, while another member of the colony wrote that his sister, having had two or three fits of fever and ague, felt that her "seasoning" was now well over.[10] It has been claimed that Virginia was relatively free of malaria in the seventeenth century, but in view of its widespread distribution, this assertion seems doubtful.[11]

[9] "Diary of John Hull," *loc. cit.*, 184; "[Simon] Bradstreet's Journal," *loc. cit.*, 44; "Diary of Noadiah Russell," in *New England Historical and Genealogical Register*, VII (1853), 59; Paltsits, "New Light on Publick Occurrences, America's First Newspaper," *loc. cit.*, 80 ff.

[10] John Clayton to Secretary, Virginia, 1687, in *Philosophical Transactions*, XLI (1739–40), Pt. 1, 143–62; Letter to Capt. Henry Fitzhugh, July 18, 1687, in *Virginia Magazine of History and Biography*, II (1895), 141.

[11] Blanton, *Medicine in Virginia in the Seventeenth Century*, 54–55, asserted that malaria did not constitute a serious problem in seventeenth-century Virginia and laid the blame for most of the summer fevers upon typhoid. Childs, *Malaria in the Carolina Low Country*, 30, declared that the contagion was highly epidemic in tidewater Virginia. Malaria was endemic in many sections of Europe and in the English and the French settlements to the north of Virginia. Under these circumstances it is highly improbable that the early settlers in Virginia were exempt from this hazard.

In eighteenth-century Virginia, malaria was a constant threat, but the victims did not seem to find this especially remarkable. Most new arrivals were "subject to Feavers and Agues, which is the Country Distemper, a severe Fit of which (called a Seasoning) most expect sometime after their arrival." Hardly a diary or personal letter of the period fails to refer to this recurrent infection. "I am now & then troubled with ye fever & ague wch. is a very violent distemper here," wrote Scottish settler George Hume to his family in 1723, adding somewhat testily that "This place is only good for doctors & ministers who have good encouragement here." [12] Toward the end of the century, malaria was mentioned with increasing frequency—evidence of the growing extent of the disorder.

Fever and ague was also a perennial complaint among the S.P.G. missionaries, and a study of their letters during the eighteenth century clearly shows the infestation of parts of New Jersey, Pennsylvania, and New York. Fever and ague was "universal" in the southern section of New Jersey, and an itinerant missionary in Pennsylvania wrote to the Society in 1738 of the difficulties confronting him: ". . . as for ye Fever & Ague unless it be in ye Winter I very rarely ever want it." From Burlington, New Jersey, which seems to have experienced all manner of colonial ills, the Reverend John Talbot wrote a dispirited letter to the Society, regretting the loss of so many missionaries, one of whom was "baited to Death with Muscatoes & blood thirst Galhuppers which wou'd not let him rest night or day." A few years later one of Talbot's successors at Bur-

[12] Erskine Hume, "A Colonial Scottish Jacobite Family," in *Virginia Magazine of History and Biography*, XXXVIII (1930), 110; Hugh Jones, *Present State of Virginia*, quoted in Blanton, *Medicine in Virginia in the Eighteenth Century*, 66–67; Tom Jones to his wife, Virginia, September 12, 1736, in Jones Family Papers, Manuscript Division, Library of Congress.

lington requested permission to return home or be moved to another parish, explaining, ". . . for my wife and I are both of us reduced to Mere skeletons by being always liable to the ffever and Ague and Grips." [13]

From Staten Island, New York, another missionary apologized to the Society in 1709 for not writing sooner and explained that he had been "sick of a ffever and Ague, Spring, Summer, and ffall." To Robert Jenney of Rye, New York, repeated malaria attacks seemed sufficient cause to ask for a transfer to some other parish. "Ever since I came to this place," he lamented, "the Ague and fever has as duly attended me and my family (sometimes alltogether) as ye Summer has come and although at present (I thank God) I am very well yet as sure as Harvest shall come so assuredly I expect ye return of that troublesome Distemper." [14]

Sections of Pennsylvania and Delaware were among the major malarial trouble spots, and it is not surprising that Thomas Crawford, the first missionary sent to Dover, Delaware, fell ill immediately upon his arrival. In his first letter to the Society in 1705 he complained that "this is not only a Seasoning in ye Country, But Fever & Ague does every year seize ye Inhabitants of the place. When I was first taken with ye fever I was credibly informed that there was not a Family in all the shire, but that either ye whole or part was sick." [15]

[13] Wickes, *History of Medicine in New Jersey*, 20; William Lindsay to Secretary, Pennsylvania, November 21, 1738, in S.P.G. MSS., B7, Pt. 1, fp. 220; John Talbot to Secretary, Burlington, N. J., September 27, 1709, *ibid.*, A5, fpp. 99–102; Robert Walker to Secretary, Burlington, N. J., October 10, 1717, *ibid.*, A12, fpp. 316–17.

[14] Aneas Mackenzie to Secretary, Richmond County, N. Y., June 13, 1709, in S.P.G. MSS., A5, fpp. 58–61; Robert Jenney to Secretary, Rye, N. Y., May 6, 1725, *ibid.*, B1, Pt. 1, fp. 302.

[15] Thomas Crawford to Secretary, Burlington, N. J., November 7, 1705, in *ibid.*, A2, fpp. 258–59.

The case of Robert Sinclair, one of the ministers sent to Pennsylvania, is typical of many in the annals of the S.P.G. On arriving at New York in 1710 he forthwith caught "a ffever and Ague." Recovering, he proceeded to his parish in Newcastle, Pennsylvania, where he was again taken ill with malaria. Two years later, his health impaired by recurring attacks, he finally resigned.

Apoquiniminck in Pennsylvania was the undoing of nearly all S.P.G. missionaries who had the misfortune to be stationed there. One of the first reported to the Society that he had been seriously ill with the infection for two out of his first three years in the parish. In the following years repeated complaints of malaria came from Apoquiniminck and other Pennsylvania towns, and Philip Reading declared in 1746 that it was "the Epidemical Distemper of this Country." [16]

Malaria was omnipresent in the Carolinas. From 1709 to 1717 three missionaries reported serious illness from the disease, and all the S.P.G. men considered it a part of the "seasoning." There is poignant heroism in the letter of Thomas Newnam, who had brought his family to Edenton, North Carolina: "Since my last lettr. to you dated June ye 29th 1722 I & my little Family have laboured under a severe fitt of Sickness the Feaver & Ague commonly known by the name of the Seasonings incident to all new Comers here; it holding one from the beginning of August to the latter end of December made me incapable of performing my Duty as I could have wish'd; but by ye blessing of God we are all now perfectly recovered." Within six

[16] Robert Sinclair to Secretary, Philadelphia, July 21, 1710, *ibid.*, A5, fpp. 359–60; *id.* to *id.*, Newcastle, Pa., September 10, 1710, *ibid.*, A5, fpp. 451–52; Alexander Campbell to George Ross, Apoquiniminck, Pa., September 10, 1727, *ibid.*, A20, fp. 152; Philip Reading to Secretary, Apoquiniminck, Pa., November 14, 1746, *ibid.*, B14, fp. 250.

months, however, Newnam was dead—of "fever and ague."[17]

Letters from the Carolina ministers show that practically all suffered from recurring and disabling attacks. From 1738 to 1742 no less than six S.P.G. workers in South Carolina wrote to the Society of their severe illness from malaria. All stated they had been incapacitated for some months, and four of them requested permission to return home, one declaring he had been afflicted with the sickness every summer for seven years.[18]

With the passage of time, malaria seemed to increase in virulence in many sections of the country, and its ravages became a recurrent theme in the correspondence of the S.P.G. missionaries located in the middle and southern colonies. So deleterious were its effects on the missionary at Lewes, Pennsylvania, reported one of his colleagues, "that from a ruddy robust young man, he looks like one just risen from the Dead; & prays, for God's Sake, that he may be moved up to his Native Hills in Pennsylvania. Sussex on Delaware is as it were the Fens of Essex, & I fear till we get one born in the Place & naturalized to it, we shall have no stable Mission there." In 1771 the missionary at Apoquiniminck explained to the Society that the church construction was not progressing very well because "In the beginning of last September the workmen fell sick of intermitting fevers, the epidemical distemper of this country: and the autumnal season was so far advanced before they

[17] Thomas Newnam to Secretary, North Carolina, May 9, 1723, *ibid.*, B4, Pt. 1, fp. 23; Vestry of Eden Town, N. C., to Secretary, November 18, 1723, *ibid.*, A17, fpp. 74–75.

[18] The missionaries were Thomas Hassell, John Fordyce, Thomas Thompson, Levi Durand, and Timothy Millechamp; Thomas Thompson to Secretary, St. Bartholomew's, S. C., September 29, 1739, in S.P.G. MSS., B7, Pt. 2, fp. 607.

recovered, that the utmost they could do was lay the floor."[19]

Letters from missionaries in New York, Virginia, the Carolinas, and other colonies bear similar testimony, as do the journals of the Moravians in North Carolina. A committee of twenty Brethren met in 1766 to consider measures against the recurring fever, but the only suggestion offered was that bitter herbs or roots be added to their beer![20]

Peter Kalm, a Swedish scientist who spent fourteen years in colonial America but did not get south of New Jersey, discussed fever and ague with several residents of New York City and learned "that the disease was not so common in New York as in Pennsylvania, where ten were seized by it to one in the former province." His informants "were of the opinion that it was occasioned by the vapors arising from stagnant fresh water, from marshes, and from rivers, for which reason those provinces situated on the sea shore could not be so much affected by it." Most of the doctors, Kalm asserted, held to the view that putrid standing water was the source of infection, a view with which Kalm agreed.[21]

Lord Adam Gordon, an English army officer who journeyed through the colonies in 1764–65, observed that though malaria was prevalent in the Carolinas, Charleston was relatively free of the disorder. The townspeople attributed this "to the air being mended by the Number of Fires in Town, as much as to its cool Situation, on a point,

[19] William Smith to Secretary, Philadelphia, October 22, 1768, *ibid.*, B21, fp. 711; Philip Reading to Secretary, Apoquiniminck, Pa., March 27, 1771, *ibid.*, B21, fp. 566.

[20] Adelaide L. Fries (ed.), *Records of the Moravians in North Carolina*, 6 vols. (Raleigh, 1922), I, 37–38; see also "Memorabilia of Wachovia," *ibid.*, I, 336.

[21] Adolph B. Benson (ed.), *Peter Kalm's Travels in North America*, 2 vols. (New York, 1937), I, 127–28; II, 193.

at the junction of the two navigable streams, called Ashley and Cowper Rivers." The real explanation lay, of course, in Charleston's porous sandy soil and its proximity to salt water, but Gordon came close to explaining the spread of malaria when he reasoned that "In general what part of South Carolina is planted, is counted unhealthy, owing to the Rice-dams and Swamps, which as they occasion a great quantity of Stagnated water in Summer, never fails to increase the Number of Insects, and to produce fall fevers and Agues, dry gripes and other disorders, which are often fatal to the lower set of people, as well White as Black." [22]

The one bright spot in the malaria picture of the eighteenth century was New England. As the infection intensified its attacks in the middle and southern colonies, its hold on the northern settlements gradually weakened. In 1791 Dr. Isaac Senter of Newport, Rhode Island, recalled that "Since my remembrance the genuine intermitting Fever, was very common in different parts of the inland country of New England; but for twenty years past has seldom been met with anywhere east of New York." A similar condition prevailed in Connecticut at this time, where a physician replied to a query: "We see no Intermitting Fevers generated here, though 35 or 40 years ago they sometimes occurred." [23] Reports from other New England colonies tell the same story. The northern margin of malaria steadily receded as the colonial period drew to a close, and by the outbreak of the Revolution, New York City constituted the northern boundary for malaria in the coastal regions.

There can be little doubt that malaria was prevalent in all American colonies during the seventeenth century.

[22] Mereness (ed.), *Travels in the Colonies*, 397, 399.

[23] Dr. Isaac Senter to William Currie, Newport, R. I., February 19, 1791, in Currie, *An Account of Climates and Diseases*, 8, 26.

Toward the end of the century and continuing into the eighteenth a rising incidence marked parts of Pennsylvania, New Jersey, Maryland, Delaware, and other colonies situated in the coastal plains region, while a corresponding decline characterized New England.

The significance of malaria in colonial history can scarcely be overrated, for it was a major hurdle in the development of the American colonies. To the newly arrived settlers or "fresh Europeans," it frequently proved fatal, and epidemics of pernicious malaria took a heavy toll of old and new colonists alike. In endemic regions the regular succession of spring and fall outbreaks, with the concomitant sickness and disability, deprived the colonies of much sorely needed labor. The case fatality rate among malaria patients was considerably lower than that for yellow fever or smallpox, but malaria was much more widespread than either of the former and affected a greater percentage of the population. In the majority of epidemic illnesses, one attack usually gave at least a temporary immunity; however, one attack of malaria was only the beginning of a long period of recurring sickness which often undermined the victim's health and left him a helpless prey to other infections. Directly and indirectly, malaria was one of the most fatal of colonial diseases and shares with dysentery first place among the colonial infections.

Dysentery

Dysentery can be classified with malaria among the fatal and debilitating colonial sicknesses. Its general symptoms include fever, diarrhea, cramps, and bloody, mucous evacuation, the latter giving rise to the common name of flux or bloody flux. Unfortunately, these characteristics are not restricted to dysentery, and accurate diagnoses of the various intestinal infections on the basis of colonial records are often impossible. More than likely some of the virulent outbreaks of bloody flux may have been typhoid or some form of cholera. In the case of amoebic and bacillary dysentery, identification is out of the question. Granting all this, dysentery, either bacillary or amoebic, probably is the infection indicated in the majority of outbreaks designated as bloody flux. No age group or area is immune from this contagion, and in colonial days it flourished from Massachusetts to Georgia. Like malaria it was endemic and epidemic. Although found in both temperate and warm climates, dysentery has a higher death rate and is more extensive in warmer regions. In the southern colonies the mortality from dysentery was roughly comparable to that from malaria. The flux was a perennial problem in the Carolinas, and the other colonies saw constantly recurring outbreaks.

Dysentery appeared early in colonial history. The first settlers in Virginia complained of "flixes" which in all probability were this infection.[24] The disorder was omnipresent, and few colonial journalists, chroniclers, historians, or private correspondents failed to mention it.

The year 1669 saw widespread outbreaks of sickness in the colonies north of New York, and one observer listed flux as the chief source of trouble. "It was a very sickly time," wrote the Reverend Samuel Danforth of Roxbury, Massachusetts, "many being visited with gripings, vomiting & flux, with a fever, which proved mortal to many infants & little children, esp'ly at Boston & Charlestown, and to some grown persons." "Gripings, vomiting & flux,

[24] Packard, *History of Medicine*, I, 64.

with a fever" could apply equally to dysentery, typhoid, or cholera, and the reference illustrates the diagnostic problems confronting the student. "A sore dysentery flux" struck down many Bostonians in 1676, and a few years later John Marshall noted that "about this time many persons dyed at Boston, especially children, of a bloody flux and feaver and some dyed of it in the Country." [25]

Fever and ague, and bloody flux constituted the chief burden of complaint of the S.P.G. missionaries in the eighteenth century, and judging by their accounts, flux was almost the worst of the two. Commissary Gideon Johnston wrote from Charleston, South Carolina, in 1710 that though "it is not now so violent either on me or my wife having put some stop to it by the use of hypocochoana & Laudanum," another missionary, "Mr. Wood is desperately ill of the flux, and in great danger. This Distemper is one of those incident to this climate, and has been fatal to a great many this year." None of the remedies, he added, effected a complete cure.[26]

Twenty-four years later Daniel Dwight of South Carolina petitioned the Society for permission to take a voyage for his health. "I find myself also in this Country vastly liable to the bloody flux," he wrote, "a distemper common here of which My worthy predecessor Mr. Maule died in this house. I have been troubled with it by turns, not to Excess half of my time for two years past; and fear what the Event of the frequent return of it may be. If therefore

[25] O'Callaghan (ed.), *Documents Relative to Colonial History*, III (1853), 185; "Rev. Samuel Danforth's Records, Roxbury, Mass.," *loc. cit.*, 300; Thomas Thacher to son, Peter, Boston, August 16, 1676, in *New England Historical and Genealogical Register*, VIII (1854), 178; "John Marshall's Diary," *loc. cit.*, 155–56.

[26] Commissary Gideon Johnston to Secretary, Charleston, S. C., July 5, 1710, in S.P.G. MSS., A5, fp. 414.

I might be permitted to take a Voyage it would probably be very advantageous as well as very grateful to me." Apparently his plea fell on deaf ears, however, for in a subsequent letter written some five months later the missionary again mentioned his "great weakness" from "the long continuance of ye Bloody flux, a Distemper most Common in this Country." [27]

Another South Carolina missionary, Stephen Roe, endured a long attack of dysentery. In 1740 he reported that all his sickness had "settled in a confirmed Dysentery, wch has followed me for about sixteen months past." The following year he repeated his complaint of fever and dysentery and requested a transfer from South Carolina.[28] Cases like these of Roe and Dwight are typical; on a number of occasions, S.P.G. missionaries died before permission to leave was granted by the Society.

From North Carolina exhausted John Macdowell, minister for the town of Brunswick, asked permission from the S.P.G. to travel for his health because of his sufferings from "an Obstinate Diarrhea, that will yield to no Medicine or Skill of the Physician." His condition was "truly pitiable," he wrote, for he had "not had one day, or one Night's Ease or rest these four Months past & . . . no less than fifteen times a night I am oblig'd to get up; and that accompanied by the Most excruciating pains in my Bowels, my back, my Loins." Alexander Stewart, the minister at Bath, North Carolina, also asking permission to leave his parish, wrote that he now had, "double Reason to renew my Intreaty, Having lost my wife by ye Flux, which has

[27] Daniel Dwight to Secretary, St. John's, S. C., April 16, 1734, *ibid.*, A25, fpp. 112–13; *id.* to *id.*, September 30, 1734, *ibid.*, fp. 131.

[28] Stephen Roe to Secretary, St. George's, Dorchester, S. C., January 6, 1740, *ibid.*, B9, fp. 311; *id.* to *id.*, December 22, 1741, *ibid.*, B10, fpp. 379–87.

Rag'd with Uncommon Violence since I wrote last, & been more mortall than ever I knew any other Distemper ye latter end of this Summer; and I myself am at present sick with it but hope in God not dangerously." [29]

The experiences of the missionaries with dysentery illustrate the long duration of the sickness. In some cases death gave quick release; in others, the patient lingered for some years before finally succumbing to the disease or to other infections. The susceptibility of the English missionaries to dysentery was probably greater than that of the native-born colonists, for newcomers to all regions, both tropical and temperate, are peculiarly susceptible to the infection if it is endemic.[30] Almost invariably "fresh Europeans" were subject to the so-called "seasonings" which apparently consisted of an attack of either dysentery or malaria, and occasionally both. Nonetheless, the colonial-born also were subject to constant and wearing encounters with the contagion.

Although it attacked all colonies, dysentery was observed in its most virulent form in the Carolinas. A serious Indian uprising in South Carolina in the spring of 1715 brought with it the usual sickness. The refugees from the Indians crowded into Charleston and other fortified areas, and the resultant overcrowded and unsanitary conditions meant that an epidemic was scarcely to be avoided. It was "hardly credible," wrote Dr. Francis Le Jau, "wt. quantity of People we have lost by the Enemy & by Sickness wch through infection in our small Garrisons & much hardship, has carried away several Persons, & children most chiefly;

[29] John Macdowell to Secretary, Brunswick, N. C., February 23, 1763, *ibid.*, B5, fp. 123; Alexander Stewart to Secretary, Bath, N. C., November 20, 1764, *ibid.*, B5, fpp. 149–50.

[30] Hirsch, *Handbook of Pathology*, III, 361.

It Pleased God of a flux of feaver July 13 in Charles-Town. We have been sick all of us; but thro' God's mercy we are pretty well at present." In 1751 a new arrival to South Carolina wrote of the "prodigious Sickness of the Country since we came here. . . . various kinds of Fevers rage fatally, & Fluxes carry off Numbers." He added that the amount of sickness was very shocking to newcomers such as himself but that he was getting accustomed to it.[31]

Reports similar to those from the Carolinas can be found for other colonies. New England, in particular, suffered heavily in the eighteenth century. The year 1732 in Salem, Massachusetts, was a "very sickly time . . . abundance being down with the Fever and bloody Flux of which several have died." Two years later fatal dysentery epidemics struck Boston and New London, Connecticut. Towards the close of summer the city began to be "very sickly," reported the Boston *News-Letter*, and "many both elder and young Persons, [were] within a few Days taken down with a Fever and Flux, of which several . . . died after less than a Weeks Illness." A newly formed medical society in Massachusetts proposed as its first work the publication of an article entitled, "A History of the Dysentery Epidemical in Boston in 1734." [32]

In the succeeding years dysentery climbed to first position among the epidemic diseases afflicting New England. Year after year outbreaks occurred and rarely did a five-year period elapse without at least one major epidemic. In 1742 "the Bloody flux, the Common Distemper," was

[31] Francis Le Jau to Secretary, Charleston, S. C., August 23, 1715, in S.P.G. MSS., A10, fp. 151; William Langhorne to Secretary, St. Bartholomew's, S. C., March 18, 1751, *ibid.*, B18, fp. 470.

[32] Boston *Weekly News-Letter*, No. 1496, September 21–28, 1732; No. 1594, August 22–29, 1734; *Diary of Joshua Hempstead*, 279; Jared Sparks (ed.), "Dr. William Douglas[s] to Cadwallader Colden," *loc. cit.*, 188.

reported "among many families" in New London, and at Shrewsbury, Massachusetts, "many children [were] taken away" in 1745 by the disease. It struck down a number of adults and children in New London again in 1753 and flared up in an explosive epidemic in many sections of Massachusetts in 1756. "In the Months of August and September last," reported a Boston newspaper in 1769, "an epidemical Fever and Flux prevailed among the young children in this Town: The Burials have been . . . In the whole 165 Whites, 14 Blacks."[33] The severity of the outbreak is shown by the fact that the annual death rate in Boston only averaged around four hundred and twenty-five at this time.

The middle colonies, too, were affected. In 1731 the flux broke out in New York City, and in Burlington, New Jersey, in the fall of 1745 "numbers of people" were "swept away by fluxes and fevers." A minister who resided outside Philadelphia made the mistake of visiting the city in the fall of 1757, and since fall was the "unhealthy season," caught the bloody flux; on his return home he passed the disease on to most of his family. Fortunately, all recovered but only after considerable sickness and much inconvenience.[34]

Naturally, with the disease so common, the colonists set their active—if not fevered—minds to work on the problem of a cure. John Winthrop declared in 1638 that "for the fluxe there is no better medicine than the Cuppe [bleeding] used 2 or 3 times." The patient was also to take some

[33] *Diary of Joshua Hempstead*, 398, 612–18; Ebenezer Parkman Diary, September 6–16, 1745, September–October, 1756; Rev. Nathan Fiske Diary, August–September, 1756; David Hall Diary, October 23, 1756; *Massachusetts Gazette and Boston Post Boy and Advertiser*, No. 634, October 9, 1769.

[34] *Pennsylvania Gazette*, No. 149, September 23–30, 1731; Colin Campbell to Secretary, Burlington, N. J., November 6, 1746, in S.P.G. MSS., B14, fp. 154; Paulus Bryzelius to Secretary, Philadelphia, September 16, 1767, *ibid.*, B6, Pt. 2, fp. 937.

"pilles . . . made of grated peper made up with turpentine, . . . and some flower withall." The *New Hampshire Gazette* recommended to its readers "Butter, or Oil, with a Proportion of Beer and Molasses," a remedy certain of popularity. "Take an Egge and Boyle it very hard," John Saffin directed his readers, "then pull off the Shell, and put it as hot as you can well endure, into the fundament of the patient Grieved and when it is much abated of the heat, put in another Egge in the same Manner and it will cure." [35]

Few armies in history have escaped dysentery, and colonial armies were no exception to the general rule. In 1690 Robert Livingston reported that the soldiers in Albany and Greenback in western New York were afflicted with this disease. General Braddock's campaign in the French and Indian War was hindered considerably by the bloody flux, and on one occasion George Washington wrote, "Our hospital is filled with sick and the numbers increase daily with the bloody flux which has not yet proved mortal to many." [36]

The terms "camp fever" and "camp disorder," names usually applied to typhus in Europe, probably indicated dysentery in the colonial wars. A chaplain in 1758 complained that he was having bowel trouble, and that he feared an attack of the "camp disorder." Even in peacetime dysentery was a constant threat to troops. Captain John Montressor in 1770 recorded his difficulties renovating Castle William. He was able to secure a working party of only forty men from the Fourteenth Regiment, since seventy-

[35] John Winthrop to John Winthrop, Jr., *c.* 1638, *Winthrop Papers,* IV, 3; *New Hampshire Gazette,* No. 209, October 3, 1760; The Note Book of John Saffin, 1665–1708.

[36] Robert Livingston to Lieutenant Governor Francis Nicholson, New York, June 7, 1690, in O'Callaghan (ed.), *Documents Relative to Colonial History,* III (1853), 727–28; *Virginia Magazine of History and Biography,* XXXI (1924), 317 n.

four of its complement of four hundred were hospitalized with bloody flux.[37]

The actual effect of dysentery on colonial health is not easily determined. The disease was so extensive as to prevent a statistical measurement in terms of cases and fatalities. Its indirect effects were serious, but here, too, one can only estimate the damage. The death rate from the infection, especially in the south, was high. Its victims were subject to long periods of incapacitating illness, which drained their vitality and reduced their resistance to other fatal disorders. In general the disease resembled malaria in its effect upon the population in that it was both endemic and epidemic, recurrent, debilitating, and often fatal. As malaria slowly relaxed its grip on New England, dysentery stepped into the breach and more than offset any gains to public health. Certainly dysentery was one of the leading colonial infections and ranks with malaria as a primary cause of sickness and death.

Typhoid Fever

Typhoid fever was undoubtedly present among the American colonists, but just how extensive it was and how early it appeared is still debatable. The symptoms of this sickness resemble those of both dysentery and typhus, a fact which adds to the difficulties confronting the student of these three diseases. The fever, cramps, diarrhea, and bloody discharge of dysentery often characterize typhoid,

[37] "Journals of Captain John Montressor," in New York Historical Society *Collections*, XIV (1881), 401–402, 410; "The Journal of the Rev. John Cleaveland," in *Historical Collections* of the Essex Institute, XII (1874), 186–87.

and the mild skin eruption of typhoid was occasionally confused with the typhus rash. Its chief distinguishing characteristic is a constant high fever, which lasts from two to three weeks. From this characteristic manifestation were derived the contemporary names—slow fever, nervous fever, continued fever, burning fever, and long fever. The putrid bilious fever mentioned in connection with yellow fever may have belonged in this classification, too.

Little agreement exists on the first appearance of typhoid fever. One medical authority declared that this disease was not epidemic until the nineteenth and twentieth centuries, while another asserted in discussing seventeenth-century Virginia that "typhoid which is a disease of the summer season, must have accounted for much of the dreaded summer sickness and probably killed off more than all the others combined." [38] Yet colonial records reveal little evidence of this malady.

The "burning fevers" which attacked the Jamestown settlers in the summer of 1607 may have been typhoid. In the colony, declared Sir Francis Wyatt, "new comers seldom pass[ed] July & Aug. without a burning fever." [39] Since it is a disease of the summer months, and since one attack usually gives immunity, the scourge of new arrivals possibly was typhoid.

"A burning and violent fever" in the Dutch colony of New Amsterdam in 1658 resulted in a long sickness and affected nearly all people, but it bore heaviest upon the young and was easiest upon the old.[40] It too may have been

[38] Allen, *The Story of Microbes*, 203; Blanton, *Medicine in Virginia in the Seventeenth Century*, 69.

[39] "Letter of Sir Francis Wyatt, Governor of Virginia, 1621–1626," in *William and Mary Quarterly*, Ser. 2, VI (1926), 117.

[40] J. Alrichs to Petrus Stuyvesant, New Amsterdam, October 7, 1658, in O'Callaghan (ed.), *Documents Relative to Colonial History*, XII (1877), 226–27.

typhoid, but these two instances are the only references found so far to possible typhoid outbreaks in the colonies during the seventeenth century.

During the eighteenth century typhoid appeared on a fairly large scale, although it was toward the mid-century before the major outbreaks occurred. Governor John Seymour, of Maryland, may have died from the infection in 1707, for the Council notified the Board of Trade that the Governor had died of "a long lingering Indisposition of a Continued Feavour." [41]

A series of fever epidemics in Connecticut and Massachusetts in the years 1727, 1734, and 1737 bear some resemblance to typhoid attacks. In the summer of 1727 Norwich, Connecticut, experienced "a very sickly and Dying Time; Hundreds of Persons [were] Sick at once, and about Forty . . . Died: . . . the Mortality fell chiefly in one Parish, where . . . Died above a Sixth part of the Heads of Families." A similar epidemic also was reported in Woodbury, Connecticut, during this year. In the spring of 1734 serious epidemic fevers were reported at New Haven and other towns in Connecticut. The fever returned again in 1737 and struck several towns in Massachusetts. A "malignant Fever" broke out "in some Towns in the County of Worcestor," and "at Sutton in one House where two Families dwelt, both the Heads of each Family died therewith, and one Child. within two Months." [42]

Meanwhile reports of typhoid came from some of the other colonies. The Reverend William Guy of St. Andrew's

[41] Council of Maryland to Board of Trade, Maryland, July 30, 1707, Public Record Office, Colonial Papers, No. 5, Vol. 717, No. 1, phototranscript in Library of Congress.

[42] *The Weekly News-Letter,* No. 44, October 26–November 3, No. 23, June 1–8, 1727; Boston *Weekly News-Letter,* No. 1578, April 26–May 3, 1734, No. 1734, May 26–June 2, 1737.

Parish, South Carolina, informed the S.P.G. that he had been sick with a "constant fever" in the fall of 1734. Four years later another missionary wrote from South Carolina that he, too, had been visited with a "continued fever." [43] Though the Society's members had been working in South Carolina for over thirty years, no mention had been made of constant or continued fevers prior to these dates.

Beginning around 1740 a series of fever epidemics broke out in New England. A considerable number were obviously dysentery, but the descriptions of many of the long, nervous, and continued fevers leave little doubt that typhoid was fighting alongside the other bowel infections. In 1741 the "long fever" killed nineteen persons in Sutton, Massachusetts, and several others in New London, Connecticut. A year later the fever brought despair to James Macsparran, the S.P.G. minister at Narragansett, Massachusetts. "Ever since February," he wrote to the Society, "I have had a nervous Fever raging in my Family among my Slaves and at this Instant my wife is in the one and Twenty-eth Day with yt Fever in the most Severe Manner So yt there is but little (tho I thank God there is this Day Some little Hopes) of her Recovery. & I was seized with it myself last Sunday being Whitsunday So yt I did not go to church and God alone knows whether I ever shall." Fortunately Macsparran and all his family recovered.[44]

The same year that the Macsparran family was attacked, another missionary at Brookhaven, Connecticut, mentioned in a letter to the Society that his wife had been very sick

[43] William Guy to Secretary, St. Andrew's, S. C., November 29, 1734, in S.P.G. MSS., A25, fp. 139; Stephen Roe to Secretary, St. George's, S. C., December, 1738, *ibid.*, B7, Pt. 1, fp. 246.

[44] David Hall Diary, April 6, 1741; *Diary of Joshua Hempstead*, 375; James Macsparran to Secretary, Narragansett, Mass., June 10, 1742, in S.P.G. MSS., B10, fp. 28; *id.* to *id.*, October 18, 1742, *ibid.*, fp. 32.

from a "distemper" which "is known here by the Name of the Long-Fever, and is generally very Mortal." In 1745 Stamford, Connecticut, suffered from a "Malignant dysentery." Only the residents on one street were affected, but seventy of them died.[45] A high mortality and the limitation of the disease to one street point to typhoid fever, a disorder most often spread by infected water or defective sewage disposal.

An outbreak of fever occurred in Albany, New York, in 1746 and exacted an extraordinary toll. Dr. Cadwallader Colden, who was in the town at the time and had opportunity to observe the epidemic first hand, unhesitatingly diagnosed it as nervous fever or typhoid. The next summer New York City was ravaged by a "raging nervous fever, which . . . carried off multitudes." [46]

Two years later dysentery and nervous long fevers prevailed in many towns in Connecticut, where they proved "very mortal," one town losing 130 inhabitants and another place losing 20. In 1751, the towns of Hartford and New Haven in Connecticut were attacked by a "fatal dysentery," [47] but the prevalence of typhoid fever in Connecticut during the previous years suggests that it played a part in these outbreaks.

Boston appears to have escaped the fever attacks which affected much of New England, although a resident of the city mentioned the death of an uncle in 1754 from a nervous fever. In Brookline, Massachusetts, the local minister died "after a few Days Illness, by a Fever, attended with

[45] Isaac Browne to Secretary, Brookhaven, Conn., July 16, 1742, *ibid.*, B10, fp. 212; Webster, *History of Epidemic Diseases*, I, 239.

[46] *Colden Papers*, III (1919), 289; William Livingston to Noah Wells, New York, October 12, 1747, Johnson Family Papers, No. 37, Yale University MSS.

[47] Webster, *History of Epidemic Diseases*, I, 241–42.

a Dysenteria, which Disorder his Parish and children have been sorrowfully afflicted with." The next year a pastor in Salem also succumbed to "a nervous fever," and "slow fever and bloody flux," caused considerable sickness at Black Point, North Yarmouth, and Falmouth, three towns in northern Massachusetts. On April 11, 1756, David Hall of Sutton, Massachusetts, noted in his diary that two of his neighbors sons had died of "a nervous fever," and that the rest of the household, nine in all, were sick with it. Three weeks later he sorrowfully recorded that his neighbor had given his "wife and 5 sons to ye Lord." [48]

Just when typhoid fever first entered Philadelphia is not known, but apparently it was familiar to Elizabeth Drinker, who, on May 31, 1759, visited a friend "who lay ill of a nervous fever." "The slow Nervous Fever, as described by Dr. Huxham, was a very common disease in Philadelphia during my apprenticeship, (from the year 1760 to 1766)," Dr. Rush recalled, "also for many years after I settled in the city, which was in the year 1769." Rush also stated that Dr. Thomas Cadwallader, who died in 1779 at the age of seventy-one, remembered that the disorder first came from Connecticut, where it was called the "long-fever." [49]

By the 1760's typhoid fever was widely prevalent in the colonies. A missionary at Dover, Delaware, mentioned in 1764 the loss of his wife from a bilious fever, one of the many names given to typhoid. Three definitely identifiable cases of typhoid fever are listed in the records of the

[48] *Papers of the Lloyd Family*, II (1927), 515–16; Boston *Weekly News-Letter*, No. 2729, October 24–31, 1754; No. 2756, May 1, 1755; Willis (ed.), *Journals of Smith and Deane*, 168; David Hall Diary, April 11, 1756.

[49] Elizabeth Drinker's Diary, May 31, 1759; Currie, *An Account of Climates and Diseases*, 120.

Moravians of North Carolina in 1764, and an S.P.G. missionary was among the victims of a 1767 outbreak in Elizabeth Town, New Jersey.[50] In New England Ebenezer Parkman mentioned the case of an individual sick with the "long fever" in 1760, who had "voided by Stool abt 2 quarts of bloody matter." "Long Fever" claimed another victim in Sutton, Massachusetts, who "was hopefully recovered but Died suddenly," and brought sickness to Hatfield in the winter of 1766–67.[51]

There is evidence, although inconclusive, of typhoid fever in Virginia and New York during the early part of the seventeenth century; however, almost a hundred years elapsed before the disorder was clearly identified. As already noted, the fact that there were many unclassified fevers in this period makes a positive assertion as to the presence or absence of any particular disease open to question. Yet the scant material relating to typhoid fever previous to the 1730's and 1740's is an excellent indication that the disease, if present, attacked on a limited scale.

It is quite clear that typhoid fever appeared on an epidemic scale in Connecticut and South Carolina shortly after 1730 and from those sections gradually spread through the other colonies. The increasing extent of the sickness and the number of deaths from the contagion in the ensuing forty years give this disorder a high rank among destructive sicknesses. Yet, for the colonial period as a whole, typhoid

[50] Charles Inglis to Secretary, Dover, Pa., November 20, 1764, in S.P.G. MSS., B3, Pt. 2, fpp. 978–81; Thomas B. Chandler to Secretary, Elizabeth Town, N. J., October 12, 1767, *ibid.*, B24, Pt. 1, fp. 267; Fries (ed.), *Records of the Moravians*, I, 280 n.

[51] Ebenezer Parkman Diary, January 23, 1760; David Hall Diary, November 9, 1766; Asahel Hart to Ebenezer Baldwin, Hatfield, Mass., November 17, 1766, S. E. Baldwin Collection, Yale Library MSS.; Sophia Partridge to Ebenezer Baldwin, January 1–8, 1767, *ibid.*

fever was only one of a large number of diseases, and it cannot be classified with the chief infectious disorders.

Typhus

Typhus, the fourth of the major fevers and one which was both extensive and fatal in Europe, was of little danger to the American colonists. A disorder which results from overcrowding, poverty, and filth, it was much less likely to prevail in America, where land was cheap and the economy predominantly agricultural. Typhus is an acute, infectious, and highly contagious disease which lasts about fourteen days. Its chief symptoms are prostration, nervous symptoms, and a peculiar eruption of the skin. It is transmitted by lice and is more frequent in temperate and cold climates than in warm. The name given to it—gaol fever, military fever, hospital fever, camp fever, contagious fever, putrid fever, ship fever, and petechial fever—are indicative of the conditions favorable to its development. Its greatest danger to the colonists lay in the passage from Europe in dirty and overloaded vessels, and it was a common disease on board ships.[52]

Typhus apparently was carried into Canada on several occasions during the seventeenth century, and the infectious

[52] A pamphlet in the University of California (Los Angeles) Library, *Matters interesting on the Score of Humanity: being Propositions relating to the Health, Comfort, and Satisfaction of British Seamen in His Majesty's Service* (n.p., n.d.), 6, shows the effect of typhus upon British sailors: "It is said 'That before Admiral Boscawen reached England on his return, upwards of 2,000 Sailors died of a Putrid or Jail Fever, which it is presumed was in a great Measure occasioned by the moist Vapour, and confined Air between Decks.' " See also John Duffy, "The Passage to the Colonies," in *Mississippi Valley Historical Review*, XXXVIII (June, 1951), 21–38.

fevers in New England mentioned by Governor Bradford may have been this same disorder.[53] The colder climate of Canada made that region more susceptible to typhus, and epidemic outbreaks developed on a number of occasions. Twice in the seventeenth century "spotted fever" outbreaks occurred in New England, but whether or not they were typhus it is difficult to say.

On the whole, the American colonies were not troubled with typhus until the large-scale importation of Germans and Scotch-Irish in the eighteenth century. Two vessels which arrived in Philadelphia with the "Palatine Fever" aroused considerable alarm, and in succeeding years the arrival of convicts, bond servants, and other immigrants greatly increased the danger from typhus despite a tightening of the existing quarantine laws and the introduction of special measures relating to immigrant vessels. In 1754 Philadelphia residents were alarmed again by a sickness which reportedly came from the Palatine ships and spread through town. The provincial council ordered the secretary to have doctors visit all ships and places in town where Palatines were housed. An epidemic of fever which broke out among the Moravians in North Carolina in 1759 took the lives of nine of the settlers and was diagnosed as typhus.[54]

Annapolis, Maryland, was troubled with a series of shipborne typhus outbreaks in the 1760's. "We hear that lately a great number of People have Died in Talbot County, especially Negroes, of a Malignant Distemper, supposed to have been brought in by a Vessel with Servants, from Ireland," reported the *Maryland Gazette* in 1764, "but it is

[53] Ashburn, *Ranks of Death*, 96.

[54] Norris, *History of Medicine in Philadelphia*, 102; *Colonial Records of Pennsylvania*, VI (1851), 169; Fries (ed.), *Records of the Moravians*, I, 206.

now somewhat abated." Two years later, a Maryland family which had undertaken the contract of a redemptioner, learned "the Imprudence of taking in a Passenger from a Convict Ship . . . Nine of the Family . . . died . . . of the Jail Fever, and Four more" were "in a dangerous Condition, from the same Disorder." "The Fever that lately raged here was of the same Kind," the editor sermonized, "and, as generally supposed, was brought in by one of these ships. Surely the many shocking instances of the like Nature, by which many Families have suffered Extremely, will make People more Cautious how they admit under their Roofs, *these Wretches,* doubly Nuisances from the Contagion of their Distempers, and of their Vices." The correspondence of Governor Horatio Sharpe of Maryland and the frequent mention of the sickness in the papers during these years show that typhus, while never endemic, was frequently introduced into the middle colonies.[55]

As indicated by the names military fever and camp fever, typhus was long a scourge of European armies. In the American colonies, however, it was not until the outbreak of the Revolutionary War that the infection manifested itself on a large scale, though at least one outbreak occurred previous to the Revolution. "I heard that the putrid fever is broke out at the old fort," a colonial officer stationed in western New York recorded in his journal in 1760, "& all men are forbade going into it on any account." Four days later he wrote: "I hear Rhoad Island regt. has got the spotted fever among them, which is as bad in an Army as the plague, as the regular doctor says."[56]

[55] *Maryland Gazette,* No. 999, June 28, 1764; *Massachusetts Gazette and Boston News-Letter,* No. 3306, February 12, 1767; Governor Sharpe to Hugh Hamersley, Annapolis, July 27, 1767, in Brown *et al.* (eds.), *Archives of Maryland,* XIV (1895), 411.

[56] "Journal of Captain Jenks," *loc. cit.,* 383.

In this case, "putrid" or "spotted" fever is almost certain to have been typhus.

Not only was typhus rarely found in the colonial period but even after the Revolution the United States remained relatively free of the infection. Inasmuch as typhus and typhoid were not clearly differentiated at this time, one suspects that the "typhus" which prevailed in Connecticut in the 1760's was actually typhoid, for the proper era of typhus in the United States began in the nineteenth century when emigration from Ireland set in on a major scale.[57] Obviously, typhus had little effect upon colonial health.

Of the four fevers treated in this chapter, malaria and dysentery were by far the most significant. In the long run they proved far more detrimental to colonial health than did the deadlier diseases such as smallpox and yellow fever. Typhoid and typhus do not belong in the same category with the two other fevers. Typhoid probably deserves greater attention than has been given to it, but it cannot be considered of determining consequence to colonial well-being. Typhus, as has been pointed out, ranks a poor fourth.

One last fever deserves mention. Many of the colonial children were subject to various types of worm fevers. These sicknesses do not belong under the heading of epidemic diseases, but their effect upon colonial health should not be disregarded. Hookworms and similar parasites were responsible for many fatalities and much sickness and suffering among the younger population.

Many fever epidemics still defy classification. No doubt most of these belong under the headings of the main disorders treated in this discussion. Granting that all these outbreaks could be identified, it is improbable that they

[57] Currie, *An Account of Climates and Diseases*, 26, 62; Hirsch, *Handbook of Pathology*, I, 572.

would make any real change in the order of importance of the four fevers listed above.

Venereal Diseases

The colonials—Puritans and planters alike—were a rugged, earthy people with little of the delicacy and prudery which later Americans have ascribed to them. Colonial newspapers published anecdotes and accounts that would jar the sensibilities of the present-day reading public. The descriptive names given to some of the illnesses of the day such as "griping of the guts" and "bloody flux" reveal little reluctance to call a spade a spade. Granting that venereal disorders were a delicate topic even in colonial times, private correspondents would have had no qualms about discussing the infection in others or mentioning it in their private diaries and journals. Hence the fact that so few references to venereal diseases can be found in the colonial records is an excellent sign that these infections were rarely present.

A minor syphilis outbreak occurred in New England in 1646, when, according to John Winthrop, the "lues venerea" was brought into Boston by a sailor who infected his wife. She in turn gave the infection to fifteen neighbors "who drew her breasts as well as suckled her baby." Among the Puritans, of course, it is inconceivable that the disease could have spread by any other method, although John Hull suggested that virtue was not completely triumphant in Boston when he noted that several young women were tried in a Boston court in 1762 "for re-iterated whoredom," and another on suspicion of keeping "a brothel-house." [1]

[1] Thacher, *American Medical Biography*, 18; "Diary of John Hull," *loc. cit.*, 232.

A few years later the ubiquitous Cotton Mather hinted that all was not as it should be in the Puritan capital. "I am informed of several Houses in this Town," he confided to his diary, "where there are young Women of a very debauched Character, and extremely Impudent; unto whom there is a very great Resort of young men, [who] are extremely poisoned by such conversation as these entertain them withal. I must address our Society, that . . . this Mischief may be extinguished." [2] Mather, a keen student of both physical and spiritual ills, unfortunately gave no clue as to whether the poisoning was material or moral.

Fortunately for the reputation of New London, Connecticut, one of its citizens was found not guilty when brought before the court in 1753 on the charge of "keeping a Bawd house." Several years later Lemuel Wood of Boxford, Massachusetts, serving with the colonial forces during one of the campaigns in New York, noted that two "campwomen" were sent back from Crown Point "by Reason of an Infectious Distemper they Carryd along with them [which is] very Common to ye Sex in these Parts." [3] However, the New Englanders looked upon the Dutch and other foreigners—and other colonials, for that matter—with much condescension, and the association of venereal diseases with *Uitlanders* has always been customary with all people. Had venereal disease been general in this area, some record of it would certainly have survived.

The only major attack of syphilis to strike North America in colonial times occurred in Lower Canada in 1773. A wide area was affected by the disease, which apparently was spread quite innocently in many cases. Doses of mercury

[2] *Diary of Cotton Mather, loc. cit.*, (1709–1724), 229.

[3] *Diary of Joshua Hempstead*, 604; "Diaries Kept by Lemuel Wood of Boxford," in *Historical Collections* of the Essex Institute, XIX (1882), 187.

finally conquered the infection and probably left a residue of mercurial poisoning in their wake.[4]

The announcements of supposed cures for venereal disorders is as good an index of the presence of the disease as any. The first of these to appear in the colonial newspapers was a "Recipe" for the curing of venereal diseases discovered by "a Negroe Man in *Virginia* [who] was freed by the Government, and had a Pension of *Thirty* Pounds *Sterling* settled on him during his Life." The remedy, which included a decoction made of the bark from Spanish oak and pine trees, and "Shoemack Root," and an ointment made from "Hogs Fat and Deer's Dung," showed that even then the way of the transgressor was hard.[5]

By the 1760's a considerable increase is noted in the advertisements relating to venereal disorders. One such announcement stated that George Weed, who "was bred to the practice of Physick & Surgery . . . undertakes to cure the Venereal Disease in all its Stages, even when attended with Ulcers." The makers of "Keyser's Famous Pills," a favorite colonial nostrum, decided in the 1770's to move into the apparently lucrative field arising from venereal complaints, and they added them to the long list of sicknesses which their pills would cure. "Keyser's Famous Pills [are] well known all over Europe, and in this and the neighboring Colonies," read one of their advertisements, "for their Superior Efficacy and peculiar Mildness, in perfectly eradicating every Degree of a certain Disease, without the least Trouble or Confinement. The Public may be assured, that this excellent Medicine is beyond any Thing in Foulness

[4] Heagerty, *Four Centuries of Medical History*, I, 131–60.

[5] Thomas Harward to Sir Hans Sloane, Boston, June 16, 1731, photo-transcript No. 4051 in Sloane MSS., Library of Congress; *South Carolina Gazette*, No. 63, March 24–31, 1733; *American Weekly Mercury*, No. 699, May 17–24, 1733.

and Impurities of the Blood, having performed many astonishing Cures in Scorbutic Eruptions, Leprosies, White Swellings, Stiff Joints, Gout and Rheumatic Disorders, etc."[6]

Obviously venereal disorders were present on occasions in colonial days, and in all likelihood the incidence increased slightly following the French and Indian War. The presence of European soldiers in the years from 1740 to 1763 plus the social and moral disruptions engendered by the war itself may explain the more frequent appearance of the disease in the later colonial period. Nonetheless, it is safe to say that the colonies were relatively free of all venereal disorders.

[6] *Pennsylvania Gazette*, No. 2019, September 3, 1767; Boston *Gazette and Country Journal*, No. 1005, July 18, 1774.

CHAPTER VIII

Conclusion

The problem of classifying epidemics in the American colonies in the order of their destructiveness would obviously be simpler if more statistical information were available. As it is, there are many discrepancies in the accounts of the major disorders: outbreaks which were not clearly identified, epidemics for which little information exists, and attacks in small towns and rural areas which were not recorded. However, few, if any, of the important epidemics passed without record, since sickness and death were given a prominent place in the diaries, letters, and other writings of the period.

The concentrated mortality of certain diseases makes them stand out far beyond their real significance. Epidemic infections such as smallpox and yellow fever struck suddenly and with devastating effect. An attack of yellow fever was an extraordinary event, and the terrible mortality it wrought among those affected made an indelible impression upon all surviving the visitation. Similar alarm was caused by smallpox, and later, by diphtheria after its virulent attacks on New England in the 1730's. Naturally these contagions aroused much attention, but many historians have overrated their importance as hindrances to colonial development. Epidemics of dysentery and malaria, which were less alarming but were chronic sicknesses occurring year after year, proved far more costly both in terms of economics and human suffering.

From the standpoint of social and economic cost, malaria and dysentery rank first among the epidemic disorders affecting the colonists—malaria because of its return year after year to plague the inhabitants of many sections of the colonies, and dysentery because it was both widespread and debilitating.

Actually, the death toll from malaria would be higher if the deaths indirectly caused by it were included. Its successive attacks drained the vitality of the inhabitants and increased their susceptibility to other diseases.

The number of deaths laid directly to dysentery appears slightly higher than from malaria, and like malaria, it was found in every colony, attacking both old and new settlers. New arrivals proved particularly susceptible to both diseases, and in all probability these two plagues exacted a heavier death toll among "fresh Europeans" than all other epidemics combined.

Respiratory diseases—colds, influenza, pleurisy, and pneumonia, for which little statistical information exists—probably should be placed third as causes of suffering and death. They affected all age groups in every section of the colonies, and in their destructiveness are close competitors with malaria and dysentery.

Unquestionably, smallpox aroused the most consternation among the colonists. It was highly contagious, extremely fatal, and of a loathsome nature—characteristics which justify the colonial terror. Fortunately, the outbreaks were often spaced many years apart, and by the time smallpox appeared more frequently, variolation was practiced on a large enough scale to mitigate the worst effects of the disease. Never endemic in the colonies during the eighteenth century, this disease proved much less of a problem than in England and on the Continent, where annual heavy tolls were exacted. Smallpox, although a major problem in the colonies, in the long run was not as costly as malaria, dysentery, or the combined group of respiratory disorders. Had it become endemic in America, as it was in other sections of the world, it undoubtedly would have rated first among specific infections. Fortunately, this did not occur, and the picture of smallpox in colonial America, although grim, is much brighter than usually depicted.

Yellow fever, like smallpox, has been given far more attention by medical historians of the colonial period than it deserves. However, because it was possibly the most malignant of all pestilences to affect North America, one can easily understand the horror with which it was regarded. No other epidemic in colonial America proved so quickly fatal, and only smallpox can compare with it in the devastation wrought by a single epidemic. But yellow fever was the exception rather than the rule. As has been pointed out, it is questionable whether the disease was present in the American colonies before 1693, and from then until the Revolution only a few outbreaks occurred. Rarely did the infection spread beyond the limits of New York, Philadelphia, and Charleston, and most of the colonists remained unaffected. This geographical restriction places yellow fever far below smallpox and the other major illnesses as a menace to colonial health.

The other epidemic sicknesses included in this study are of less importance. Diphtheria and scarlet fever, although appearing late in colonial history, were of more importance than measles, whooping cough, and mumps. Diphtheria did not assume its virulent form until the last forty years of the colonial era, but it left a heavy mark on any community it affected. In an age of high infant mortality, it was a severe blow to lose the older children to diphtheria. It is not pleasant to picture the plight of parents in certain New England towns where the "putrid sore throat" almost wiped out all children, or the helplessness with which they were compelled to watch their children slowly strangle to death. Yet the disease appeared late in colonial times and was not nearly so extensive as other disorders. Aside from the fatalities among children, diphtheria did not cause much disruption of economic and social life, and little time was lost by the effective working population. From this viewpoint diphtheria and scarlet fever cannot be classed with the more virulent epidemics.

Typhus proved fatal on the voyages from Europe, but was negligible in the colonies. Typhoid fever was of doubtful importance, although it may be underrated. The three remaining epidemic sicknesses—measles, whooping cough, and mumps—were present in the colonies but proved neither extensive nor especially fatal.

Undoubtedly, infectious diseases took their heaviest toll among immigrants. The term "seasoning" is in itself proof of the frequent sicknesses attacking newcomers. The fact that there were many fatalities among early settlers helps to explain the slow growth of the colonies during the seventeenth century. Most of the settlers were immigrants, and it was not until a native colonial population developed that health conditions improved. The development of a more permanent society with a higher standard of living was an important factor in promoting better health. Nearly all writers on early colonial history have commented on the three forces—disease, famine, and war—which constantly decimated the early settlements. With the development of a sounder economy and a larger population the threats of both famine and Indians were diminished, and with a better and increased food supply came greater resistance to disease.

The excessive mortality among new arrivals is well illustrated in the case of the S.P.G. missionaries, whose work did not begin until the eighteenth century. From 1700 to 1750 about sixty-two missionaries were sent to the Carolinas, fifty to South Carolina and twelve to North Carolina. All were relatively young men who had been carefully selected for arduous work in the mission fields. Nonetheless, within five years of their arrival in the colonies twenty-seven, or 43.6 per cent either had died or had resigned because of ill health. By following the careers of the missionaries for ten years, it was found that the deaths, and resignations for reasons of health, reached 56.5 per cent. In actuality the casualty toll was probably higher, since a number who resigned for reasons unknown were assumed to have been in good health when they left the Society's service.

One might ask whether the Carolinas are a fair example of the American colonies as a whole. The climatic adjustment which Europeans were called upon to make was greater than in the colonies to the north, and epidemics of all types ravaged Charleston with considerable violence. However, the corresponding figures for missionaries in the middle colonies show a similarly high death toll. The S.P.G. sent twenty-six missionaries in a fifteen-year period to New York, Pennsylvania, and Delaware. Of this group, five, or 19 per cent, died within five years, and during the ten-year period three more died, bringing the mortality rate to approximately 31 per cent. While the percentages cited for the middle colonies are slightly lower than those for Carolina the death rate is still alarmingly high. Although the S.P.G. missionaries did not penetrate the New

England colonies until late in the colonial period, their casualty rate there was comparable with that in the other sections.[1]

The mortality figures for missionaries are probably an accurate index for the colonists as a whole. However, certain reservations should be kept in mind. In the first place, the relative percentage of immigrants in the eighteenth century was not so large as it had been in the previous century, and consequently, the majority of colonials were native-born. The missionaries, on the other hand, as newcomers, could be expected to have a higher death rate than the American-born colonists. Further, the ministers were constantly exposed to infection through their visits to the sick, and because the size of their parishes compelled them to travel constantly, they were exposed to all sorts of weather. Unquestionably, the main cause for the high fatality rate among the S.P.G. ministers was their position as "fresh Europeans." The other factors are secondary and can be greatly discounted. Even allowing for all possible explanations, the amount of sickness and death among the missionaries presents a grim picture and indicates the prevalence of disease in the colonies. The same disorders which bore so heavily on the missionaries were also ravaging the colonists, as evidenced by the recurrence of such phrases as "epidemical disorder" and "general distemper" in the Society's correspondence.

The eighteenth century brought a definite improvement in colonial health. The rising standards of living already

[1] This data was compiled from a study of the S.P.G. records. Some of the information can be found in C. F. Pascoe, *Two Hundred Years of the S.P.G.*, 2 vols. (London, 1901); Dalcho, *An Account of the Episcopal Church in South-Carolina*; and David Humphreys, *An Historical Account of the Incorporated Society for the Propagation of the Gospel in Foreign Parts* (London, 1730).

mentioned and the development of a colonial-born population were primarily responsible for this change. It must be remembered that this improvement was relative and is not to be judged by twentieth-century standards of hygiene and sanitation. The medical profession contributed little to the improved health conditions, though through immigration and the education of colonials in European medical schools the number of doctors in the colonies increased. This latter factor can easily be overrated, however, for medical practice varied little from the preceding century, and the number of medical practitioners was always far short of the needs of the colonists. The quack doctors who throve in the absence of trained physicians did much harm and no doubt helped to justify Dr. William Douglass' remark that occasionally "nature gets the better of the doctor and the patient recovers." [2]

One notable improvement in medical treatment was the introduction of variolation, a practice which arose despite the opposition of most outstanding medical men. By the second half of the century the worst epidemics of smallpox were over as a result of this somewhat dangerous but effective method of smallpox inoculation. A great step forward was made in the treatment of malaria with the widespread use of cinchona bark, a medicine introduced into England in the late seventeenth century. One other factor aiding in improved health was the retreat of malaria from New England. Because of better drainage or for other reasons the colonies to the north of New York City were almost completely free of this fever by the outbreak of the Revolution. The absence of malaria undoubtedly enhanced New England's reputation for salubrity.

Bad as conditions were in the colonies, the chances for

[2] Douglass, *British Settlements*, II, 351.

survival were still better than for the crowded thousands in the slums of England's cities and towns. With the exception of yellow fever, all the diseases in America prevailed in England. Malaria was not such a problem as in the colonies, but smallpox, typhus, and other disorders proved far worse in the mother country. The demand for labor in the colonies forestalled the creation of a depressed economic class and thereby promoted general health. Slaves, the exception to this statement, were looked on as valuable property and were usually well cared for from the standpoint of physical needs. Their condition contrasts with that of the lower economic groups in England, who lived in abject poverty, perpetuating typhus, smallpox, and various infections which were then periodically passed on to the other classes.

Epidemics played a notable role in eliminating the Indian menace. Far more Indians died of white men's diseases than ever died from their weapons. Smallpox was the greatest of these Indian scourges, but influenza and other plagues contributed to the desolation of the red men. In peace and in war epidemic diseases were transmitted to the Indians with devastating results. Because they possessed no immunity to European disorders, little conception of the need for quarantine, and only the crudest methods of treatment, the mortality rate from smallpox among them was many times that of the whites. Incidents in which villages and tribes were wiped out by smallpox, as was the reported fate of the Pemlico Indians of South Carolina in 1698–99, seem credible, in view of the susceptibility of Indians to smallpox as late as the nineteenth century. Governmental records show case fatalities among certain tribes at that time ranging from 55 to over 90 per cent. The whites were not unaware of the potency of this weapon, and authenticated instances of Europeans deliberately spreading this pestilence by means of infected blankets are found in colonial records.[3] Occasionally, the infection was returned to the white men with a new virulence. However, the damage sustained by the whites on this account does not compare with the ravages of smallpox among the Indians. Unquestionably, the way for the white man was rendered easier by his advance guards of diseases.

Insofar as the effect of epidemic diseases upon Negroes is concerned, the Africans generally possessed more immunity to smallpox, yellow fever, and malaria than Europeans. It was their immunity to this last disease which made possible the development of rice plantations in South Carolina. Coming from one of the chief focal centers of smallpox, it was only natural that slaves should bring the disease with them to the colonies. Several major smallpox outbreaks among the colonists were traced to slave ships, and often slaves transmitted the infection directly to the Indians. The Negroes appear to have been susceptible to respiratory complaints, for the phrase "pluretical disorders" appears repeatedly in connection with sickness among them and the fatalities from respiratory diseases appears much higher than for Caucasians. On the whole, however, epidemics in the colonies affected the Negroes much the same as the whites.

The effect of epidemic diseases upon colonial development is by no means clear. The loss of life from outbreaks was enormous, and the cost of sickness is impossible to estimate. The disruption of normal activities during major outbreaks was an additional burden, and one can only wonder how society managed to survive the numerous devastating epidemics. Yet despite all this destruction and desolation,

[3] Stearn and Stearn, *Effect of Smallpox on the Amerindian*, 13–15.

the colonies increased in wealth and population. How to reconcile the ghastly picture of suffering and death caused by diseases with the steady growth of colonial economic prosperity is difficult. Boston, New York, Charleston, and other cities were repeatedly desolated by epidemics, only to recover in a short time. This same held true for entire provinces, but no matter how severe the outbreak, it was no more than a temporary check to the social and economic development of the country. Part of the answer, as has been pointed out, lies in the relatively healthful conditions in the colonies as compared with Europe. An American historian, writing a few years after the Revolution, stated that in New Hampshire the annual death rate was not more than one in seventy, "except when some epidemic disorder prevails." [4] Indeed, the general health of the New Englander was good. In the southern colonies, too, the claims to a healthful climate put forth by Alexander Hewat, Lionel Chalmers, and others probably have some justification.

Though immigration was a big factor in increasing the seventeenth-century colonial population, by the eighteenth the high birth rate probably provided the larger increment. Early and productive marriages were the order of the day. Gottlieb Mittelburger observed that the city of Philadelphia was "fairly swarming" with children. "If one meets a woman," he declared, "she is either with child, or she carries a child in her arms, or leads one by the hand." In 1736 a missionary wrote to the Society that several old members of his church had died, but added that it was no great loss to the church since "ye Membrs. of it are Increased, by Reason of the Children, wherewith most Houses are well stocked, growing up, marrying & settling by themselves, who thereby become so Many New Heads of Fam-

[4] Belknap, *History of New-Hampshire*, III, 232.

ilies."[5] The missionaries themselves usually had large families, and their appeals to the Society for more money were largely based upon sickness and the needs of their growing families. In an area where labor was scarce and land plentiful, children were a valuable asset. Under the colonial economy no necessity existed for deferred marriage, and it was only natural that large families ensued.

The seventeenth and eighteenth centuries saw a steady increase in the population of western Europe and the American colonies. Regardless of the destructive effects of smallpox and the various diseases which ravaged entire countries, the population grew steadily and wealth increased. As one major pestilence disappeared, another one took its place. In Europe, plague and then smallpox winnowed the population, but in New England, where smallpox was rare, diphtheria proved exceptionally fatal.

Isolation and lack of congested urban areas gave the American colonies a decided advantage in the matter of health, and this helps explain their rapid development. Thus, while England, where health conditions were deplorable, was steadily expanding in wealth and population, the improved health conditions in the American colonies promoted a development which exceeded even that of the mother country.

[5] Carl T. Eben (trans.), *Gottlieb Mittelberger's Journey to Pennsylvania in the Year 1750 and return to Germany in the Year 1754 . . .* (Philadelphia, 1898), 107; Paul Stoupe to Secretary, New Rochelle, New York, June 1, 1736, in S.P.G. MSS., A26, fp. 274; James Duane's draft of Governor Tryon's "Report on Certain Heads of Enquiry Relative to the Present State and Conditions of the Province of New York, 1774," p. 85, New-York Historical Society MSS.

Bibliography

MANUSCRIPTS

The omnipresence of disease in the colonies makes every written record a potential source of information, but certain of the manuscript collections more than repay the researcher for his time. One of the most fruitful collections is the records of the Society for the Propagation of the Gospel in Foreign Parts, particularly the letters, Ser. A, Vols. 1–26, Ser. B, Vols. 1–25, journals, Vols. 1–8, supplementary letters and papers, Pgs. 1–7, and the Fulham Palace manuscripts. Aside from the material relating to this study, these collections provide a picture of colonial life which set the background for specialized work. The missionaries, required to report regularly to the secretary of the Society, wrote detailed accounts of their observations, and because of their social consciousness, few events passed without notice. Their own health and that of their congregations was a matter of considerable importance to them and was duly noted in their reports. The early letters from American clergymen in the Simon Gratz and the Ferdinand J. Greer Collections in the Pennsylvania Historical Society Library also are useful, but their value is limited because the majority were written in the nineteenth century.

The Toner Collection in the Library of Congress contains a fund of information relating to medical history, but only parts of it concern epidemics. Some of the most useful are the manuscript transcripts: "A Collection of References to Scattered Medical Items and Contributions by early Medical Men found in American Newspapers and Periodicals Printed before 1800, Selected and Alphabetically Arranged in Two Volumes, (1886)"; "Extracts from Newspapers Published in Charleston, South Carolina from the year

1732 to the year 1800 both inclusive, Collected by Wm. H. Bailey, M.D. for J. M. Toner, M.D."; "Index to Medical Matters found in Pennsylvania Gazette from its first issue to the close of 1800, prepared by J. M. Toner"; and "A List of Laws Affecting Public Health in British Colonies in America." The Toner Collection also includes many pictures of early medical men which would be of value to those working in the field of medical biography.

The volumes of the Public Record Office, Colonial Office 5, in the Library of Congress were examined and found to contain certain useful material on military and political affairs but surprisingly little information on social conditions in the colonies. Much the same can be said of the Sloane Manuscripts and the King's Manuscripts from the British Museum. The following papers in the Library of Congress supplied some material relating to colonial health: Thomas Amory Papers, including the Business Letterbooks and Family Papers; Joseph Ball Manuscripts; Ebenezer Hazard Manuscripts; Jones Family Papers; and Ezra Stiles Diary, 1770–1775. Citations were also made from the Robert Treat Paine Papers, Massachusetts Historical Society Library, and the S. E. Baldwin Collection and the Johnson Family Papers in the Yale University Library.

The unpublished Cadwallader Colden Papers in the Library of Congress and the New-York Historical Society Library were of some use, although the best material has already been edited in the New-York Historical Society *Collections*. "Dr. John Mitchell's Acct. of the Yellow Fever in Virginia in 1741–42, Written in 1748, transcription by Dr. John Redman Coxe," in the Library of the College of Physicians, Philadelphia, is noteworthy, since Mitchell's account of yellow fever is the only source of information for this outbreak. In this same library under the heading "Manuscripts Relating to Yellow Fever" are a number of documents concerned primarily with the yellow-fever outbreak of the 1790's.

Among the best of the journals and diaries are three in the Massachusetts Historical Society Library: the David Hall Diary, 1740–1789; the Diary of Benjamin Bangs; and a series of diaries kept by Jeremiah Belknap in *Ames Almanacks* for the years 1758–61, 1769. In the American Antiquarian Society Library the Ebenezer Parkman Diary is a very useful source and can be supplemented by the diaries of the Reverend Nathan Fiske in *Ames Almanacks* for most of the years from 1754 to 1773.

The most informative of the diaries and journals in the Pennsylvania Historical Society is Elizabeth Drinker's Diary, 1758–1775, parts of which have already been published. Another valuable manuscript is the Journal of Benjamin Pomroy, 1758–1768.

Useful papers in the New-York Historical Society Library, in addition to those already mentioned, are The Note Book of John Saffin, 1665–1708; Charles Lodwick's Account of New York, May 20, 1692; and the draft in James Duane's handwriting of Governor William Tryon's "Report on Certain Heads of Enquiry Relative to the Present State and Conditions of the Province of N. Y., 1774."

PRINTED SOURCE MATERIAL

Contemporary histories

Nearly all contemporary colonial historians give some picture of health conditions. Dr. William Douglass in his work, *A Summary, historical and political, of the first planting, progressive improvements, and present state of the British Settlements in North America*, 2 vols. (London, 1760), commented on the diseases of his time with considerable discernment. Two historians whose works illustrate health conditions in particular areas are Jeremy Belknap, *The History of New-Hampshire*, 3 vols. (Boston, 1791–92), and Alexander Hewat, *An Historical Account of the Rise and Progress of the Colonies of South Carolina and Georgia*, 2 vols. (London, 1779). Belknap gives an excellent account of the diseases in New England, especially the throat distemper outbreak. Hewat does a similar job on the infectious disorders incident to the southern colonies.

Two standard contemporary histories are John Oldmixon's *The British Empire in America*, 2 vols. (London, 1741), and Thomas Salmon's *Modern History, or the Present State of All Nations*, 4 vols. on America (London, 1736–38). Oldmixon copied much of his material verbatim from earlier writers, therefore his volumes are of value only where the original work is not available. Salmon's four books on America are vols. 28–31 in his set. Like Oldmixon, Salmon has little new material. Other contemporary historical works used include Robert Beverly, *The History and Present State of Virginia* (London, 1705); *Bradford's History of Plymouth Plantation 1606–1646*, in J. Franklin Jameson (ed.), *Original Narratives of Early American History* (New York, 1908); David Humphries, *An Historical Account of the Incorporated Society for the Propagation of the Gospel in Foreign Parts*, 2 vols. (London, 1730); Thomas Hutchinson, *The History of the Province of Massachusetts-Bay from the Charter of King William and Queen Mary in 1691 until the year 1750*, 3 vols. (Boston, 1767); Cotton Mather, *Magnalia Christi Americana: or the ecclesiastical history of New-England from its first planting in the year 1620 unto the year of our Lord, 1698,* . . . (London, 1702); Thomas Prince, *A chronological history of New-England in the form of annals . . . from the discovery by Capt. Gosnold in 1602 to the arrival of Governor Belcher, in 1730. . . ,* 2 vols. (Boston, 1736 and 1755); Alexander S. Salley, Jr. (ed.), *Narratives of Early Carolina, 1650–1708* (New York, 1911); William Smith, *The History of the Province of New York* (London, 1776); and John Winthrop, *The History of New England from 1630 to 1650*, 2 vols. (Boston, 1825–26).

Medical Accounts

The best of the early medical works from the standpoint of epidemics is Noah Webster, *A Brief History of Epidemic and Pestilential Diseases* . . . , 2 vols. (Hartford, Conn., 1799). Considering the limited medical knowledge of his time, Webster did a remarkable job. Despite many mistakes, his studv is still helpful for its wealth of facts and accurate clinical descriptions of colonial diseases. Another publication by Webster, but one of limited value for the purpose of this study, is his *Collection of Papers on the subject of Bilious Fevers prevalent in the United States for a few years past* (New York, 1796). Two other noteworthy medical accounts are those of Lionel Chalmers, *An Account of the Weather and Diseases of South Carolina*, 2 vols. (London, 1776), and William Currie,

An Historical Account of the Climates and Diseases of the United States of America . . . (Philadelphia, 1792). Both writers are most effective when discussing the sicknesses of their own times. Currie is particularly good on yellow-fever outbreaks. A medical writer who came a little late for the colonial period, but who wrote extensively on yellow-fever epidemics, Benjamin Rush, *Medical Inquiries and Observations*, 4 vols. (2d ed., Philadelphia, 1805, and 4th ed., Philadelphia, 1815), was a keen observer and made good use of his opportunity to study at firsthand two yellow-fever attacks in the eighteenth century.

Smallpox and variolation brought forth a series of pamphlets and essays in England and the colonies. The first and most famous of these is Thomas Thacher, *A brief rule to guide the common people of New-England how to order themselves and theirs in the Small Pocks, or Measles* (Boston, 1677). Following the introduction of variolation, a bitter pamphlet war ensued. The Mathers immediately jumped into the fray with Increase Mather's *Several Reasons Proving that inoculating or transplanting the Small Pox, is a lawful practice, and that it has been blessed by God for the saving of many a life* (Boston, 1721), and Cotton Mather's *Sentiments on the Small Pox Inoculated.* These two works have been reprinted with an introduction by George Lyman Kittredge (Cleveland, for private distribution, 1921). In 1722 two of the opponents of inoculation replied: William Douglass, *The Abuses and Scandals of some late Pamphlets in Favour of Inoculation of the Small Pox, Modestly obviated, and Inoculation further considered in a Letter to A—— S——, M.D. & F. R. S.* (Boston, 1722), Toner Collection, Library of Congress; and Edmund Massey, *A Sermon against the Dangerous and Sinful practice of Inoculation. Preach'd at St. Andrew's Holborn, on Sunday, July the 8th, 1722* (London, 1722). Zabdiel Boylston, the first physician to practice inoculation in the colonies, published his views in a work entitled *An Historical Account of the Small-Pox Inoculated in New England, upon all sorts of persons, white, blacks, and of all ages and constitutions. . .* (London, 1726). Three other treatises cited in connection with variolation are James Kilpatrick, *An Essay on Inoculation, Occasioned by the Smallpox being brought into S. Carolina in the year 1738* (London, 1743); William Cooper, *A reply to the objections made against taking the small pox in the way of inoculation from principles of conscience* . . . (Boston, 1730); and William Douglass, *A practical essay concerning the smallpox* (Boston, 1730). Additional pamphlet material relating to variolation can be found in the Rare Book Room of the Library of Congress.

Two useful accounts of yellow-fever outbreaks are included in John Lining, *A Description of the American yellow fever, which prevailed at Charleston, in South Carolina, in the year 1748* (Philadelphia, 1799), and John Redman, *An Account of the Yellow Fever as it prevailed in Philadelphia in the Autumn of 1762* (Philadelphia, 1865).

The throat distemper aroused considerable interest in the 1730's and 1740's and was noted by many writers. William Douglass was one of the first to describe its ravages in his work *The practical history of a New Epidemical Eruptive Military Fever* . . . (Boston, 1736). Another excellent narrative is that of Samuel Bard, *An Enquiry into the Nature, Cause and Cure, of the Angina Suffocativa, or, Sore Throat Distemper* . . . (New York, 1771). A description of diphtheria in eighteenth-century England which has since become one of the medical classics is John Fothergill, *An Account of the Sore Throat Attended with Ulcers* (London, 1748). Fothergill's clear picture of the clinical symptoms is helpful in identifying the infection in America.

Cotton Mather, *A Letter About a Good Management under the Distemper of the Measles, etc.* (Boston, 1739), is one of the colonial medical classics. Not only does it contain an excellent clinical picture of the disease but Mather's common sense approach to its treatment makes this short work a shining light amid the quackery of the period.

Other eighteenth-century works cited are Charles Buxton, *An Inaugural Dissertation on the Measles* (New York, 1793); and John Tennent, *An Essay on the Pleurisy* (Williamsburg, reprinted in New York, 1742).

Travel and Description

Little can be said of travel and description works other than that occasionally the researcher finds useful bits of information.

Many accounts are valueless, but often travelers would note the prevalence of specific diseases. The standard collections used in this study were John Harris, *A Complete Collection of Voyages and Travels*, 2 vols. (London, 1748); and Newton D. Mereness (ed.), *Travels in the American Colonies* (New York, 1916). Among the other narratives two deserve special mention: Adolph B. Benson (ed.), *Peter Kalm's Travels in North America*, 2 vols. (New York, 1937), which gives a good discussion of malaria and dysentery in New York, and Carl T. Eben (translator), *Gottlieb Mittelberger's Journey to Pennsylvania in the year 1750 and return to Germany in the year 1754 . . .* (Philadelphia, 1898). Although he wrote with the aim of exposing the plight of the German emigrants, Mittelberger presents a fairly accurate picture of the health problems in Pennsylvania and other colonies. Other travel records cited include R. R. Wilson (ed.), *Burnaby's Travels through North America, 1759* (New York, 1904); Timothy Dwight, *Travels in New-England and New-York*, 4 vols. (New Haven, 1821); Henry C. Murphy (ed. and trans.), *Journal of a Voyage to New York, 1679–80*, in *Memoirs* of the Long Island Historical Society, I (New York, 1867); and Bartlet B. James and J. Franklin Jameson (eds.), *Journal of Jasper Dankaerts*, 1679–80, in Jameson (ed.), *Original Narratives . . . Series* (New York, 1913).

Correspondence and Diaries

As with travel and description, the search for medical information in the diaries and correspondence of the colonial period is largely a hit-or-miss proposition. Some diarists took little note of sickness and disease, whereas others wrote both extensively and accurately. Business correspondence was found to be unfruitful in general, but Francis Norton Mason (ed.), *John Norton & Sons, Merchants of London and Virginia* (Richmond, 1937), gives a clear picture of the spread of smallpox through the careless practice of variolation. Also useful were Edward Armstrong (ed.), *Correspondence between William Penn and James Logan and Others, 1700–1750* (Philadelphia, 1870), in *Memoirs* of the Historical Society of Pennsylvania, IX; and Anne Row Cunningham (ed.),

Letters and Diary of John Rowe, Boston Merchant, 1759–1762, 1764–1779 (Boston, 1903).

Among the most serviceable of the diaries are those of William Byrd. In his detailed journals Byrd mentions nearly all sicknesses affecting the colonists, and his frequent references to malaria and dysentery are a good index to their prevalence in Virginia. See L. B. Wright and Marion Tinling (eds.), *The Secret Diary of William Byrd of Westover, 1709–1712* (Richmond, 1941), and Maude H. Woodfin and Marion Tinling (eds.), *Another Secret Diary of William Byrd of Westover, 1739–1741* (Richmond, 1942).

For the illnesses troubling New England, William Willis (ed.), *The Journal of the Rev. Thomas Smith and the Rev. Samuel Deane* (Portland, 1849); *Diary of Joshua Hempstead of New London, Connecticut, 1711–1758,* in New London County Historical Society *Collections,* I (New London, 1901); George Francis Dow (ed.), *The Holyoke Diaries, 1709–1856* (Salem, Mass., 1911); and the *Diary by Increase Mather, March, 1675–December, 1676, Together with Extracts from Another Diary by Him, 1674–1687,* introduction and notes by Samuel A. Green (Cambridge, Mass., 1900), are invaluable. Edwards A. Parks, *Memoir of the Life and Character of Samuel Hopkins, D.D.* (Boston, 1854), is of some use.

The letters and works of Benjamin Franklin contain many notations on medical matters, the best of which have been culled out by William Pepper, *The Medical Side of Benjamin Franklin* (Philadelphia, 1911). Jared Sparks (ed.), *The Works of Benjamin Franklin,* 10 vols. (Boston, 1839–47), also was useful. Another work of some value for the middle colonies is *A Journal of the Life and Travels of Thomas Chalkley, Friends Library,* II (Philadelphia, 1835).

Only a few of the pamphlets and broadsides examined were of any significance. The Library of Congress has Cotton Mather, *Seasonable Thoughts upon Mortality. A sermon occasioned by the many deaths of our brethren there* (Boston, 1712), and the Library of the University of California in Los Angeles has an equally interesting pamphlet, *Matters interesting on the Score of Humanity: being Propositions relating to the Health, Comfort, and Satisfaction of British Seamen in His Majesty's Service* (London, 1793).

Newspapers

Colonial newspapers are a fertile field for exploration. Frequently the course of an epidemic in Boston can be followed through the successive issues of papers in other cities—and on occasions—in the Boston papers. Since a summary of the outbreak in terms of cases and fatalities was often printed, the seriousness of the epidemic can be determined. The masthead on colonial newspapers was subject to frequent changes; hence, for convenience, the name of the paper at the date cited is given. Citations were made from the following journals: Boston *Weekly News-Letter;* Boston *News-Letter; Weekly News-Letter; Massachusetts Gazette and Boston Weekly News-Letter; Massachusetts Gazette and Boston Post Boy and Advertiser; Green and Russell's Boston Post Boy and Advertiser;* Boston *Chronicle;* Boston *Evening Post;* Boston *Post Boy; New England Weekly Journal;* Newport *Mercury; New Hampshire Gazette;* New York *Gazette;* New York *Gazette Revived in the Weekly Post-Boy;* New York *Mercury; American Weekly Mercury; Pennsylvania Gazette;* and *South Carolina Gazette.* Other newspapers have been listed in footnotes, but in these cases the quotations were taken from printed source collections, such as the *Documents Relating to the Colonial History of the State of New Jersey.*

Collections and Proceedings

Printed source collections were exceedingly helpful for the type of research required to trace colonial epidemics. One of the most valuable of these works is the Massachusetts Historical Society *Collections* (Cambridge, 1792——). The correspondence, diaries, journals, and the other records published in these volumes present an excellent cross section of life in the New England colonies. Included in the *Collections* are the *Belknap Papers, Winthrop Papers, Belcher Papers, Sewall Papers, The Letter-Book of Samuel Sewall,* and the *Diary of Cotton Mather.* Equally useful are the Massachusetts Historical Society *Proceedings* (Boston, 1859——); American Antiquarian Society *Proceedings* (Worcester, Mass., 1812 ——); *Historical Collections* of the Essex Institute (Salem, 1859

——); and the *Publications* of the Colonial Society of Massachusetts (Boston, 1892——). Local records of some value may be found in J. H. Tuttle (ed.), *The Dedham Historical Register*, 14 vols. (Dedham, Mass., 1890–1903), issued under the auspices of the Dedham Historical Society, and the *Boston Record Commissioners*, VIII (Boston, 1883). For New Hampshire, Nathaniel Bouton (ed.), *Provincial Papers, Documents and Records Relating to the Province of New-Hampshire, from the Earliest Period of its settlement: 1623–1776*, 7 vols. (Concord, 1867–73), is helpful, especially for the study of smallpox and the quarantine measures used against it, and the New Hampshire Historical Society *Collections* (Concord, 1824——) also contains much helpful material. Two good printed source collections are available for the province of Rhode Island: John R. Bartlett (ed.), *Records of the Colony of Rhode Island and Providence Plantations in New England*, 10 vols. (Providence, 1856–65), and *The Early Records of the Town of Providence*, 21 vols. (Providence, 1892–1915).

New York, like Massachusetts, has a wealth of printed source material. The *Collections* of the New-York Historical Society (New York, 1868——) rank with the best of the historical society publications. Among the most valuable records in this set are the nine volumes of the *Letters and Papers of Cadwallader Colden* (New York, 1918–37), and the two volumes of the *Colden Letter-Books* (New York, 1877–78), as well as the two volumes in Dorothy C. Barck (ed.), *Papers of the Lloyd Family of Lloyd's Neck, New York* (New York, 1927). Another series of volumes essential for a study of colonial New York is E. B. O'Callaghan (ed.), *Documents Relative to the Colonial History of the State of New York . . .*, 11 vols. (Albany, 1856–61). Much useful material relating to colonial health is contained in this work, and, in addition, it is one of the few collections with an adequate index. A later addition to O'Callaghan's set is Vol. XII, entitled *Documents Relating to the History of the Dutch and Swedish Settlements on the Delaware River*, trans. Berthold Fernow (Albany, 1877). For New Jersey, W. A. Whitehead *et al.* (eds.), *Documents Relating to the Colonial History of the State of New Jersey*, 30 vols. (Newark, 1880——), is helpful.

The *Colonial Records of Pennsylvania, Minutes of the Provin-*

cial Council of Pennsylvania, 10 vols. (Harrisburg, 1851–52), throw light on health conditions in both Pennsylvania and the surrounding colonies. Other collections used include Samuel Hazard (ed.), *Pennsylvania Archives,* Ser. 1, 12 vols. (Philadelphia, 1852–56), and Edward Armstrong (ed.), *Memoirs* of the Historical Society of Pennsylvania (Philadelphia, 1826, republished in 1862).

In connection with Maryland and Virginia, William Hand Brown *et al.* (eds.), *Archives of Maryland,* 32 vols. (Baltimore, 1883——); William Waller Hening (ed.), *The Statutes at Large* ..., 13 vols. (Richmond, 1819); John P. Kennedy (ed.), *Journals of the House of Burgesses of Virginia,* 1761–1765 (Richmond, 1907), and 1766–1769 (Richmond, 1909), also proved helpful. The two volumes by Kennedy have a good index and were useful in tracing the outbreaks of yellow fever and smallpox in Virginia.

For the Carolinas, Adelaide L. Fries (ed.), *Records of the Moravians in North Carolina,* 6 vols. (Raleigh, 1922); *Collections* of the South Carolina Historical Society, 5 vols. (Charleston, 1857–97); and Bartholomew R. Carroll (ed.), *Historical Collections of South Carolina,* 2 vols. (New York, 1836), were used. Carroll is helpful when the original work is not available.

Reuben G. Thwaites (ed.), *The Jesuit Relations and Allied Documents,* 73 vols. (Cleveland, 1896–1901), contributes only slightly to the history of epidemics in the English colonies, but is a mine of information for health conditions among the French and Indians. The index is complete and includes all references to sickness and disease.

The *Philosophical Transactions of the Royal Society of London* (London, 1666——), particularly volumes XX to LXV covering the period of 1699 to 1775, were examined. The introduction of variolation into England and the American colonies aroused the interest of members of the Society on both sides of the Atlantic, and a considerable discussion ensued. The correspondence of the American members with the Society supplies much data on colonial epidemics and general medical problems. The *Transactions of the American Philosophical Society* come too late to be of much value for the colonial period, but Vol. I, published in Philadelphia in 1789, for the years 1769–71, was used. Technically the *Gentlemen's Magazine* (London, 1731–1904) does not belong with this group of publications, yet from the standpoint of colonial epidemics it fills a role akin to that of the *Philosophical Transactions.* The volumes from 1731 to 1775 contain a fund of information relating to the colonies. The journal was read widely in America, and few major colonial epidemics escaped the notice of the editors or the American correspondents.

PERIODICALS

Medical

The Index-Catalogue of the Library of the Surgeon General's Office was used as a guide to articles relating to colonial health, but most of the essays on medical history written prior to 1920 were too brief and too general to be of much value.

The most useful of the medical periodicals were the *Bulletin of the History of Medicine* (Baltimore, 1933——) and the *Johns Hopkins Hospital Bulletin* (Baltimore, 1889——). *Medical Classics,* 5 vols. (Baltimore, 1936–41), which reprinted the best accounts of disease by early physicians, was helpful. Other medical journals cited include *Annals of Medical History,* 10 vols. (Baltimore, 1917–28), new series, 10 vols. (Baltimore, 1929–38), series 3, 4 vols. (Baltimore, 1939–42); *Bulletin of the Society of Medical History of Chicago,* II (Chicago, 1917–22); *The New England Journal of Medicine and Surgery,* XIV (Boston, 1825); *Ciba Symposia,* III (New Haven, Conn., 1942); *Yale Journal of Biology and Medicine,* XV (New Haven, Conn., 1943); and the *London Medical Journal,* III (London, 1783).

General

A number of regional historical magazines supplied considerable information. One of the best is the *New England Historical and Genealogical Register* (Boston, 1847——). The diaries, journals, and early records of New England towns and villages published in these volumes are invaluable for research in health conditions in colonial New England. Outstanding journals publishing materials relating to the southern section include the *Virginia Maga-*

zine of History and Biography (Richmond, 1893——); *William and Mary College Quarterly Historical Magazine*, 1st series, 27 vols. (1892–1919), 2d series, 23 vols. (1921–43), 3d series (1944——); *North Carolina Historical Review* (Raleigh, 1924——); and *South Carolina Historical and Genealogical Magazine* (Charleston, 1900——). The *Mississippi Valley Historical Review*, XXXVIII (Cedar Rapids, 1951), was also cited.

Medical Works

A few studies dealing with epidemics in general have been published. Charles Creighton, *A History of Epidemics in Britain*, 2 vols. (Cambridge, 1894), is the standard work on English epidemics. It is an exhaustive factual study, but many of Creighton's conclusions need reinterpreting in the light of modern medical knowledge. Another outdated but still useful work is August Hirsch, *Handbook of Geographical and Historical Pathology*, trans. Charles Creighton, 3 vols. (London, 1883–86). Hirsch surveys epidemics affecting Europe and the rest of the world. His study presents, as does Creighton's, an amazing amount of detailed information but is limited by the state of contemporary medical knowledge. For Canada the definitive work is John J. Heagerty, *Four Centuries of Medical History in Canada and a Sketch of the Medical History of Newfoundland*, 2 vols. (Toronto, 1928). Heagerty, who gives a complete picture of the ravages of epidemic diseases, has left little else to be done on this aspect of Canadian medical history.

No comprehensive history of epidemics in the United States has been written, although epidemics are given some treatment in many of the medical histories. Francis R. Packard, *History of Medicine in the United States*, 2 vols. (New York, 1931), one of the best medical works, covers epidemics in one chapter. Other American medical histories give an even more cursory treatment to this phase of colonial health. Among the better works on medicine in America are Henry E. Sigerist, *American Medicine* (New York, 1934), a short, readable account by a leading European medical student and former William H. Welch Professor of the History of Medicine at Johns Hopkins University; James G. Mumford, *A Narrative of Medicine in America* (Philadelphia, 1903); and James Thacher, *American Medical Biography, or Memoirs of Eminent Physicians who have Flourished in America*, 2 vols. in one (Boston, 1828). Maurice Bear Gordon, *Æsculapius Comes to the Colonies, the Story of the Early Days of Medicine in the Thirteen Original Colonies* (Ventnor, N. J., 1949) is a series of biographical sketches of colonial physicians taken largely from a few secondary sources.

The general histories of medicine supplied background for the colonial health picture. Charles Singer, *A Short History of Medicine* (New York, 1928), is a well-written treatise by a leading English medical scholar. A good brief manual is M. G. Seelig, *Medicine, An Historical Outline* (Baltimore, 1931).

Another study of value primarily for the nineteenth and twentieth centuries is Edward B. Vedder, *Medicine, Its Contribution to Civilization* (Baltimore, 1929). For the medieval period, David Riesman, *The Story of Medicine in the Middle Ages* (New York, 1936), is satisfactory. Other works include Elisha Bartlett, *The History, Diagnosis and Treatment of Fevers of the United States* (4th edition, revised by A. Clark, Philadelphia, 1856), and Cecil K. Drinker, *Not So Long Ago: An Analysis of Philadelphia from the Diary of Elizabeth Drinker, The March of Medicine* (New York, 1940).

Probably the most profitable of the medical histories are those dealing with particular states. Wyndham B. Blanton's *Medicine in Virginia in the Seventeenth Century* (Richmond, 1930), and *Medicine in Virginia in the Eighteenth Century* (Richmond, 1931), provide the best medical history of any state. Blanton's chapters on epidemics are exceptionally well done. Samuel Abbott Green, *History of Medicine in Massachusetts* (Boston, 1881), and Henry R. Viets, *A Brief History of Medicine in Massachusetts* (Boston and New York, 1930), survey this state adequately. Viets gives a good discussion of the throat-distemper outbreak in New England, 1735–36. For New York and New Jersey, Stephen Wickes, *History of Medicine in New Jersey, and of Its Medical Men from the Settlement of the Provinces to A.D. 1800* (Newark, 1879), which is largely biographical, and James J. Walsh, *History of Medicine in New York*, 3 vols. in one (New York, 1919), a more comprehensive medical work but not too useful from the standpoint of epidemics, were helpful. Two other local medical histories of some value are George William Norris, *The Early History of Medicine in Philadelphia* (Philadelphia, 1886), and John R. Quinan, *Medical Annals of Baltimore from 1608 to 1880* (Baltimore, 1884).

A series of special studies on aspects of medical history have contributed much toward clarifying the picture of early medicine. P. M. Ashburn, *The Ranks of Death, a Medical History of the Conquest of America* (New York, 1947), is a work of considerable merit. Ashburn discusses thoroughly the sicknesses and diseases afflicting the early settlers in Central and South America from the time of Columbus up into the eighteenth century. However, the British settlements in North America are treated cursorily, and it is evident that the author is at his best in working with the Spanish sources. An excellent introduction to the great American plague malaria is given in St. Julien Ravenel Childs, *Malaria and Colonization in the Carolina Low Country, 1526–1696* (Baltimore, 1940), in Johns Hopkins University *Studies in Historical and Political Science*, Ser. 58, No. 1. Another good short study is E. Wagner Stearn and Allen E. Stearn, *The Effects of Smallpox on the Destiny of the Amerindian* (Boston, 1945), which, although placing the major emphasis upon the nineteenth and twentieth centuries, is still useful for the earlier period.

The best account by far of the outbreak of throat disease in New England during 1735–36 is the work by Ernest Caulfield, *A true history of the terrible epidemic vulgarly called the throat distemper, which occurred in His Majesty's New England Colonies between the years 1735 and 1740* (New Haven, Conn., 1939).

Frank MacFarlane Burnet in his work *Virus as Organism, Evolutionary and Ecological Aspects of Some Human Virus Diseases*, in Harvard University *Monographs in Medicine and Public Health* (Cambridge, 1945), shows how changes have occurred in certain virus infections. His work may explain our inability to identify certain colonial infections. Other special studies cited are Henry R. Carter, *Yellow Fever, An Epidemiological and Historical Study of Its Place of Origin*, eds. L. A. Carter and W. H. Frost (Baltimore, 1931); R. Hingston Fox, *Dr. John Fothergill and His Friends* (London, 1919); and Clifford Allchin Gill, *Seasonal Periodicity of Malaria and the Mechanism of the Epidemic Wave* (London, 1938).

Of the many medical histories written for popular consumption, the following have been cited: Paul William Allen, *The Story of Microbes* (St. Louis, Mo., 1938); Howard W. Haggard, *The Lame, the Halt, and the Blind* (New York, 1932); Ralph N. Major, *Disease and Destiny* (New York and London, 1936); and Wade W. Oliver, *Stalkers of Pestilence, the Story of Man's Ideas of Infection* (New York, 1930).

GENERAL WORKS

The majority of the general histories have only limited value for a study of colonial epidemics. A few, however, deserve special mention. An excellent account of the epidemic diseases affecting South Carolina can be found in David Ramsay, *The History of South Carolina from Its First Settlement in 1670 to the Year 1808*, 2 vols. (Charleston, 1809). Ramsay gives a particularly good account of the smallpox and yellow-fever outbreaks. Health conditions in colonial Virginia have received considerable attention, and among the useful works for this colony are Alexander Brown's *The First Republic in America* (Boston and New York, 1898) and *The Genesis of the United States*, 2 vols. (Boston and New York, 1890). Brown was one of the first historians to survey the effects of disease and food shortages upon the settlers in the seventeenth century. A more recent historian of seventeenth-century Virginia, Thomas J. Wertenbaker, has produced *The Planters of Colonial Virginia* (Princeton, 1922) and *Virginia under the Stuarts* (Princeton, 1914). Wertenbaker, like Brown, devotes considerable space to the problems of sickness and disease and has made a notable contribution to this phase of colonial history.

For any student delving into the mass of S.P.G. records, an indispensable work is C. F. Pascoe, *Two Hundred Years of the S.P.G.*, 2 vols. (London, 1901). The short biographical sketches of all missionaries employed by the Society which are to be found in the Appendix to Vol. II are especially useful. A much older, but still valuable history relating to the S.P.G. is Frederick Dalcho's *An Historical Account of the Protestant Episcopal Church in South Carolina* (Charleston, 1820).

Health conditions among a large segment of the colonial population have been treated thoroughly in Abbot E. Smith, *Colonists in*

Bondage, White Servitude and Convict Labor in America 1607–1776 (Chapel Hill, N. C., 1947). Smith's material on shipboard conditions during the journey to the New World is particularly good. An earlier but still sound work dealing with emigration to America in the early colonial period is Edward Eggleston, *The Transit of Civilization from England to America in the Seventeenth Century* (New York, 1901). Eggleston's treatment of health conditions in the colonies surpasses that found in many of the more recent social histories.

Other works cited include Ralph Boas and Louise Boas, *Cotton Mather, Keeper of the Puritan Conscience* (New York and London, 1928); Philip Alexander Bruce, *Institutional History of Virginia in the Seventeenth Century*, 2 vols. (New York and London, 1910); F. B. Dexter, *Estimates of Population*, in American Antiquarian Society *Proceedings*, N. S., V (1887); John Hayward, *A Gazetteer of Massachusetts* (Boston, 1847); Thomas Babington Macaulay, *The History of England from the Accession of James II*, 5 vols. (Philadelphia, 1887 ed.); John Marshall, *A History of the Colonies Planted by the English on the Continent of North America* (Philadelphia, 1824); Edward McCrady, *The History of South Carolina under the Proprietary Government, 1670–1719* (New York, 1897); James Mease, *The Picture of Philadelphia* (Philadelphia, 1811); *A Century of Population Growth*, Government Printing Office (Washington, 1909); William J. Rivers, *A Sketch of the History of South Carolina to the Close of Proprietary Government by the Revolution of 1719* (Charleston, 1856); Isaac Newton Stokes, *The Iconography of Manhattan Island, 1498–1909*, 6 vols. (New York, 1922); and Justin Winsor, *The Memorial History of Boston*, 4 vols. (Boston, 1886).

Index